ESP

A Scientific Evaluation

ESP

A SCIENTIFIC EVALUATION

by **C. E. M. HANSEL**

Professor of Psychology,
University College of Swansea, University of Wales

INTRODUCTION BY

EDWIN G. BORING

Edgar Pierce Professor of Psychology Emeritus,
Harvard University

New York · CHARLES SCRIBNER'S SONS

ACKNOWLEDGEMENTS

I am deeply indebted to Professor Emeritus R. T. Birge of the University of California for his detailed examination of my manuscript. I was fortunate to begin correspondence with Professor Birge in 1959, when he became interested in parapsychology, and since then have had the benefit of his generous assistance and advice.

I am also particularly indebted to the American science writer, Martin Gardner, who has assisted me in every possible way and who has been mainly responsible for getting this book published.

I gratefully acknowledge further indebtedness:

To the American author Clayton Rawson, who has kept me in touch with events in the United States and advised me on my manuscript.

To Christopher Scott, now Regional Statistical Adviser to the United Nations in Addis Ababa, who first interested me in ESP research many years ago and who has given me the full benefit of his wide knowledge of activities in that field.

To Ronald C. Read of the Department of Mathematics, University College of the West Indies, who also contributed to my early interest in ESP research and who read my early manuscript.

To J. B. Rhine, formerly Director of the Parapsychology Laboratory, Duke University, for arranging and financing my visit to his laboratory.

To Eric Dingwall, keeper at the British Museum, who probably knows more about "strange experiences," spiritualism, and mental mediums than any man alive, for reading and commenting on the chapters dealing with those subjects.

To the Society for Psychical Research for allowing me the use of their Library.

To Graham Reed of the Department of Psychiatry, Manchester University, for his assistance with the chapter on mental mediums.

To Professor John Mann of the Graduate School of Arts and Sciences, New York University, for his advice on the manuscript.

To all those others who have assisted me in various ways and, in particular, to Professor John Cohen of the Department of Psychology, Manchester University, for his continued encouragement and support.

Finally, to my wife, Gwenllian Hansel, who has spent many laborious hours sorting out the text and references.

v

TABLE OF CONTENTS

LIST OF ILLUSTRATIONS

LIST OF TABLES

INTRODUCTION

PARANORMAL PHENOMENA: Evidence, Specification, and Chance

THIS is really a book about human belief, in this case, the belief that certain inexplicable events are evidence of the operation of a hidden general principle that, were its nature revealed, would constitute an explanation of the occurrences in question. Such a faith in an occult principle readily emerges from an ignorance of the nature of the principle by which the phenomena operate, and the history of science shows how ignorance perpetually directs man's ingenuity toward dispelling it, how mystery is an inevitable invitation to attempt its own dissolution. In other words, curiosity promotes science. Nevertheless, ignorance, the stuff on which science feeds, is much too plentiful always to stimulate research: science has to choose, its curiosity has to be selective.

In the case of the various phenomena with which this book is concerned, the selection is determined in part by the ancient distinction between mind and matter. Mind is mysterious, being, as the French philosopher René Descartes said, "unextended substance." Yet how can mind be in the body and still occupy no space there? It seems reasonable to suppose that so impalpable an essence could act in strange ways. For instance, if the mind or the soul—the two used not to be distinguished—can be here and yet take up no room, may not the mind or its effects be both here, there, and everywhere, like light or, as now, the radio waves? When in 1860 the German physicist and philosopher Gustav Theodor Fechner, one of the founders of experimental psychology, first measured sensation—a mental thing, mind you—his achievement commanded instant attention, because measuring this elusive psychic entity was like harnessing it and forcing it, for all its impalpability, to become an object of scientific examination.

In this volume, Professor Hansel gives the whole history of what were at first called *psychic phenomena* because they had the evanescent characteristics of what is mental. Later, the phenomena came to make up the subject matter of *parapsychology,* a term that still emphasizes their mental nature. Hansel tells about the strange raps of the Fox sisters and about the rise of spiritualistic mediums who claimed to bring one into contact with deceased persons. William James's interest in Mrs. Piper is another story in that department of the paranormal field. Hansel also tells about the physical phenomena—table lifting, trumpet blowing, flying objects in the air—produced by such famous mediums as Eusapia Palladino and Margery Crandon. Most of all, he stresses the recent phase of the somewhat better controlled experiments on telepathy and clairvoyance, now called *extrasensory perception* (ESP), and *psychokinesis* (the modern phrase to describe the mind's moving of physical objects), associated most often with the work of J. B. Rhine in America and S. G. Soal in England. All this is set forth clearly, and there is no need for me to anticipate the exposition except to point out that for three centuries and more persons have been more ready to expect mystery in the realm of the mind than in that of matter.

What do people really want when they come up against supposed paranormal phenomena? They try to resolve the enigma, explaining the events in familiar physical, physiological, or psychological terms. If they succeed, are they pleased, or are they a little regretful that their investigatory ingenuity has crushed the mystery out of what seemed so hopefully inexplicable? I think they are sorry at their success. Fundamentally, they hope to fail so as to preserve a sense of being in a world where mind is powerful.

That failure is success in psychic research is a consequence of the fact that ESP is negatively defined. ESP is said to be communication without the intervention of the ordinary sensory channels. It was believed that bats, for instance, dodge wires in the dark because of their clairvoyance; that is to say, investigation failed to reveal how they did it. Then research succeeded in finding a sensory explanation, and the clairvoyance evaporated: bats can locate wires by the reflection of the sound of their own squeaking, which is pitched above the limit of human audibility.

This scientific success was, however, a parascientific failure, and so it will always be. To prove that ESP exists requires confirmation that communication can and does occur by no known sensory channel. It is easy to establish one's own ignorance of the channel, but not of a universal necessity for the ignorance, which may suddenly evaporate as it did in the case of the bats. A universal negative of this sort cannot be proven. Ignorance is too plentiful. Unexplained communication always remains inexplicable until at last it is scientifically accounted for. It seems quite probable that the world of intellectual debate may never be completely without the persons who feel that they have gained something of value in failing to discover, for some case of communication, a natural means of transmission.

Professor Hansel's book is, for the most part, a history of the failure to prove the universal negative of ESP. Again and again, when a medium or a "sensitive" subject is caught in trickery, the believer in paranormal phenomena raises the question of whether some of the phenomena in question are not after all "genuine" (inexplicable), even though some portion has been accomplished by fraud.

Spirit "controls" also resort to this saving principle. Margery's control (her deceased brother Walter) used to "say" that, because convincing the public of the actuality of the spirit world is such exhausting work, he used trickery to persuade his investigators of what was already established as truth and resorted to genuine phenomena only on special occasions. Just so, William James saved a crucial moment in an important lecture-demonstration when a turtle's heart should have beat and did not: he used his finger to twitch the string that connected the heart with a movable pointer whose shadow was projected upon a screen, thus making the demonstration clear. A correct demonstration it was, but by noncardiac pedagogy with the true cause inscrutable to the audience.*

* Sometime in the early 1880's, William James accepted responsibility for the physiological demonstrations of a well-known popular lecturer, Newell Martin. They had rigged a string from a turtle's heart to a pivoted straw that went up and down as the heart pulsated so as to cast its shadow on a large screen. The heart, alas, was dying, and it stopped readily enough when the lecturer stimulated the inhibiting nerves but failed to start again when the accelerating nerves were innervated. What to do? "I was terrified at the fiasco," wrote James, years afterward, "and found myself suddenly acting like one of those military geniuses who on the field of battle convert disaster into victory. There was no time for deliberation; so, with my forefinger under a part of the straw that cast no shadow, I found myself impulsively and automatically imitating the rhythmical movements which my colleague had prophesied the heart would undergo. I kept the experiment from failing. . . . I established in the audience the true view of the subject. . . . 'There is no worse lie than a truth misunderstood.' . . . The heart's failure would have been misunderstood by the audience and given the lie to the lecturer. . . . Even now as I write in cool blood I am tempted to think that I acted quite correctly. I was acting for the *larger* truth, at any rate." [1]

It is quite clear that interest in parapsychology has been maintained by faith. People want to believe in an occult something. In fact, the common citizen comes with the case of an inexplicable phenomenon and says, "Don't you think there is Something in that?" What would "Something" be? Great scientists as well as ordinary citizens believe. Among the notable believers in ESP in the last century, Hansel mentions Augustus De Morgan (mathematician and logician), Alfred Russel Wallace (naturalist and independent inventor of the theory of evolution), Sir William Crookes (physicist famed for early research in radioactivity), Henry Sidgwick (philosopher and ethicist), Sir William Fletcher Barrett (physicist, known for his studies of magnetism, heat, sound, and vision), Sir Oliver Lodge (physicist, known for his investigations of electromagnetic phenomena), and many others.

Hansel tells how Sidgwick, when elected President of the Society for Psychical Research, said: "We must drive the objector into the position of being forced to admit the phenomena as inexplicable, at least by him, or to accuse the investigators either of lying or of cheating or of a blindness or a forgetfulness incompatible with any intellectual condition except absolute idiocy." Throughout history religious faith has produced stronger diatribes than that, and one senses here the same spirit. Faith is always more aggressive than evidence. And what about the Chief Judge of the Supreme Consular Court at Shanghai, Sir Edmund Hornby, who, as Hansel tells us, was so sure of the details of the apparition of the court reporter and then later, when inconsistencies were established, changed his story? Was his forgetfulness indicative of "absolute idiocy," or was he, in spite of his distinction and judicial calling, merely human?

Clearly, it is not possible to hold a strong faith in the existence of parapsychological phenomena without accepting some incompatibles in the repertoire of beliefs, although the contradiction is apt not to be recognized by the person who holds to it. If ESP has no definition, that is to say, if its definition is negative and is thus no definition at all, if it has no specification of conditions that will tell you when ESP is working and when it is not, why then belief in the existence of ESP has to be a matter of faith and preference, since there can be no proof. Yet it is said, even occasionally by distinguished men of science notable for their erudition, "Now that the existence of ESP is established, we should bend our energies toward discovering its nature and the conditions under which it occurs." How can they say that? Only by accepting incompatibles in their beliefs.

The Stanford University psychologist, Leon Festinger, and his associates have coined the term *cognitive dissonance* for this kind of unwitting acceptance of contradictions. They gave it a vivid meaning by the publication in 1957 of *When Prophecy Fails,* an account of unfulfilled prophecies and disappointed messiahs, concerned especially with a prophecy of an enormous destructive flood that would occur, according to information revealed to a particular sensitive woman by beings from another planet, on December 21 of a recent year.[2] The group of believers in this prophecy was infiltrated by psychologists, and the group's rational resolutions when the prophecy was not fulfilled are described. Accounts of these beliefs differ from the histories of persistent beliefs in paranormal phenomena only in that in this case men of great prestige were not among the believers.

On the other hand, it is not fair to reproach these men of faith. Cognitive dissonance shades off into prejudice, delusion, trickery, dishonesty, and fraud. Perhaps the last three should be defined as despicable, but the others are the inevitable limitations of honest men.

Take the common prejudice in favor of believing oneself right, the need for the great man to defend his important theory. The great American geologist, Louis Agassiz, for example, held out against the theory of evolution until his death. This is the same egoism that produces the motivation that keeps the scientific investigator at work. It is much better for science to accept these individual biases and to let criticism amend error eventually, even at times to wait a hundred years for correction by posterity. Belief always has to be exercised in the face of insufficient evidence, and any decision based on insufficient evidence creates a dissonance.[3] That is why William James wrote *The Will to Believe:* he felt that faith must be held to be beyond reproach—in religion and also in science, as James's own suspended judgment on psychic research showed.[4]

It is evident that modern ESP research is psychical research gone quantitative. It has had a great deal to do with statistics and thus with the theory of probabilities, the foundation of statistics. One is told that a paranormal phenomenon exists because a difference was found in relative frequencies, a difference for which there was only 1 possibility in a billion (or in a million, or in 10^8, 10^{21}) of the phenomenon's being "due to chance." These differences that, within reason, cannot be due to chance must (if you are a determinist, as even parapsychologists are) be due to "Something," and that is the mysterious Something that began this whole affair. We have avoided the need to define the Something, but now our trouble lies in specifying the nature of Chance.

There are many definitions of chance. Some are mathematical, relating immediately to the logic of the theory of probabilities and not to actual occurrences. There are tables of chance made out, long lists of randomly distributed numbers which scientists accept when they come near fitting the mathematical model.[5] Such definitions need not concern us, for they apply only when shown to fit empirically observed frequencies. In the case of ESP, chance occurrence is usually determined without observation. It is supposed to be ½ for the heads or tails of a coin, ⅕ for drawing a card from an ESP pack, which consists of equal numbers of 5 kinds of cards.

How does one know that the chance of each side turning up is ½ for each coin toss, that a thousand tosses will give somewhere near 500 heads and 500 tails? One does not. It has been said that the frequency of near ½ has been tested out empirically by numerous tosses, but how can this be unless the conditions of the test are specified? The most reliable observation would employ mechanical tossing instead of a dependence on the casual variability of an uncontrolled toss. Yet, if one had a well-designed mechanical tosser, it ought always to work the same way and everything would depend on whether the coin was put in the machine heads up or tails up. If it were always put in the same way, there would always be the same result, and the probability of heads would be 0 or 1; or ½ could be achieved by alternating heads and tails as the coin is put in the machine.

At this point in the argument, he who has statistical faith is apt to become outraged. "You have rigged Chance with a machine!" is the charge. But does not science want rigid conditions? Are not statisticians determinists in a situation like this? And what would chance be for these people? It might well be the heads-tails frequency of coins in the subway fare box, where every coin is tossed by a different person whose habits of tossing and of keeping change in his pocket must remain inscrutable. Chance in this case is immutable ignorance.* The relative frequency is whatever it is found to be when the conditions of tossing have been specified, but, if the conditions are changed, the frequency can be either 1 or 0 or something in between—perhaps ½, perhaps not.

Determining chance frequencies with a pack of cards that is shuffled is even less sure. The shuffler's intent is to cut the deck in half and then riffle the cards of each half into one another, with their alternation as the ideal. Even the dictionary supports this view of the shuffler's purpose. Suppose this intent is accurately realized by dividing the deck exactly in half and carefully arranging it by selecting cards from each half by alternation. What happens? A deck of 52 cards comes back into its original order every eighth shuffle. Sixteen cards repeat their order after only 4 shuffles, but 12 cards take 10. It takes 20 such shuffles before an ESP pack of 25 cards resumes its original order. Does shuffling then give randomness? Of course, in actual repeated shuffling the cards do not repeat their order, and that is because the shuffler fails to realize his own intent. The order of the cards depends not on what he tries to do, but the ways in which he has bungled his intention. Here is another case of immutable ignorance constituting the conditions for chance, a delusion that there would be an equal distribution of bungles.[11]

How can one really be scientific about this matter? Conditions ought to be kept constant, exactly specified so that the experiment can be repeated. Suppose one is testing clairvoyance with an ESP pack of 25 cards, 5 cards of each of 5 kinds. Let the subject without any ESP guess the cards and note the frequencies of right and

---

* The assigning of equal probabilities to events that are not known to differ in probability was called "the equal distribution of ignorance" by the nineteenth-century English mathematician George Boole.[6] The assumption was called the Principle of Insufficient Reason by the nineteenth-century German scientist Johannes von Kries, who spoke of Cogent Reason when evidence was available.[7] It was named the Principle of Indifference by J. M. Keynes,[8] the twentieth-century English economist and philosopher. The point for us to remember is that "there are no laws of chance in the sense that the laws dictate the pattern of events."[9] On the logical dissonance that the use of the Principle creates, see E. G. Boring, "Statistical Frequencies as Dynamic Equilibria."[10]

wrong guesses, whether ⅕ right or something else. That is the control series. Then have a subject with ESP take his turn, and let the researcher find out how many right guesses he makes. That can be done 20 times, the *probable error* for each series (experimental and control) can be found, as can the probable error of the difference between the two and the ratio of the difference to its probable error (the critical ratio). There would be no need to go further to compute the probability of whether or not the difference is due to chance, for the critical ratio would show when the difference is large enough to be significant, and one would compare this statistic with one's experiences with measured differences of such phenomena and decide whether to be excited enough to publish.

In science, a fact is always a difference, a value is always relative to something. There must be a standard of reference or a control.[12] Both phenomenon and control need equal precision of specification so that chance is not assumed on the basis of immutable ignorance but is observed as a frequency in the control series.

Still, I have been talking nonsense about ESP for there is no sure way of turning ESP off and on so that control and experimental observations are separated. Might a "sensitive" subject be used for the experimental and an "insensitive" for the control data? Hardly, for ESP has no real definition, and, if the supposed insensitive was right more times than the supposed sensitive, the conclusion would be that you did not know how to distinguish between sensitivity and insensitivity. So everything comes back to the fact that ESP lacks clear specification.

Clearly, there are insidious logical weaknesses when concepts of probability are applied to the validation of ESP. This introduction is, however, not the place to discuss the details of this complex logical problem; yet no harm can have been done in exhibiting this rather special dissonance to which some keen thinkers adhere without realizing how insecure is the support these elaborate statistics and gigantic probabilities in parapsychology afford.*

* There is an extensive literature on the application of the theory of probabilities to empirical data, and the reader can enter it by way of the studies cited (Boole, von Kries, Keynes, Boring in 1941, and Ayer) and the various other works that they cite. For specific discussion of card-guessing by ESP in this context, see works by Boring[13] and Ayer.[14]

Actually, if I had written this book, I think I should have done what Professor Hansel has done: take these preposterous relative frequencies, the billion to 1 odds—take them tongue-in-cheek, it is true—and display them to my reader to impress him. Every scientist knows what these chance values in statistics imply—not what you would actually get if you made a billion experiments as nearly identical as possible, but a difference that is so very large in respect of its variability that it just cries out for explanation. One of the most effective tactics at Professor Hansel's disposal has been to turn these very probabilities against the proponents of ESP. How can it be argued that in the actual ESP experiments, with all the deficiencies Professor Hansel points out, the probability of error or deception is so enormously remote? All agree that a great relative magnitude of difference implies a cause, and what can a cause be if no specification can be written for it?

EDWIN G. BORING
Harvard University

ESP

A Scientific Evaluation

CHAPTER 1

The Origins
of Psychical Research

MOST persons learn through experience that awareness of objects in the world outside of them arises through the use of the senses. Scientific knowledge explains how this comes about—we see an object because light is reflected from it into our eyes—and also makes clear, indirectly, the conditions under which seeing cannot take place—light is necessary for vision; therefore, without it we cannot see.

Personal experience also tells us that our thoughts remain private unless expressed by voice or action. Another person's thoughts can be guessed, but few would claim to be able to know them as they would if the person were thinking aloud. There are exceptions. On the stage, men appear to see when blindfolded and to read thoughts; but such performances are classified as magic, and it is known that the magician uses tricks that enable him to appear to do what common sense says is impossible.

During the past 30 years, however, the public has become aware of reports that abilities such as clairvoyance and telepathy have been demonstrated in the laboratory by means of rigorously controlled experiments. These claims are puzzling to many persons who are interested in natural processes and scientific experimentation, for the investigators appear to have established, by means of carefully planned experiments and conventional statistical analyses, the reality of phenomena that conflict with well-established principles.

Experimental evidence has been produced for four such processes to date:

1. *Telepathy,* a person's awareness of another's thoughts without there being any communication through sensory channels.

1

2. *Clairvoyance*, knowledge acquired of an object or an event without the use of the senses.

3. *Precognition*, knowledge a person may have of another person's future thoughts (*precognitive telepathy*), or of future events (*precognitive clairvoyance*).

4. *Psychokinesis*, a person's ability to influence a physical object or an event, such as the fall of a die, by thinking about it.

Since the first three of these processes involve an act of perception or cognition and also because they are, by definition, independent of activity in the sense organs, each is commonly referred to as a kind of *extrasensory perception*, or ESP.

It will be seen that these four terms are restatements in systematic language of beliefs that have long been a part of folklore and superstition. Telepathy is a new name for mind reading; clairvoyance for second sight; precognition for divination or premonition; and psychokinesis is another name for levitation or for the process whereby a man thinks, for example, that he can get good weather for his holiday by praying for it. For this reason the experiments, if they can be relied on, would imply that much of what has in the past been regarded as superstition must now be included in the domain of natural science.

THE FOUNDATION OF THE SOCIETY FOR PSYCHICAL RESEARCH

Preoccupation with these beliefs was responsible for the emergence at the end of the nineteenth century of *psychical research*, the study of ESP and related phenomena, as an organized discipline. At that time there was a great deal of speculation about the possibility of strange, new human powers. Stories of extraordinary happenings that seemed to contravene accepted scientific principles were popular, just as they are today. In the latter half of the nineteenth and well into the twentieth century much publicity was given to *spiritualist mediums*, who supposedly received messages from the dead and whose exploits attracted considerable scientific interest.

But at that time science displayed a unity in that when a discipline, such as biology, revealed new facts, they were always consistent with other scientific knowledge. Thus, principles of physics and chemistry operated in the new discoveries of biology. As D'Arcy Thompson (1860–1948), the Scottish biologist, wrote, ". . . no physical law, any more than gravity itself, not even among the puzzles of stereo-chemistry, or of physiological surface-action and osmosis, is known to be transgressed by the bodily mechanism."[1]

In the realm of the senses, the eye was found to employ principles known to optics and the ear to contain mechanisms that might be expected from the study of sound. Messages were transmitted along nerve fibers from the sensory organs to the brain, and the nervous system behaved in a manner that was consistent with knowledge of other physical systems.

While it was not clear at that time whether psychological events would ever be fully explicable in terms of the natural laws already known to science, nothing in human behavior seemed at variance with known processes. The precise changes arising in the brain that were responsible for, say, memory were not known, but remembering displayed no very strange characteristics; similar processes, such as the camera's recording of a photographic image or the creation of a charge in a condenser, were well understood. However, if a man had shown himself to be capable of knowing about things before they happened, that would have involved a process of quite a different order, as if the photograph could emerge before the film had been exposed in the camera.

While telepathy seemed unlikely but not impossible—for it was conceivable that some sixth sense lay undiscovered—precognition displayed characteristics foreign to science, since, in this case, an effect seemed to precede its cause.

Not all the scientists were skeptical about the reports of what appeared to be paranormal happenings. A number of eminent British scientists, including the chemist, Sir William Crookes (1832–1919), the physicists Sir William Fletcher Barrett (1844–1925) and Sir Oliver Joseph Lodge (1851–1940), the mathematician Augustus De Morgan (1806–1871), and the biologist Alfred Russel Wallace (1823–1913), thought that there was more in the reports than orthodox science would admit. After some early unsuccessful attempts to bring these matters to the serious attention of the scientific world, a group of scholars at Cambridge University decided that the time had come to set up a learned society to examine those faculties of man, real or supposed, that appeared inexplicable to science. As a result, the Society for Psychical Research was founded in 1882, with Henry Sidgwick (1838–1900), Professor of Moral Philosophy at Cambridge, as its first president. An American society for psychical research was established a few years later, with the distinguished astronomer Simon Newcomb (1835–1909) as its president; today there are similar groups in 17 countries.

Since those early beginnings, a considerable amount of research has been conducted by the societies, by private individuals, and in universities. Today, psychical research, or *parapsychology* as it is now known, has come to be regarded by many as an accepted field of scientific study; investigations are in progress in numerous university departments; several laboratories and associations are committed to full-time research; and higher degrees are awarded in the topic.

ATTITUDES TO ESP

For the student of psychology, the position is extremely puzzling. Most of the leading British psychologists, for example, who have had anything to say on the matter of extrasensory perception, including Sir Cyril Burt, Margaret Knight, Robert H. Thouless and H. J. Eysenck, leave no doubt that they regard its existence as proved. For example, Mrs. Knight, who is lecturer in psychology at Aberdeen University and is well known to the British public wrote: "But as Thouless convincingly argues it is a waste of time to conduct further laborious experiments merely to demonstrate the occurrence of ESP. This has now been established beyond reasonable doubt." [2]

Professor Eysenck, head of the Department of Psychology at the Maudsley Hospital, London, known as a hard-headed and critical scientist wrote:

Unless there is a gigantic conspiracy involving some thirty University departments all over the world, and several hundred highly respected scientists in various fields, many of them originally hostile to the claims of the psychical researchers, the only conclusion the unbiased observer can come to must be that there does exist a small number of people who obtain knowledge existing either in other people's minds, or in the outer world, by means yet unknown to science.[3]

The student finds a similar viewpoint expressed by other well-known philosophers and scientists. Yet parapsychology probably does not appear in his curriculum, nor do any of his textbooks contain a reference to extrasensory perception in their indexes.

If he questions his teachers, he will probably find that they know very little about psychical research, or, if they are critical of it, that they have few facts with which to support their criticisms. Thus, Samuel George Soal, a mathematician at London University and Britain's best-known parapsychologist, wrote:

> There is, of course, no shortage of people who feel that, because they are qualified in Psychiatry or Psychology they are competent to pass judgment on the work of the parapsychologist. The "expert" knowledge of such persons is usually based on some quite elementary books on the subject which omit the essential experimental details without which a proper evaluation of the work is not possible. It would be interesting to meet the psychiatrist or psychologist who has perused every page of the 49 volumes of the *Proceedings* of the Society for Psychical Research, and who remains a sceptic. It is no coincidence that those most sceptical of ESP research are almost invariably those who are least acquainted with the facts.[4]

Even in the beginnings of psychical research, the conflict between skeptic and believer existed. The members of the new Society for Psychical Research thought that a strong a priori case for telepathy and kindred phenomena existed in the numerous reports of inexplicable experiences; many scientists adopted the attitude that any such phenomena were, a priori, so unlikely in view of existing knowledge that there was no point in bothering about them.

Toward the end of the nineteenth century, the great German scientist, Hermann Ludwig von Helmholtz (1821–1894) expressed this viewpoint when he declared: "Neither the testimony of all the Fellows of the Royal Society, nor even the evidence of my own senses, would lead me to believe in the transmission of thought from one person to another independently of the recognized channels of sense." [5] Helmholtz was speaking with some authority, since he was the greatest living expert on sensory communication. To him, the manner in which information is acquired through the activity of the sense organs and the relationship between bodily processes and mental processes made the idea of telepathy as scientifically untenable as that of a flat earth.

A similar viewpoint has been expressed more recently by D. O. Hebb, a Professor of Psychology at McGill University, Canada.

> Personally, I do not accept ESP for a moment, because it does not make sense. My external criteria, both of physics and physiology, say that ESP is not a fact despite the behavioral evidence that has been reported. I cannot see what other basis my colleagues have for rejecting it; and if they are using my basis, they and I are allowing psychological evidence to be passed on by physical and physiological censors. Rhine may still turn out to be right, improbable as I think that is, and my own rejection of his views is—in a literal sense—prejudice. [6]

The well-known English author, Aldous Huxley (1894–1963), commented on Hebb's statement in *Life* magazine: "That a man of science should allow a prejudice to outweigh evidence seems strange enough. It is even stranger to find a psychologist rejecting a psychological discovery simply because it cannot be explained. Psi [the process of ESP] is intrinsically no more inexplicable than, say perception or memory; it is merely less common." [7]

Thouless, Reader in Psychology at Cambridge University and a former president of the British Society for Psychical Research, also has attacked those who refuse to accept the findings of research on extrasensory perception. In a paper he read to the Royal Institution of Great Britain in 1950, he said:

> In all science an unexpected experimental result is a challenge to the basis of our expectations and so becomes a possible starting point of theoretical advance. The failure of the Michelson-Morley experiment to reveal the expected motion of the earth relative to the ether made necessary the reconstruction of the theory on which the expectation of a detectable ether drift was based. By good fortune, this situation also produced the genius of Einstein who

was able to take the essential step in the reconstruction of theory which made the Michelson-Morley result explicable.

I would suggest that the discovery of the *psi* phenomena has brought us to a similar point at which we must question basic theories because they lead us to expectations contradicted by experimental results. . . . I can only suggest that we must be ready to question all our old conceptions and to distrust all our habits of thoughts.[8]

The case cited by Thouless is perhaps not so apt as it appears at first sight. The Michelson-Morley experiment—which attempted to measure the velocity of the earth through the ether (postulated as the medium through which light in space traveled) through the effect of this velocity on the velocity of light—failed to show any movement of the earth relative to the ether. Scientists did not, from this result, conclude that the earth was stationary and that the rest of the solar system moved around it; this would have contradicted too much of what was known and already accepted as true. Instead, they looked afresh at the process of measurement and the assumptions underlying it. The result, of course, was a new concept of the nature of light and its motion. Parapsychologists, on the other hand, ask critics to accept ESP as proved and to change the rest of science so that it can include this new phenomenon.

What Thouless is implying is, however, quite clear. No one can ignore a mass of empirical data provided that it conforms with all the safeguards and requirements of science.

In Helmholtz's time, the evidence for telepathy was almost entirely of an anecdotal nature, but during the last 80 years, numerous full-scale experiments have been carried out. It is claimed that they provide overwhelming evidence for the existence of ESP. It may be that any a priori theoretical objections must now be relinquished in the light of empirical evidence, but before such a drastic step is taken, it is necessary to be quite certain that the experimental results obtained by parapsychologists are due to paranormal rather than to normal processes and that the experiments establish this fact beyond all doubt.

A close inspection of the work of the parapsychologists is, in any case, important for two reasons: if their claims are justified, a complete revision in contemporary scientific thought is required at

least comparable to that made necessary in biology by Darwin and
in physics by Einstein. On the other hand, if ESP is merely an
artifact, it is then important to understand how conventional
experimental methods can yield results leading to erroneous conclusions.

CHAPTER 2

The Subject Matter
of Psychical Research

IN order to identify more exactly the processes in which parapsychologists are interested, it is necessary to describe the way in which they are investigated in the laboratory. It is not implied, however, that experiments have been conducted in precisely the manner described in this chapter.

AWARENESS OF EXTERNAL EVENTS

Knowledge of objects in the external environment is normally acquired through stimuli acting on the sense organs, in which some sort of physical action must take place. For that reason, some form of energy must pass from the object to the sense organ, or, in the case of the organs for taste and smell, particles of the substance that is sensed must be received. Activity at the sense organs constitutes the first step in a chain of processes ultimately resulting in knowledge of the external object. Before there can be this awareness, the individual has had to learn to react to a complex of stimuli that denotes a specific object. When we say we see a dog, a particular pattern of light and shade is recognized as having been due to the presence of a dog, that being an object we have seen before and learned to identify by this name.

TRANSMITTING A MESSAGE

A *message*, some form of information, is normally communicated by one person—the sender—through the means of voice, gesture, or some other activity involving the use of his muscles. This generates stimuli that can be detected by another person—the receiver—through the medium of one or more of his senses. The receiver thereby can become aware of what the sender is doing or of the message he is transmitting. Most messages involve the use of *language*, that being a means whereby sounds are encoded to signify objects or actions; but any other code can be used, so long as both the sender and the receiver employ the same system.

The number of methods of communication is limited by the ways in which the sender can, with his muscles, initiate activity detectable by the receiver. An instrument, such as a megaphone or a telescope, may be employed to increase the distance over which messages can be transmitted. The sender may also use apparatus to produce disturbances that cannot be detected by the unaided sense organs but that can be detected by means of suitable apparatus, such as a television set or telephone. However, in all these cases the sender has to initiate activity by using his muscles, and the receiver ultimately has to detect stimuli by means of his sense organs.

TELEPATHY

For telepathy to exist, the receiver, or *percipient*, must learn what the sender, or *agent*, is thinking about without the use of his sense organs. It is also usually implied that there is no special activity on the part of the agent. That is, his thoughts become known to the receiver, whether he wishes it or not and without his making any effort at communication.

Furthermore, in telepathic communication, information passes from one person to another without the use of any special apparatus. It does not involve the setting up of disturbances, such as those created by voice or movements, and it does not require any activity of the known senses. Telepathy therefore implies abilities of human beings thus far unknown to psychology and physiology and properties of matter unknown to physics.

To read someone's thoughts does not necessarily involve the idea of telepathy. Any normal person may at times have some idea of another's thoughts by utilizing cues such as facial expression, skin color, and posture. He will not know the verbal content, but he may obtain some idea of the other person's emotional state and from this deduce the type of thought that he is having.

In experiments carried out to demonstrate telepathy, the percipient tries to guess the nature of a symbol about which the agent is thinking. If the percipient could invariably guess correctly, or even could know when he had done so, there would be no difficulty in demonstrating telepathy. The experimenters themselves have, however, admitted the inability of their subjects to do either of these things.

The task of the percipient is made easier as the number of possible things about which the agent may be thinking is reduced. Thus, when the agent has complete freedom of choice, the percipient's job is at its most difficult; if he knows that the agent has been instructed to think of a digit between 0 and 10, then his task is greatly simplified. But even under the simplest conditions—namely, when the agent is instructed to think of 1 of 2 possible symbols—no percipient has ever guessed correctly all the time. The experimenters merely claim that some persons, while they do make mistakes, produce more correct guesses than are likely to arise by chance.

Most investigators of telepathy have preferred to use 5 symbols, and the percipient is informed that when he makes his guess the agent will be thinking about 1 of these 5. An experiment consists of a number of *trials*, or guesses; during each, while the agent looks at a card bearing 1 of the 5 symbols, the percipient tries to guess which symbol the agent is seeing. A subject might be tested by giving him 200 trials, broken up into 8 *runs* of 25 trials each. If the symbols are presented to the agent in random order, a person with no telepathic ability would be expected to guess correctly an average of ⅕ of the trials. If he made 200 guesses, he would therefore be expected to obtain about 40 successes.

It is claimed that under such conditions subjects sometimes obtain scores that are highly unlikely to arise by chance. If, for example, a subject obtains 60 successes in 200 trials and then goes on achieving similar scores on further runs, it soon becomes clear that something other than chance is responsible for his scores.

CLAIRVOYANCE

Clairvoyance differs from telepathy in that only one person is involved; the percipient can become aware of an event or the characteristics of an object without the involvement of a second person acting as transmitter.

If clairvoyance is possible, the agent in a telepathy experiment might appear to play a minor role, since there would be little point in his transmitting a message giving the symbol on a card to a percipient, who can identify it by clairvoyance. In the United States, investigators have obtained high scores as easily in clairvoyance experiments when no agent is employed, as in telepathy experiments. In Great Britain, many efforts to demonstrate clairvoyance have been made with subjects who have been successful in telepathy experiments; however, these attempts have not succeeded.

In the majority of the clairvoyance experiments, a subject attempts to guess the identities of symbols depicted on cards. One such experiment is similar to the telepathy study described above, except that the agent, instead of looking at the symbol displayed on the face of a card, merely touches its back and does not see the symbol; the percipient then attempts to guess it. In a more ambitious type of experiment, a pack of cards is shuffled and placed on a table in front of the percipient. He attempts to guess the identity of the cards in their order in the pack while it is left undisturbed.

PRECOGNITION

In a variation of the last experiment, the pack is shuffled after the subject has guessed at the identities of the cards. If scores at above the chance level are observed when the subject's guesses are checked against the cards as they exist *after the shuffle,* he is said to display precognitive clairvoyance.

In another test, the percipient takes part in a telepathy experiment in which he has to guess cards seen by an agent at the rate of 1 every 2 seconds. He scores significantly above the chance level when each of his guesses is checked against the card to be seen next by the agent; it is as if the guesser anticipates the person having the thought. He is then said to display precognitive telepathy.

Here there is no possibility that the agent transmits information to the percipient, for there is no means by which he could do so, since he is unaware of the symbol until 2 seconds after the guess has been recorded. The agent could, in fact, be talking freely to the percipient and still be unable to affect his scores.

In the major experiments on precognition, it has always been necessary for there to be an agent who later saw the symbol about which the percipient guessed. Percipients' scores have been above the chance level when the agent was instructed to look at the symbols on the cards during each trial, but only at the chance level when he merely touched the backs of the cards. A positive result in the latter instance would have been attributed to precognitive clairvoyance.

What is defined as precognition under these experimental conditions differs to some extent from popular usage of the term in which to have precognition would imply that a person had foreknowledge of something that he himself was going to experience. If precognition were possible, it is indeed reasonable to expect that the percipient would more easily precognize his own thoughts than those of someone else. An experimental situation to test this would require the percipient to see a series of symbols at, say, 6-second intervals and to guess the next 2 seconds before seeing it.

PSYCHOKINESIS

Psychokinesis differs from the processes already described in that a person is said to influence a physical object by thinking about it. Thus, he causes something to happen in the external world, rather than being influenced himself by an external event. The subjects in psychokinesis experiments, for example, may attempt to influence the fall of a die so that a particular face will land uppermost.

SPONTANEOUS DATA

Extrasensory perception and psychokinesis are usually regarded as being well-suited to investigation in the laboratory, but not all the phenomena studied in psychical research readily lend themselves to experiment. In the past, considerable attention has been paid to spontaneous events reported from everyday life that seemed to permit of no normal explanation, and a great deal of attention has been directed to the study of spiritualistic phenomena. In fact, there was greater scientific interest in the phenonomena of the séance rooms in the first part of this century than there is today in

all of extrasensory perception. At that time, interest was mainly
directed to the possibility of communication with the dead, but
today many parapsychologists regard mediums simply as persons
with highly developed telepathic and clairvoyant abilities. Some
parapsychologists would go further and say that the study of
spontaneous data and of telepathy, as demonstrated by the mediums, can provide more satisfactory evidence for ESP than can
laboratory experiments. It is also a fact that many people claim to
have had psychical experiences, and for most people, personal
experience provides more convincing evidence than any number of
experimental findings. However, because experimental material
can be commented upon more concretely, it will be discussed first
and the spontaneous data will be dealt with in the final chapters.

CHAPTER **3**

Examining the Evidence

FEW people have time to examine and test the evidence in parapsychology for themselves. They have to rely on authoritative statements made by investigators and by others who have studied the research. The same is true in any branch of science. A chemist, for example, cannot hope to verify every new claim reported in his field, but he has good reasons for believing that a mistake will be revealed by those specializing in the topic concerned.

How then is an authoritative opinion of extrasensory perception to be obtained? If there were no doubt about the existence of such phenomena, they would be dealt with as aspects of psychology. However, orthodox psychologists, to judge from what they teach in universities or include in their books, do not regard extrasensory perception as an established process, and if a psychologist is consulted, ESP is likely to be quickly dismissed. On the other hand, if a parapsychologist is asked, he is likely to have no doubts about the existence of ESP.

THE AMOUNT OF EVIDENCE

Experiments testing for the presence of extrasensory perception are fortunately of such a nature that anyone of reasonable intelligence can understand them and even try them out for himself. Many persons are put off at the start, however, because they have a false impression of the amount of evidence that has accumulated. For example, the well-known Hungarian-born English author Arthur Koestler wrote in *The Observer* of May 7, 1961:

The card-guessing and dice-throwing experiments repeated over millions of experimental runs with thousands of random experimental subjects—often whole classes of schoolboys who have no idea what the experiment is about; the more and more refined experimental conditions and methods of statistical breakdown; the increasingly elaborate machinery for mechanical card shuffling, dice-throwing, randomising, recording, and what-have-you, have turned the study of extra-sensory perception into an empirical science as sober, down-to-earth and also too often as dreary as teaching rats to run a maze or slicing up generations of flatworms.[1]

Few parapsychologists would claim, however, that millions of guesses have been made by thousands of subjects under good experimental conditions or that results providing conclusive evidence for ESP have been reported from many universities.

The experiments differ markedly in complexity; thus, an experiment may be relatively simple, involving, say, 4 persons who meet one afternoon and record 200 trials at guessing card symbols, or it may be highly complicated. Some of the telepathy experiments have, in fact, consisted of a large number of sittings in which the conditions have been changed from one sitting to another. With this latter type of investigation, it becomes particularly necessary to emphasize 3 principles that should be considered when assessing a study.

1. Each experiment must be considered solely on its own merits. A weakness cannot be excused because it was absent in a second experiment, which may have its own weaknesses; if it has not, the first experiment should be ignored and conclusions obtained only from the second.

Professional magicians often rely on the fact that their audience does not practice this kind of assessment. The magician, for example, may demonstrate "thought transference." The essential features of his trick are that a member of the audience takes a card from a pack of playing cards, looks at it, and replaces it. The magician later identifies it. A second member of the audience takes a card. This time, he is allowed to retain it, and the magician again names it. If a member of the audience isolates these essential features of the trick, he may be puzzled as to how it was carried out. He may decide after the first trick that the magician is somehow getting sight of the card after it is replaced in the pack. But on the second occasion, since the performer does not touch the pack after the card is drawn, this possibility would appear to have been eliminated.

Any professional magician is likely to have many variations of a simple trick of this nature. He may, for example, attempt to force the choice of a card, the identity of which is known to him, on each occasion. If he is successful in doing so, the card need not be replaced in the pack. If he is unsuccessful, he has to ask that it be put back so that he can bring it to the top of the pack by sleight of hand and somehow see its face. Few magicians announce in advance exactly what they are going to do.

2. An experiment that has any defect such that its result may be due to a cause other than ESP cannot provide conclusive proof of ESP. In parapsychology research, the process being investigated is both hypothetical and a priori extremely unlikely. Any possible known cause of the result is far more likely to be responsible for it than the hypothetical process under consideration.

A possible explanation other than extrasensory perception, provided it involves only well-established processes, should not be rejected on the grounds of its complexity or because it seems unlikely to be the true one.

For example, in the case of a particular experiment, it may be necessary to decide between two explanations accounting for the scores observed: extrasensory perception, which posits a new process, or a second one that, although complex, is dependent only on known processes. The latter may appear unlikely, but it is *possible*. It must be eliminated or its probability greatly reduced in further tests before the explanatory hypothesis of extrasensory perception can be entertained.

3. An experiment must be judged on the weakest part of its design. Inadequacy of control at one point cannot be overcome by extreme control at another.

For example, in the telepathy experiments with George Zirkle as subject, described on page 53, there is a weakness in that reliance must be placed entirely on the accuracy of an experimenter who also acted as agent and who recorded both the symbol she had been thinking about and the guess of the percipient. However stringent the controls of other features of the experiment, they cannot offset this weakness.

THE EFFECTS OF ERROR AND TRICKERY

In addition to the above, no factor that could influence the results of an experiment must be overlooked. If there is the slightest possibility that any or all participants in the experiments did anything to influence the result that is not noted in the experimental report, this possibility must be fully considered.

It is necessary to discuss openly possible trickery or cheating by participants to produce a spurious conclusion. If the result could have arisen through a trick, the experiment must be considered unsatisfactory proof of ESP, whether or not it is finally decided that such a trick was in fact used. At this point, the concern is with evaluation of the experiment rather than with a decision about whether a particular individual tried to influence the result. As a further step it may be necessary to establish whether there is any evidence to show that trickery did in fact take place.

It may be objected that any experiment can be condemned on the grounds that all of those taking part in it, including the researchers, may be indulging in a trick, and that trickery is a well-established process whereas ESP is not; therefore, no single experiment can be conclusive. This is so. But normally in science anyone who suspects an experimental result can repeat the experiment himself and check its conclusions.

Repetition after repetition of an ESP experiment by independent investigators renders the possibility of deception or error extremely unlikely and thus, if the original result is confirmed, the probability of ESP becomes increasingly likely.

INITIAL ASSUMPTIONS

Psychical research in many ways is like a game and some of the investigators have emphasized that those taking part in the experiments should treat them as games if they hope to obtain positive results. It may be that conditions required to conduct card-guessing experiments are necessarily somewhat similar to those in which a magician endeavors to demonstrate his powers. The magician has to elaborate the proceedings so that the obvious explanations are ruled out; the psychical researcher, so that normal means of gaining information and of trickery are eliminated. The researcher attempts to remove all loopholes, but the magician has to leave one so that he can perform his trick.

An ESP experiment can be analyzed in much the same way as one tries to discover how the conjurer performs his trick. For example, a girl is sawed in half by a magician. First, she is seen, a complete female figure; later the legs are seen sticking out of one end of a box, the head, out of the other end. A saw is passed through the region that corresponds with the girl's abdomen. The assumption is that the girl has not, in fact, been sawed in half, since she is intact at the conclusion of the experiment. Thus no part of the girl was in the space through which the saw passed. Then either the sawing was an illusion, or she was not in the place through which the saw passed. At a further demonstration, the head and legs that are sticking out are inspected, and the conclusion that is reached is that they could not be where they are and belong to the same person unless there was a torso in the area through which the saw passed—that is, unless either the head or the legs were an illusion. But other observers examine the head and legs and convince us that they are real. Then, the legs belong to some other person than does the head.

The hypothesis is now formed that two girls are inside the box, so arranged that we see the head of one and the legs of the other and so that there is an empty space between them through which the saw can pass. This analysis of the conjuring trick starts with the assumption that what the conjurer claims to do, or appears to have done, is not what he does in reality, since it contradicts too much of what is known about the properties of things.

Thus, in analyzing an experiment that purports to prove ESP, it is wise to adopt initially the assumption that ESP is impossible, just as it is assumed that the conjurer cannot saw the same girl in half twice each evening.

To assume that ESP is impossible is not unreasonable, since there is a great weight of knowledge supporting this point of view, and the main evidence contradicting it is that of the experiment being analyzed. If analysis shows that this assumption is untenable, then the possibility of ESP has to be accepted.

THE STATISTICAL EVALUATION OF AN EXPERIMENT

It will be found that there are enormous odds against the scores produced in many of the experiments under discussion having arisen by chance. Thus, in Soal's experiments with Mrs. Stewart, discussed on pages 127–128, the odds are quoted as 10^{70} to 1 against chance. In mathematical notation, the superscript numeral is the power to which a number is raised, that is, the number of times it is multiplied by itself. If a man bet a penny on a horse at these odds and won, he would have a very difficult task disposing of his fortune. If he gave a million dollars to every man alive, for that matter if he included every man who has ever lived, he would still have plenty left. After repeating that whole gift a million times every second for a million million years, he would not have made the slightest hole in his capital. He would certainly still have a million million times as much money as he had given away.

The great odds against a particular score arising by chance are sometimes quoted as if they are proof that the experiment really does prove the existence of ESP. Thus, in a review of the Soal-Goldney experiment on Basil Shackleton (see pages 105–124), C. D. Broad, Professor of Philosophy at Cambridge University, came to the conclusion that it provided evidence "which is statistically overwhelming for the occurrence not only of *telepathy,* but of precognition." [2]

Professor Broad appears to have assumed that the result could have been achieved only if the percipient possessed precognitive telepathy. However, if there is even the smallest possibility of some other explanation, the results of the experiment support it as much as they support the hypothesis of precognition. The probability (10^{-35}) obtained in the experiment is that of the score having arisen by chance. It tells us nothing about the probability of precognitive telepathy. To provide statistically overwhelming evidence for the occurrence of ESP in experiments of this nature requires satisfaction of two conditions: (i) the scores achieved by the subject must be such as are very unlikely to arise by chance, and (ii) the experimental conditions must be such that only ESP could account for them.

The first condition is quite simple to assess. The percipient's score is compared with the one expected to arise by chance, and the frequency with which such a score would be expected to arise in a large number of such experiments if the guesses were made purely at random is calculated. Thus, in the case of the Shackleton experiment, it was found that his score would be expected to arise by chance only once in about 10^{35}.

The second condition causes the difficulties. For any interpretation as to why the experimental result differs significantly from the chance expectation is dependent on what is known about the conditions under which the experiment was carried out. A low probability that a certain result will occur, as noted in the first condition, reveals nothing about the probability that ESP does or does not exist. This is entirely dependent on the second condition. An example will make this clearer.

When a magician performs a thought-reading act, he correctly identifies 50 cards, each drawn from a pack of 52 and then replaced; the pack is shuffled before each draw. The odds against his guessing these cards by chance are 52^{50} to 1, and this is even more impressive a result than was achieved by Shackleton. It is, however, unlikely that the magician's score is due to ESP, for it is known that he is performing a trick. In this case, the probability of ESP in the second condition is 0, and the total probability of the result being due to ESP is 0.

The weight attached to an experiment's supposed proof of ESP is entirely dependent on how certain one can be that any alternative explanations of the result are completely eliminated. The subject's score and the probability of its arising by chance serves merely to indicate whether an assessment of the experiment should be made at all.

The second condition is the more difficult to assess. The experimental conditions may be examined most meticulously and no flaw found, but there is no certainty that nothing has been missed. The conclusion that an experiment provides statistically overwhelming evidence for the appearance of ESP is misleading if no allowance is made for the possibility of error in the experimental setup. The incidence of trickery, deception, and error in psychical research is such that the probability of their occurrence is certainly far from insignificant. Professor Broad's statement, quoted earlier in this chapter, is based on assumptions that the experiment he is quoting is completely watertight and that there is no probability of error or trickery or that it is small enough to be ignored. It could, however, be argued that the probability that ESP exists is insignificantly small and the probability of fraud quite appreciable. In that case, it could be said that the experiments provide overwhelming evidence for trickery or error. If it can be shown that these conditions could account for the results, a more likely hypothesis can be established. If, on the other hand, it can be reasonably ascertained that trickery or error have been eliminated through the employment of a completely watertight experimental procedure, then the experiment can provide evidence to support the hypothesis of extrasensory perception. If the result is confirmed by other investigators, ESP eventually will cease to be a hypothesis and will be accepted as fact. If a process really does exist in nature, this fact eventually will silence all objections, since it is as difficult to maintain erroneous criticism as it is to demonstrate the existence of something that is nonexistent. Criticism must be thorough, just as experimental research seeking to establish the facts must be thorough.

EXPLORATORY AND CONCLUSIVE METHODS

Few people are likely to have time themselves to check through all the experiments on ESP that have been conducted. It is therefore necessary to make a selection of the data, which must include all those experiments generally agreed to provide the strongest evidence for the presence of ESP. Fortunately, several of the most prominent workers in this field have surveyed the literature and selected such studies. At the same time, they have rejected experiments that contain weaknesses in design or in which explanations other than a manifestation of ESP can account for the result.

Two of the best-known American parapsychologists, Joseph B. Rhine, Director of the Institute for Parapsychology, and formerly Director of the Parapsychology Laboratory, Duke University, and Joseph G. Pratt, formerly associated with the Laboratory, stress the fact that not every experiment is designed with the object of establishing the existence of ESP. Thus, in their most recent book, *Parapsychology: Frontier Science of the Mind,* they differentiate between experiments employing an exploratory method and those employing a conclusive method.

Exploratory methods are employed, they say, "on the assumption that final conclusions will require a more cautious type of experiment." [3] According to them, "The chief characteristic of the exploratory stage of scientific inquiry is that in it the explorer is permitted to range widely, venture freely, and look into everything that might be important to his interest without being burdened with too much precautionary concern. It is a more venturesome, a more extravagant phase of investigation. It is always a first stage, of course, but only because of the natural order of investigation. While it is obvious that without this exploratory stage there would be little or nothing for science to verify or establish, it is equally true that with it alone no results would ever be firmly established." [4]

Rhine and Pratt state four requirements of a conclusive experiment:

1. Sound measurement.
2. Satisfactory experimental safeguards against normal sensory communication.
3. Care in recording. Here they remark that the responsibility of recording data should be shared between two responsible persons in such a way that no error made by either could go undetected.
4. Precautions against deception on the part of the experimenters themselves.

Proof for the existence of ESP must obviously depend on conclusive experiments, but only a small number of all such experiments are considered to fall into this category, and parapsychologists are not agreed among themselves which of the experiments should be regarded as conclusive. This was pointed out by J. Fraser Nicol, Research Officer of the American Society for Psychical Research, at an international symposium on extrasensory perception organized by the Ciba Foundation and held at Cambridge University, England, in 1955. (The Ciba Foundation was founded by CIBA Ltd. of Switzerland and is administered independently by a board of British trustees. Among other activities it organizes international conferences on scientific topics.) After comparing the selection of conclusive experiments provided by different authors, Nicol concluded by saying: "Clearly there is no unity of opinion among leading psychical researchers as to what constitutes valid evidence." [5]

WHICH ARE THE CONCLUSIVE EXPERIMENTS?

In a section of *Parapsychology,* "The Evidence for Psi," Rhine and Pratt name four experiments that they consider as providing conclusive evidence for ESP. These are:

1. The Pearce-Pratt series.
2. The Pratt-Woodruff series.
3. The Soal-Goldney series.
4. The Soal-Bateman series.

An earlier survey,[6] published in 1940, by 5 members of the Parapsychology Laboratory at Duke University, isolated the following conclusive experiments after surveying 145 reported up to that time:

1. The Pratt-Woodruff series.
2. The Pearce-Pratt series.
3. An experiment by Lucien Warner.
4. The Turner Ownbey series.
5. An experiment reported by B. F. Riess.
6. An experiment reported by Murphy and Taves.

A further survey contained in *Modern Experiments in Telepathy,* by Soal and Bateman, published in 1954, lays stress on

1. The Soal-Goldney series.
2. The Soal-Bateman series.

and also mentions without criticism:

3. The Pearce-Pratt series.
4. The Pratt-Woodruff series (mentioned as "fairly good," although no specific feature of the experiment is criticized).
5. A test known as the Martin-Stribic series.

The Riess experiment is dismissed as questionable, and the experiments of Warner and of Murphy and Taves are not mentioned. Speaking of the Turner-Ownbey series, Soal and Bateman state that the result must be accepted or else the two experimenters (Miss Ownbey and Dr. Rhine) were in collusion to deceive.

While it is of the greatest importance that each of the conclusive experiments be included in an assessment of the evidence for ESP, it is also necessary that weak experiments not be selected for criticism with the intention of extending such criticism to the research in general. The following remarks, made by R. A. McConnell, of the Department of Biophysics, Pittsburgh University, at the CIBA symposium express this view:

A final point about which I want to say something is that, at least in the United States in my own experience a certain class of critic, who is in a related field and who might be presumed by his colleagues to have some opinion about ESP—I am thinking particularly of certain psychologists—has managed to confuse the thinking of the scientific fraternity as a whole by a very simple procedure. Whenever the question comes up as to what is wrong with the ESP experiments that have been performed, the tactic which has been followed—and I can only conclude it has been followed consciously—is to describe the weaknesses in those experiments which are not the best experiments; to point out all the things that are wrong with the poor experiments and quietly to ignore the experiments which cannot be explained away.[7]

McConnell did not specify the poor experiments that should be ignored, but in the paper in which the above statement was made, he mentioned only 2 experiments with approval. These were the Pearce-Pratt series and the Riess study. In *E. S. P. and Personality Patterns* by McConnell and G. R. Schmeidler, Professor of Psychology at City College, New York, published in 1959, there is, however, a chapter, "Evidence that ESP Occurs," in which the following experiments are named:

1. The Pearce-Pratt experiment.
2. The Pratt-Woodruff experiment.
3. The Riess experiment.
4. An experiment carried out by Brugmans, Heymanns, and Weinberg in 1919.
5. The Soal-Goldney experiment.

Thus a small number of experiments are named in most of the surveys that have been made, and a number of other experiments receive occasional mention. It is the purpose of this book to analyze all those investigations that have been called conclusive. A full chapter is given to the Pearce-Pratt, the Pratt-Woodruff, and the Soal-Goldney series, since they have received unanimous approval. In addition, a chapter is devoted to an investigation of the supposed telepathic abilities of 2 Welsh schoolboys carried out by Soal after the above surveys were made. This experiment may appear out of place, since it has been extensively criticized by several parapsychologists in the United States. In Britain, however, it has been acclaimed by most reviewers, including the eminent psychologist formerly at London University, Sir Cyril Burt, as providing the final evidence for telepathy.

Other experiments will be described when they are of historical interest or illustrate the manner in which experimental error may arise. Some details are also given of experiments conducted in the Soviet Union and elsewhere, since this work has been well received by American parapsychologists. The available details of this research are hardly sufficient, however, for a full appraisal to be made.

CHAPTER 4

Early Investigations

BRITISH RESEARCH

SOON after the formation of the Society for Psychical Research, a Committee on Thought Reading was set up, headed by William Barrett, then Professor of Physics in the Royal College of Science for Ireland, together with Edmund Gurney (1847–1888), who devoted his energies to psychical research, and Frederic Myers (1843–1901), an inspector of schools, both formerly fellows of Trinity College, Cambridge. Later in the year, Frank Podmore (1855–1910), a post-office official, joined the committee. Henry Sidgwick, in his presidential address to the Society in July 1882, introduced the first report of this committee by saying:

> We must drive the objector into the position of being forced either to admit the phenomena as inexplicable, at least by him, or to accuse the investigators either of lying or cheating or of a blindness or forgetfulness incompatible with any intellectual condition except absolute idiocy.
>
> I am glad to say that this result, in my opinion, has been satisfactorily attained in the investigation of thought-reading. Professor Barrett will now bring before you a report which I hope will be only the first of a long series of similar reports which may have reached the same point of conclusiveness.[1]

Sidgwick lived to eat his words, for the investigation described in that report concerned the 5 young daughters (Mary, Alice, Maud, Kathleen, and Emily) of an English clergyman, the Reverend A. M. Creery. During sitting after sitting, the girls and a young servant, Jane, convinced the investigators of their telepathic abilities. Then, 6 years later, in 1888, they were caught using a code and admitted to having deceived the researchers.

27

In the first report of the committee, mention was also made of a G. A. Smith, whose telepathic abilities supposedly were developed to the highest degree.[2] The second and third committee reports contained details of tests carried out on Smith, and it was claimed for nearly 20 years that these tests provided a watertight case for telepathy.

THE SMITH-BLACKBURN EXPERIMENTS

The affair started on August 26, 1882, after the publication of a letter by Douglas Blackburn, editor of *The Brightonian,* in the spiritualist magazine *Light,* which said, in part:

> The way Mr. Smith conducts his experiment is this: He places himself *en rapport* with myself by taking my hands: and a strong concentration of will and mental vision of my part has enabled him to read my thoughts with an accuracy that approaches the miraculous. Not only can he, with slight hesitation, read numbers, words and even whole sentences which I alone have seen, but the sympathy between us has developed to such a degree that he rarely fails to experience the taste of any liquid or solid I choose to imagine. He has named, described, or discovered small articles he has never seen when they have been concealed by me in the most unusual places, and on two occasions, he has successfully described portions of a scene which I either imagined or actually saw.

This letter came to the attention of Myers and Gurney, who forthwith went to Brighton and carried out tests on Smith and Blackburn.

They found that Smith, when blindfolded, could name words that had been shown to Blackburn even when there was no contact between the two men. Smith was also able to reproduce drawings of simple figures shown to Blackburn, provided he touched him. The two subjects then went to London and were investigated in a long series of tests carried out by the Committee on Thought Reading. One of the tests was later vividly described by Blackburn:

> These were the conditions: Smith sat in a chair at the large table. His eyes were padded with wool, and, I think, a pair of folded kid gloves, and bandaged with a thick dark cloth. His ears

were filled with one layer of cotton-wool, then pellets of putty. His entire body and the chair on which he sat were enveloped in two very heavy blankets. I remember, when he emerged triumphant, he was wet with perspiration, and the paper on which he had successfully drawn the figure was so moist that it broke during the examination by the delighted observers. Beneath his feet and surrounding his chair were thick, soft rugs, rightly intended to deaden and prevent signals by foot shuffles. Smith being rendered contact proof and perfectly insulated, my part began.

At the farther side of the room—a very large dining room— Mr. Myers showed me, with every precaution, the drawing that I was to transmit to the brain beneath the blankets. It was a tangle of heavy black lines, interlaced, some curved, some straight, the sort of thing an infant playing with a pen or pencil might produce, and I am certain absolutely indescribable in words, let alone in a code. I took it, fixed my gaze on it, pacing the room meanwhile and going through the usual process of impressing the figure upon my retina and brain, but always keeping out of touching distance with Smith. These preliminaries occupied perhaps ten or more minutes, for we made a point of never hurrying. I drew and re-drew many times openly in the presence of the observers, in order, as I explained and they allowed, to fix it on my brain.[3]

Blackburn went on to describe how he then stood in silence behind Smith's chair while Smith produced an almost line-for-line reproduction of Myers' original drawing.

As a result of their tests, the investigators concluded that they had eliminated the possibility of information reaching Smith through any of the known senses.

As Sidgwick suggested, a skeptic at the time could have concluded that all of the investigators were liars or idiots. He would more likely, however, have suspected that Smith and Blackburn had been using tricks. In fact, the results of the investigations were of such a nature that this would have been the only reasonable alternative to telepathy.

Not everyone accepted the claims of the Committee on Thought Reading. Sir Horatio Donkin (1845–1927), a physician and a prominent critic, stated in the *Westminster Gazette* of November 26, 1907, that he had been told of two occasions when outside observers were invited to see Smith and Blackburn in action. Once, precautions taken to prevent possible auditory communication put a stop to the thought transference; on the other occasion, precautions against visual communication had a similar effect. Donkin pointed out that no mention was made in the published accounts of the presence of these observers nor of the tests they applied and the effects that were observed.

One of the observers, Sir James Crichton-Browne (1886–1938), a neurologist, confirmed these observations in the *Westminster Gazette* of January 29, 1908. He, together with the British scientist Francis Galton (1822–1911), had been present as an observer at one sitting. After witnessing demonstrations of telepathy by Smith, the two had improved the effectiveness of his blindfold and ear plugs. Further tests then showed "not the smallest response on the part of Mr. *S* to Mr. *B*'s volitional endeavours. There was no more flashing of images into his mind. His pencil was idle. Thought transference was somehow interrupted." [4]

Notwithstanding these objections, Smith and Blackburn were accepted as authentic by the Society for Psychical Research. Both became members of the group, and Smith acted as Gurney's secretary, assisting him until his suicide in 1888 by producing a number of other Brighton youths who gave convincing demonstrations of telepathy after being hypnotized by Smith. For their services to science the youths received financial benefits. After 1888, the experiments were continued by Mrs. Henry Sidgwick, helped by other members of the Society, and successful results were reported until 1892, when Smith left the employment of the Society. Telepathic phenomena ceased with his departure except for one occasion in 1894, when he again helped with an experiment. By 1898, the Society had given up all hope of finding subjects who could display telepathy under hypnosis.

Smith came into the news again on December 5, 1908, when Blackburn revealed in a popular magazine, *John Bull,* that he and Smith had used tricks during the 1882 telepathy investigations. Fuller details were given by Blackburn in the *Daily News* of September 1, 1911, from which the following extract is taken:

> For nearly thirty years the telepathic experiments conducted by Mr. G. A. Smith and myself have been accepted and cited as the basic evidence of the truth of Thought Transference.

Your correspondent "Inquirer" is one of the many who have pointed to them as a conclusive reply to modern sceptics. The weight attached to those experiments was given by their publication in the first volume of the proceedings of the Society for Psychical Research, vouched for by Messrs. F. W. H. Myers, Edmund Gurney, Frank Podmore, and later and inferentially by Professor Henry Sidgwick, Professor Romanes, and others of equal intellectual eminence. They were the first scientifically conducted and attested experiments in Thought Transference, and later were imitated and reproduced by "sensitives" all over the world.

I am the sole survivor of that group of experimentalists, as no harm can be done to anyone, but possible good to the cause of truth, I, with mingled feelings of regret and satisfaction now declare that the whole of those alleged experiments were bogus, and originated in the honest desire of two youths to show how easily men of scientific mind and training could be deceived when seeking for evidence in support of a theory they were wishful to establish.[5]

Blackburn went on to describe how mediums abounded at the end of the nineteenth century and how he had started an exposure campaign. He had then met Smith and together they had perfected a thought-reading act. One of their performances, after being described in *Light,* had brought them to the notice of the Society for Psychical Research. He explained how they were then approached by Gurney and Myers and "saw in them only a superior type of spiritualistic crank" by whom they were pestered daily. Their first private demonstration was accepted so unhesitatingly, and the lack of reasonable precautions on the part of the investigators was so marked, that Smith and he felt it their duty to show how utterly incompetent these investigators were.

Blackburn concluded by writing:

In conclusion, I ask thoughtful persons to consider this proposition; if two youths, with a week's preparation, could deceive trained and careful observers like Messrs. Myers, Gurney, Podmore, Sidgwick and Romanes, under the most stringent conditions their ingenuity could devise, what are the chances of succeeding inquirers being more successful against "sensitives" who have had the advantage of more years experience than Smith and I had weeks? Further, I would emphasise the fact that records of tele-

pathic rapport in almost every instance depend upon the statement
of one person, usually strongly predisposed to belief in the occult.[6]

Smith denied all the charges, but Blackburn then provided so
much detail of the techniques employed that there was little doubt
that tricks has been used. After describing the test in which Smith
had been swathed in blankets, Blackburn continued:

> I also drew it, secretly, on a cigarette paper. By this time I was
> fairly expert at palming, and had no difficulty while pacing the
> room collecting "rapport," in transferring the cigarette paper to
> the tube of the brass projector on the pencil I was using. I conveyed
> to Smith the agreed signal that I was ready by stumbling against
> the edge of the thick rug near his chair.
>
> Next instant he exclaimed: "I have it." His right hand came
> from beneath the blanket, and he fumbled about the table, saying,
> according to arrangement: "Where's my pencil?"
>
> Immediately I placed mine on the table. He took it and a long
> and anxious pause ensued.
>
> This is what was going on under the blanket. Smith had con-
> cealed up in his waistcoat one of those luminous painted slates
> which in the dense darkness gave sufficient light to show the figure
> when the almost transparent cigarette paper was laid flat on the
> slate. He pushed up the bandage from one eye, and copied the
> figure with extraordinary accuracy.
>
> It occupied over five minutes. During that time I was sitting ex-
> hausted with the mental effort quite ten feet away.
>
> Presently Smith threw back the blanket and excitedly pushing
> back the eye bandage produced the drawing, which was done on a
> piece of notepaper, and very nearly on the same scale as the
> original. It was a splendid copy.[7]

If Blackburn had kept his secret, this series of experiments
might well have gone down in the history of parapsychology as one
of the conclusive investigations providing irrefutable evidence for
telepathy, since critics such as Donkin and Crichton-Browne get
little publicity and are soon forgotten. As it is, the outcome of the
investigations of the Creery sisters (see page 27) and of Smith
and Blackburn, merely demonstrate the fact, confirmed time after
time, that intelligent men can be deceived quite easily when their
powers of observation are biased by their underlying beliefs.

CHARACTERISTICS OF EARLY EXPERIMENTS

The investigations reported during the first years of the Society for Psychical Research were remarkable for the ease with which subjects produced feats that no investigator today would consider worth investigating. Playing cards selected from a pack were identified with relative ease, and fairly complex drawings having a striking resemblance to those being looked at by some other person were produced under what the investigators invariably claimed were absolutely watertight conditions. By the time Blackburn made his confession, this type of experiment had almost disappeared.

The early experiments in Great Britain had been more in the nature of party games than serious scientific investigations. The energies of the Society for Psychical Research had been directed largely to the study of spontaneous events and phenomena reported from the séance room. But between 1910 and 1930, the experiments became simpler and less ambitious. During this period, the use of *statistical analyses* began, necessitating suitable types of experimental material and a systematic test procedure. In statistical analysis, the results of many runs are analyzed and compared with what chance scores would be.

MUSCULAR MOVEMENTS

Although all the investigations supporting ESP carried out before 1930 have been criticized on the ground that experimental conditions were unsatisfactory, they are of considerable interest in revealing the pitfalls that await the researcher. Some of them illustrate the fact, known from the start, that involuntary cues could influence a result and that such cues might be utilized by the percipient without his being aware of their presence.

Many supposedly supernatural phenomena were already known to be due to involuntary muscular movements. In 1852, the English chemist and physicist Michael Faraday (1791–1867), after experimenting on table turning—the phenomenon in which a group of persons sit around a table, touching its surface, resulting in a movement of the table, supposedly without the use of any muscular power—had decided that the table turner exerted pressure on the table without being aware that he was doing so. The French chemist Michel Eugène Chevreul (1786–1889) had demonstrated in 1854 that a pendulum held in the hand of a suggestible subject could be caused to swing owing to his involuntary muscular movements and that the direction and amplitude of the swings could be controlled by suggestions, even when the subject was unaware of receiving them.[8] Later, Barrett and Theodore Besterman, the Research Officer of the Society for Psychical Research, extended this type of investigation and showed that in water divining, the twig moved because of the muscular movements of the diviner.[9]

Such involuntary movements are used as cues by performers to detect hidden objects. They may do this when clasping hands with someone who knows where the object is hidden, thus detecting small muscle movements, or by watching the responses of the audience as they move around in the attempt to locate the object. Such abilities are not confined to human beings. It was found that a horse known as Clever Hans, which was claimed to make mathematical calculations, was in fact detecting small involuntary movements made by its trainer.[10]

MENTAL HABITS

Another source of error in the early investigations was due to the subjects' preferences for guessing particular symbols and their mental habits in making successive guesses. The manner in which such preferences can give a spurious result is illustrated by early experiments on psychokinesis where the subject tried to make a particular die face, selected by himself, land uppermost (see page 156). The subjects tended to want a 6, and there was also a slight bias on the die, owing to the indentations denoting the spots; this shifted the die's center of gravity, tending to cause a 6 to arise on more than ⅙ of the throws.

Again, a person who thinks he is guessing symbols at random is likely to produce far fewer guesses of some symbols than would arise in a randomly generated sequence—as by tossing a coin. The experiment (described on pages 37–38) carried out by an English electrical engineer and past president of the Society, G. N. M.

Tyrrell (1879–1952) demonstrates how such mental habits may influence the result of an ESP test.

RECORDING ERRORS

Again, errors in recording guesses or results may occur in cases where the recorder holds a particular belief or where the data may support his own hypothesis. They may easily arise when there is any ambiguity due to lack of visibility in visual information. These errors are particularly likely to occur when the recorder has to pay attention to more than one factor at a time, which divides his attention, or when he has to see or hear something that is not clearly defined.

THE BRUGMANS EXPERIMENT

The result of an experiment carried out in 1919 at the University of Groningen, Holland, by a psychologist, H. J. W. F. Brugmans (1885–1961), who was assisted by two other members of the University psychology department, may have been influenced by factors of this nature.

The subject, a young man named Van Damm, sat at a table with his head and shoulders inside a wooden framework covered with black cloth. He had the back of his head toward the open side of this enclosure, and his right arm extended through an opening so that he could touch any point on a board lying flat on the table in front of him. This board was divided into 48 squares with 8 columns labeled A through H and 6 rows numbered 1 through 6.

A hole had been cut in the ceiling directly above Van Damm. It was covered with 2 sheets of glass, placed so that there was an air cushion between them. The experimenters, sitting above the glass, looked down through it at the board in front of Van Damm and tried to "will" him to point to a particular square.

Before each trial, slips of paper were drawn from bags. The first slip determined which column the square occupied, the second its row. The subject moved his hand over the board and gave a double tap on it with his forefinger to indicate his choice.

Van Damm obtained 60 successes in 187 trials, and this result had clearly not arisen by chance. Some of the trials were made with the experimenters in the same room as the subject, but although he also succeeded under these conditions, his scores were not as high as when they were in the room above him.

There were three serious weaknesses in this research. First, the experimenter who recorded Van Damm's choice of square was also aware of the correct target; second, he had to observe the choice from a distance and through 2 thicknesses of glass; third, the men in the room above the subject could provide, quite involuntarily, auditory cues with their feet on the floorboards that would have guided Van Damm as he moved his hand over the board.

Soal, in a most interesting account of his investigations of a stage performer named Marion, found how the most minute cues could be utilized by Marion to find a hidden object, provided a person was present who knew its location. Discussing the experiment on Van Damm, Soal wrote: "We would suggest that this subject may have been a sensitive of Marion's type, and that telepathy may have played no part in the performance." [11]

To eliminate the possibility that the recorder might affect the scores, he should have been kept ignorant of the real target and have been seated beside Van Damm where he could observe the subject's choice accurately. Van Damm should have signified his selection of a square by a completely definite signal.

The greatest difficulty would, however, have been experienced in eliminating any chance that the experimenters who were trying to "will" Van Damm to point to a particular square were inadvertently supplying cues to him. This difficulty could be overcome today by using closed-circuit television to observe the subject.

SOME TELEPATHY EXPERIMENTS

In another series carried out during the years between 1910 and 1929, Gilbert Murray (1866–1957), Regius Professor of Greek at Oxford University, often demonstrated his own telepathic abilities before a small audience consisting of his daughter and friends. After Murray had left the room, the persons present would write down a "subject," such as a quotation or a description of some incident from literature or current events. Murray would return and state what he thought the subject was. His statement was recorded and compared with the original. Under these conditions, he displayed uncanny knowledge of the subject that had been written down and described during his absence. If Murray's success was due to telepathy, he should have had no difficulty in convincing skeptics by demonstration rather than by discussion and persuasion; but although he referred to these tests in his presidential address to the Society for Psychical Research, and they were reported in the *Proceedings* of the Society, he made no attempt to display his abilities under reasonable test conditions.

In 1927, V. J. Woolley, with the support of Sir Oliver Lodge and the English biologist Julian Huxley, conducted a mass telepathy test in cooperation with the British Broadcasting Corporation. Postcards were sent in by 24,659 listeners, who guessed objects seen by agents in the studio, but no evidence was obtained for telepathy.

An investigation on clairvoyance reported by Miss Ina Jephson in 1929 illustrates the need for strict supervision of the subject in ESP tests.[12] Her subjects were left unsupervised to test themselves in their own homes. They were instructed to take a pack of playing cards, to shuffle it thoroughly, and then to draw one out, keeping it face downwards. They then had to record their guess of which card had been drawn. After that, the subjects were to turn the card over, record it, and then return it to the pack. Each subject made 5 guesses on each of 5 days. Miss Jephson accumulated 6,000 guesses in this manner and found that her subjects were successful in guessing suit, denomination, and color of the card at well above the rate expected to arise by chance.

This experiment was repeated by her in collaboration with Besterman and Soal.[13] The procedure was changed, however, so that the subjects could not influence the result in any manner. A total of 9,496 guesses was recorded, but the result showed no evidence for extrasensory perception.

An experiment carried out by Tyrrell and reported in 1936 is of considerable interest, since he employed mechanical means for presenting targets and recording errors and successes.[14] Tyrrell constructed a machine consisting of 5 wooden boxes, each containing an electric lamp, that were placed in front of the subject. At each trial the experimenter pressed a key that lit a lamp in one of the boxes when its lid was raised. The subject, Miss Johnson, raised the lid of the box that she thought contained the lighted lamp. Since the circuit to the lamp was not completed until the lid of the box was raised, it remained unlit until the subject had made her choice; thus, there was no possibility of light leaking from the box and being used as a cue. In this experiment, the subject learned after each trial whether she had secured a hit, since after a success she saw a lamp light.

Tyrrell then introduced a further refinement. The circuits were rearranged by means of a commutator so that when the experimenter pressed the key, he did not know which box constituted the target. The test was now for clairvoyance rather than telepathy.

After long practice sessions with the apparatus, the subject had obtained scores high above chance probabilities. However, when the commutator was introduced, scores dropped to the chance level; but she eventually again obtained above-chance scores.

It was, however, demonstrated by G. W. Fisk, a member of the Society for Psychical Research, who took part in the experiments, that anyone could obtain high scores similar to those obtained by Miss Johnson by following a simple procedure. The guesser merely selected one target and continued calling it until he secured a success, after which he selected some other one. Fisk's system worked because the target series was generated by the experimenter. When a person selects targets according to his own whim, he tends to produce not a random series, but one in which repetitions of a particular target are relatively infrequent. This fact may easily be confirmed by the reader writing down the 2 symbols H and T at random until he has covered, say, 2 columns of a sheet of paper. The number of times either symbol is followed by the other and also the number of times either symbol is followed by itself should be counted. In a random series a symbol is likely to be followed by itself approximately 50 per cent of the time, but most people will display a strong tendency to change the symbol at each trial rather than to produce a repetition. Thus, runs in which the same symbol occurs twice tend to be infrequent, and longer runs of the same symbol are rarer still in comparison with the expected frequencies.

The author conducted a group of tests with student subjects in which they were asked to write a random series of 50 symbols from a choice of the letters A, B, C, D, and E. It was found that the frequency with which repetitions occurred was low and that runs of the same symbol repeated more than once hardly occurred at all. Some subjects simply wrote the 5 symbols in some particular order and in the following 5 entries listed them in a different order, repeating this process throughout their series.

If the experiment used a nonrandom series, it would have been a simple matter for the subject to produce high scores either by deliberately using a system such as Fisk's or by acquiring suitable response habits during the long training series without being aware of the fact. It is in fact possible to improve on Fisk's system. Thus, after obtaining a hit, the probability of success on the following trial is nearer 0.25 than 0.2 if a fresh target is selected. If a further hit is obtained, a target other than the 2 previous targets may be selected for the following trial. The chances of success on this trial are now improved even further, and this process ensures greater probability of success as the run of successes increases.

In later tests, Tyrrell introduced a mechanical randomizer, and it is of considerable interest to see how it affected the results. Miss Johnson failed to obtain above-chance scores when the randomizer was used directly, but when Tyrrell employed it to prepare lists of random digits and then used these in the experiment to determine which key was to be pressed on each trial, scores were again well above the chance level. The reason for this last result will become apparent if the action of the randomizer is considered in detail.

It consisted of a *stepping switch*, or uniselector, as used in automatic telephone switchboards; this is a rotary switch in which a double-ended arm sweeps through an arc, making contacts at its end with any one of 25 positions situated around a half circle. The arm is moved by a ratchet mechanism and an electromagnet. When the electric current flows through the electromagnet, a claw is pulled forward; when it ceases, the arm is pulled to its next position. An interrupter also is operated by the moving claw so that the circuit is broken at the top of its stroke. Thus, the arm of the uniselector moves in a series of steps until the electromagnet is disconnected. Tyrrell wired the first 5 positions of the switch in order 1, 2, 3, 4, 5. For the remaining sets of 5 positions, this order was changed. All the 1 positions were then connected together so that if the arm came to rest at any of them, box 1 would be selected. The same was done with each of the other numbered positions. Thus, when current flowed, the arm would move past the contacts and the particular target selected would depend on its position when the current was interrupted. If the uniselector was left running for a reasonable length of time between each trial, a random series would be produced, but if the arm was moving relatively slowly and if the current was applied for only brief intervals, the series produced would by no means be random. For example, if the switch arm was operating at 10 contacts per second, and the length of time the current was on to generate each number was less than a ½ second, a series would be produced in which there would be a tendency not to repeat any symbol.

Tyrrell went to the effort of producing a list of nearly 8,000 numbers with his randomizer. It is thus unlikely that he had it running for long intervals before recording each number. Even if merely a part of the series was generated by using only short bursts of current, there would still be a nonrandom feature in the sequence that would permit above-chance scores to be obtained.

Soal reported tests for randomness that he had applied to 2,000 numbers generated on Tyrrell's machine. These did not show any evidence of nonrandomness. It is not clear, however, whether the 2,000 numbers supplied to Soal were part of the 8,000 used with Miss Johnson or whether they were specially generated for him.

In spite of the above criticism, Tyrrell's experiment represented a worthwhile attempt to employ some sort of mechanical control of the ESP test. It is remarkable that his work was not followed up more fully and his methods improved.

COOVER'S RESEARCH

The first major experimental research on telepathy to be carried out in an American university was that of John E. Coover, Professor of Psychology at Stanford University, in 1915. It was of particular interest owing to Coover's use of a control series.

The use of a control series is of particular importance in an experiment that may involve a number of known variables as well as possibly unknown variables the investigator can only suspect may be present. In such an experiment, two series of observations —the experimental and the control series—are observed. Conditions under which the two series are studied are identical except for one factor that is present or absent only in the experimental series. Any difference in the result obtained in the two series is then credited to the effect of that one factor, since it constitutes the only difference between them.

Coover realized that there might be factors operating in his experimental conditions of which he was unaware or that were difficult to control; but any such factors would operate in both the experimental and the control series. In his experimental series, the subjects guessed the identities of cards seen by another person. Conditions were similar in the control series, except that no one saw the target cards. Therefore, if telepathy existed, it was a factor that could operate only in the experimental series, and any difference in scores could be attributed to telepathy.

In one of his experiments, the subjects had to guess the identity of a playing card in a pack from which the face cards had been removed, thus leaving 10 cards in each suit. Before each run of 40 guesses, a die was thrown to decide whether another person should look at the target card, thereby making telepathy possible and putting that observation into the experimental series, or whether no one should see the card, putting the observation into the control series. Altogether, 10,000 guesses were recorded, and it was found that the difference between the mean score of the experimental series and that of the control series was not statistically significant.

Later, critics of Coover pointed out that if the scores in the experimental and control series were lumped together, the combined score was significantly above the chance level. This, of course, proves nothing and is a completely illegitimate procedure, since all control over the experimental conditions brought about by using a control series is then lost. Coover himself considered that auditory cues possibly operated in favor of above-chance scores in both series.[15]

A small number of experimental investigations on telepathy and clairvoyance were carried out in the United States before 1920, but ESP research suddenly made great strides in the United States during the early 1930's. This activity was due to the work of an American, J. B. Rhine, whose work will be discussed in the next chapter.

CHAPTER 5

Salad Days
at Duke University

IN 1920, William McDougall (1871–1938), the well-known British psychologist, was appointed to the chair of psychology at Harvard University. McDougall at that time was president of the British Society for Psychical Research, having become interested in the subject while a student at Cambridge. He found a history of psychical research at Harvard, for 10 years earlier, the German psychologist, Hugo Munsterburg—McDougall's predecessor in the chair at Harvard—had exposed the great Italian medium Eusapia Palladino, and an experiment on telepathy had been carried out there by L. T. Troland, a professor of psychology in the department in 1916.

Psychical research flourished during the 1920's at Harvard. McDougall found funds for the work lying idle and quickly put them to use. Experiments on telepathy were conducted by the psychologists Gardner Murphy and G. H. Esterbrooks, and before long McDougall, together with most of the staff of his department and several senior members of the university, was involved in the investigation of "Margery," a Boston medium, which was to provide one of the most colorful episodes in the history of psychical research.

While at Harvard, McDougall was contacted by a young Chicago botanist, Joseph Banks Rhine. Rhine and his wife Louisa had become interested in psychical research, partly through hearing a lecture on spiritualism given by the English author and physician Sir Arthur Conan Doyle (1859–1930). Rhine began a correspondence with McDougall, and in 1926 he joined the Harvard psychology department as a research assistant. When McDougall joined the faculty of Duke University in 1927, Rhine went with him.

Rhine's first publication on telepathy appeared in 1929 and concerned a telepathic horse named Lady.[1] In view of the considerable doubts about this experiment and the fact that Rhine admitted that the owner of the horse had later resorted to using signals, there is little point in considering it in detail.

In 1934, he published *Extra-Sensory Perception*,[2] in which he gave details of research at Duke University and claimed to have found overwhelming evidence for the existence of extrasensory perception. Further research followed, and in 1940 the Duke Parapsychology Laboratory was formed with Rhine as its director.

EARLY EXPLORATORY TESTS

The first part of the research described in *Extra-Sensory Perception* consisted of exploratory tests made under comparatively loose conditions in which the aim was to discover subjects who would be used in later research.

Some of the major tests carried out during this exploratory period (1930–1932) are detailed below:

1. In the summer of 1930, children at a summer recreational school were asked to guess a number (0–9) seen by the experimenter. Approximately a thousand trials were made in this manner, but not a single child was discovered whose performance warranted any further investigation.

2. In the fall, Rhine in collaboration with a colleague in the psychology department, K. E. Zener, carried out clairvoyance experiments on students in class. Tests were made using 3 types of material: numbers (0–9); letters of the alphabet; and Zener cards. The latter, so named because they had been chosen by Zener, consisted of 5 different symbols: a circle, a rectangle, a plus sign, wavy lines, and a star. In a total of 1,600 trials, the scores were close to the chance expectation, and after the experiment Zener became too burdened with other work and dropped out of the research.

3. In the winter of 1931–1932, Rhine obtained what he called his first really convincing result. A clairvoyance test using Zener cards on 24 subjects yielded an over-all score of 207 hits in 800 trials. As there were 5 different symbols, the score expected to arise by

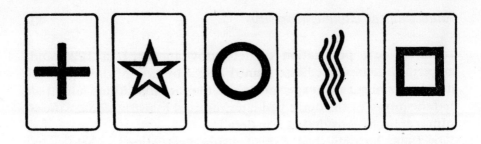

FIGURE 1. *ESP cards (formerly called Zener cards)*

chance was 160 hits, and the odds were greater than 1 million to 1 against a score of 207. Twelve of the 24 subjects obtained an average of 5 hits or more in 25 trials, while the other 12 subjects scored below chance. Of the latter group, Rhine said that none of them "developed," and few were tried again. But as, on the average, fewer than 14 trials were made with each of these low-scoring subjects, it is difficult to see how they were given much chance to develop. A surprising feature of these tests was, in fact, the small number of trials some of the subjects made. During each the subject might look at the back of the card and pick it up before making his guess; but this would hardly have taken more than about 5 seconds for each guess. Even so, several subjects recorded only 50 or fewer trials, and the 12 low-scoring subjects averaged less than 14 trials—about 1½ minutes' work each.

4. Two further experiments yielding significantly high scores were carried out at this time by Dr. Rhine's assistants, but in neither case were the exact conditions of the experiments stated. Charles E. Stuart tested 9 subjects and J. G. Pratt, 15. In each case, the over-all score for the group had high odds against arising by chance. From the meager details given, it would appear that the experimenter sat at a table with the subject and handed him a pack of Zener cards. The subject took each card in turn, holding it face downward, and made his guess, which was recorded by the experimenter. The guesses were, on some occasions, checked for hits after a run of 5 and on the other occasions after a run of 25 trials had been completed.

These "early and minor tests," Rhine stated, were published so that the reader might see the whole of the group's work in its infancy. They included 23,550 trials, and the over-all score achieved had odds greater than 1 billion to 1 against arising by chance. But as Rhine commented: "Some of the weaknesses of these beginnings one only has to read here to avoid."

A feature of the early tests was the fact that among a large number of subjects who were tested at this time, only two—A. J. Linzmayer and Stuart, both undergraduate students—later showed themselves capable of obtaining consistently high scores. The experiments gave results that were statistically significant because the groups of subjects scored slightly above the chance level over a large number of trials.

In 1930 and early 1931, progress was slow, and subjects with ESP seemed hard to find; but later in 1931 there were dramatic changes, and by the end of 1932 almost everyone tested among the graduate psychology students at Duke was found to have some ability. Thus, Rhine stated in *Extra-Sensory Perception* that of the 14 graduate students in psychology present in the last 2 years, 6 showed ESP ability that was statistically significant; another had been reported to have done work appreciably significant; and the remaining 7 students had not to his knowledge been tested.

TESTS ON HIGH-SCORING SUBJECTS

The second part of Rhine's research consisted of investigations carried out on 8 high-scoring subjects. Each of them in a relatively short time displayed remarkable powers of ESP, and his final assessment of the combined score of his subjects gave odds greater than 10^{1000} to 1 against chance occurrence.

Various types of tests were used, but they had a common characteristic: the subject guessed 1 of 5 different symbols, which were either depicted on cards or were thought of by some other person. The cards were in packs of 25 containing 5 of each of the different symbols. When a subject guesses the order of such a pack, provided he is not told whether he is correct or not after each trial, an average score of 5 hits per run of 25 is expected to arise by chance. A subject's score will vary in different runs of 25 trials; thus, in 100 runs, several scores of 9, one or two 10's, and, with luck, a 12 would probably arise. A score of 13 would not be extraordinary (odds are about 6 to 1 against getting a score of 13 in

100 runs), but a 14 would be unlikely. A score of exactly 5 hits would be expected to arise on about 40 occasions.

Rhine's high-scoring subjects would often average 8 or 9 hits over a large number of runs. Thus, the most outstanding subject, Hubert E. Pearce, a student for the Methodist ministry in the School of Religion at Duke, averaged 8 hits per run over 690 runs, constituting a total of 17,250 trials. This performance would not seem remarkable unless an observer were well acquainted with the probabilities of the different-sized scores arising by chance. But, in fact, if a person could average even 5.3 hits per 25 trials over 690 runs, there would be odds greater than 1 million to 1 against this result arising by chance, although the subject would only be averaging 1 extra hit in each 76 guesses.

The experimental techniques employed by Rhine were:

1. BT (*Basic Technique*, later referred to as "Before Touching" technique). The pack was shuffled, cut, and placed face downward on the table. The subject attempted to guess the first card, which was then removed and placed in a separate pile. He then attempted to guess the second card, and the process continued until he had guessed at the identity of each of the 25 cards in the pack. On some occasions, the subject himself took the card from the pack, held it face downward, attempted to guess it, and then placed it in a second pile.

2. DT (*Down Through*). The pack was shuffled, cut, and placed face downward on the table. The subject attempted to guess the cards 1 by 1, from the top, without disturbing the pack.

3. PT (*Pure Telepathy*). Here no cards or records of the targets were used; the aim was to study telepathy as distinct from clairvoyance. Thus, a second person, the agent, had to think of a symbol; but it was argued that if a pack of cards was used, the subject might obtain above-chance scores by clairvoyance. And so, the agent thought of a symbol that did not exist as a card in a pack or as an entry on a list. He thought of 5 of the ESP symbols in a particular order, and the subject called aloud his guesses. The agent made a record of each of the subject's calls and checked them for correctness as he recorded them.

In *Extra-Sensory Perception,* Rhine commented that success or failure depended very much on the conditions under which the tests were made, and he listed the following suggestions to those who might care to repeat his experiments.

1. The subject should have an active interest in the tests and be fairly free from strong bias or doubt. These would, of course, hinder effort and limit attention. An open-minded, experimental attitude is all that is required. Positive belief is naturally favorable but not necessary.

2. The preliminary tests should be entered into very informally, without much serious discussion as to techniques, or explanations or precautions. The more ado over techniques, the more inhibition is likely; and the more there is of explanations, the more likely is introspection to interfere. Playful informality is most favorable.

3. If possible to do so honestly, it is helpful to give encouragement for any little success but no extravagant praise is desirable, even over striking results. The point is that encouragement is helpful, apparently, but only if it does not lead to self-consciousness. If it does, it is quite ruinous. Many subjects begin well, become excited or self-conscious, and then do poorly.

4. Some begin more easily with *P.T.* [Pure Telepathy] and some with *P.C.* [Pure Clairvoyance]. It depends upon personality, I think, but I cannot explain it except to link sociability with P.T. preference. However, both conditions should be tried, following the subject's preference in the beginning.

5. It is highly important to let the subject have his own way, without restraint, at first. Later, he can be persuaded to allow changes, after he has gained confidence and discovered his way to ESP functioning. Even then, it is better for him to have his way as far as experimental conditions can allow. It is a poor science that dictates conditions to Nature. It is a better one that follows up with its well-adapted controls and conditions.

6. It is wise not to express doubts or regrets. Discouragement seems to damage the delicate function of ESP. Here again no doubt personalities differ. One subject, I know, has worked in the face of doubt expressed; but she is exceptional in this.

7. Above all, one must not, like several investigators, stop with only 25 or 50 or even 100 trials per subject. Most of my good subjects did not do very well in the first 100. With few exceptions, the first 50 to 100 trials give the worst scores. With all my major

subjects this is true. Several different occasions or sittings, too should be allowed, for there is with most subjects an adjustment phase at first that may take some time.

8. It is best at first to have the subject alone with the agent in P.T. and in P.C. to leave him alone entirely. If not, he may be inhibited from the start; but, once he has a start, he can gradually work back to other conditions. When he has observers present, the experimenter should do all he can to put the subject at ease.

9. Simple cards with 5 suits seem best as a compromise of several features of concern: easy calculation, easy recall, easy discrimination of images, etc.

10. Short runs are desirable, say 5 at a time, with a check-up after each 5. Then it is best to go casually and quietly on without too much discussion of results.

11. It is advisable not to bore or tire the subject. When he wants to stop, or even before he expressly wishes to, it is better to stop work.

12. It is best to try good friends for P.T. at first—or couples, single or married, who feel certain they have thought-transference; and, above all, to try those people who say they have had "psychic" experiences or whose ancestors conspicuously have had.

These are suggestions, not rules, for we do not yet know enough of the subject to lay down rules. They will help toward success, without endangering conclusions. One can always tighten up on conditions before drawing conclusions later. But any investigator must first of all get his phenomena to occur—or exhaust the reasonable possibilities in trying to.[3]

Linzmayer, the first of the high-scoring subjects, had been noticed as promising in the early 1930 tests. When tested again in 1931, he first produced a score of only 4 hits in 20 trials, which is exactly that of chance expectation. In the next series, made on May 21, 1931, he was far more successful, however, achieving 25 hits in 45 trials with 9 of these hits on successive cards. However, the conditions in this test could hardly be considered stringent. Rhine took a card from a shuffled pack. After first looking at it, he held it face downward under his hand and tried to visualize the symbol. He did this rather than thinking of its name so that, as he put it, the "involuntary whispering ghost need not haunt us."

Ten days later, Linzmayer was given a further 535 trials, making a total of 600. Of these, 360 were made under conditions in which the experimenter knew the symbol being guessed (described as undifferentiated ESP, Telepathy and Clairvoyance); and 240 trials were made in which the symbol was unknown to anyone (described as Pure Clairvoyance Condition). In the over-all 600 trials, Linzmayer got 238 successes, and there are odds well over 10 million to 1 against this result arising by chance.

The conditions under which the tests were carried out are nowhere described in detail. The following report is, however, given of one test in which Linzmayer produced his most remarkable feat. Linzmayer and Rhine were seated in Rhine's car, with the engine running. Linzmayer was leaning back so that he looked at only the roof of the car, and there were no mirrors or shiny surfaces to assist him in seeing the cards. Rhine held the pack out of sight, face down, and shuffled it several times during the series. He drew the card with his right hand, keeping it concealed as he leaned forward; then he tilted it a little, glanced at it, and laid it on a large record book resting on Linzmayer's knees. About 2 seconds after it was laid on the book, Linzmayer made his guess aloud. Rhine then said whether Linzmayer had been right or wrong and laid the card on the appropriate pile. The hits were counted and recorded "at the end of the 15 calls, here, and then at the end of each five calls after." On this occasion, Linzmayer was successful in 21 out of 25 trials. He also obtained 15 consecutive hits, the odds being 30 billion to 1 against the chance achievement of such a feat.

Linzmayer obtained significantly above-chance results with each of the three experimental techniques given on page 46, but he was unsuccessful when tested with the cards at a distance from him. Eventually, his results started declining until, at the finish, he was unable to score above chance.

Charles E. Stuart, the second of the high-scoring subjects, was an assistant in the psychology department. He was successful both as a subject and an experimenter with the BT technique; but this was in part due to the fact that in most of his observations he used himself as subject. He was unsuccessful when tested with the DT and PT techniques.

Following a successful result in one of the early exploratory experiments, Stuart started making ESP tests in the autumn of

1931. In a total of 7,500 unwitnessed trials carried out on himself under conditions that are not stated, he obtained 1,815 hits as compared with the expected number of 1,500. There are enormous odds against this result arising by chance.

Hubert E. Pearce, the divinity student, was by far the most versatile of all the high-scoring subjects and produced high above-chance scores when tested with each of the three techniques. He was successful with the BT and DT techniques only when seated at a table with the cards, but he succeeded in making high scores with the PT technique when at a distance of 8–30 feet from the agent. His most impressive result was in an experiment, later known as the Pearce-Pratt experiment (see Chapter 7), being con-ducted during the writing of *Extra-Sensory Perception*. Here, he obtained high scores in sitting after sitting when he was situated more than 100 yards from the cards.

The results for the remaining 5 high-scoring subjects were presented as a group in *Extra-Sensory Perception*. These subjects were all psychologists: George Zirkle and Sarah Ownbey being graduate assistants, while May Frances Turner, June Bailey, and T. Coleman Cooper were students in the psychology department.

George Zirkle was unsuccessful with the BT and DT techniques, but when tested with the PT technique, he averaged 11 hits per 25 trials over 3,400 trials. On several occasions he obtained 22 hits in 25 trials, and on one occasion he got an unbroken run of 26 successes. Zirkle was also able to obtain high scores when at distances of up to 10 feet from the agent when PT was used.

Miss Ownbey resembled Stuart in that she was successful both as an investigator and as a subject. Like Stuart, she really succeeded as a subject only when tested by herself. She carried out the first ESP test at Duke University in which the cards were at a consider-able distance from the subject.

Miss Turner, the subject in the above long-distance test, Cole-man Cooper, and Miss Bailey were all successful when using BT and PT, but obtained only moderate success with the DT tech-nique.

The combined data from these last 5 subjects gave an average score of 8.4 hits in each run of 25 over a total of 26,950 trials. The odds against such a result arising by chance are astronomical.

WEAKNESSES IN THE EXPERIMENTAL TECHNIQUES

BT has the obvious danger that the subject may recognize the cards by marks on their backs or sides; in addition, if he handles them, he may recognize a particular card by its feel.

In 1937, when ESP cards were first supplied to the public, it was shown that they could be read quite easily from their backs and sides (see pages 60–62). It is thus of considerable significance that subjects could obtain above-chance scores with the basic technique only when seated close to the cards, and that as soon as they were moved away, their scores dropped to the chance level.

A second difficulty that arises with this technique is that the cards may tend to cut at a particular symbol. It was mentioned in *Extra-Sensory Perception* that some of the early cards were found to be unsatisfactory because one of the symbols was printed on a slightly larger card than the others. Such a pack would tend to cut so that the larger one would fall toward the bottom and one of the four remaining symbols toward the top of the pack. During the shuffling, cards of a particular size might also tend to come together, so that it would be possible to obtain extra hits in other positions than at the top and bottom of the pack.

With BT, the subject's score was checked, on some occasions, at the end of 25 guesses (BT25), on other occasions after 5 (BT5). It is significant that in BT25, the hits tended to arise in the first 5 and last 5 cards of the pack. Details are not given of the scores on the first- and last-card hits, but they were clearly very high, since in 60 runs of the BT25 type, Pearce got 52 of his last calls correct.

Experiments with Pearce using BT took the following form: Pearce shuffled the pack, since he claimed it gave more real contact, and the observer cut it. Pearce would then pick up the cards and remove the top one, keeping the pack and the removed card face down on the table. The observer would record the call after either 5 or 25 calls—the two conditions being used about equally. The cards would be turned over and checked against the calls recorded in the book. The subject was asked to help in the checking by laying them off. For the next run, another pack of cards would be used.

When the BT5 technique was employed, correct scores followed a cyclical effect, being the highest for positions 2, 7, 12, 17, and 22; second highest for positions 1, 6, 11, 16, and 21; and relatively low for the remaining positions. Since, after each 5 guesses, the cards were sometimes replaced in the pack, which was shuffled and cut before the next 5 were recorded, this effect could have arisen because particular symbols tended to be brought to the top and bottom of the pack.

The down-through technique suffers from the same drawbacks as the BT25 procedure, and again it is significant that when it was employed, the subject scored most of his hits on the first and last 5 cards. Details are not given of the scoring rate at each position in the pack, but it is recorded that in 40 of Pearce's DT runs, he correctly called 33 last cards. It also appears that the DT procedure was partially originated by Pearce himself.[4]

The salient question in connection with both the basic and down-through techniques is what would happen if the cards were no longer visible to the subject? In one experiment, Pearce was tested at three distances: across a table, at 8–12 feet from the cards, and at 28–30 feet from the cards. Using both the BT and DT techniques, the scores were significantly above chance when Pearce was close to the cards, and with both techniques, scores dropped when he was at any distance from them.

The pure-telepathy technique is by far the most unsatisfactory of the three. Anyone who tries to carry out the duties of the experimenter will find them extremely difficult and tiring to perform. The possibility that errors will arise is large under these conditions, and there is no check on them if they are made.

The procedure adopted was for the experimenter to think of 5 Zener symbols in any order he liked, and then concentrate his attention on each one as its turn came while the subject made his guess. The experimenter, after signaling the subject with a key that he was to say his guess, noted down the guess and whether it was correct. After the first 5 targets had been guessed, another 5 would be preselected in some order, usually different from the first, and the process continued.

Under these conditions, high scores would be expected to arise owing to the already discussed manner in which people behave when they think they are generating a random series.

Also, each run of 5 trials tends to contain all 5 of the symbols arranged in a fresh order each time. Under these conditions, the subject's chances of obtaining high scores are greatly increased. In such cases there are 120 possible arrangements of the 5 different symbols, and the subject would expect to achieve 5 hits once in each 120 attempts, whereas in a true random distribution, the number of arrangements of the 5 symbols is 3,125 (5^5). If the experimenter tended to include all 5 symbols in each run, and the subject tended to avoid repeating his calls, the mean score would be augmented considerably.

George Zirkle, who was able to obtain high scores only when using the PT technique and only when tested by Miss Ownbey—who later became his wife—averaged 10.7 hits per 25 guesses in 5,025 trials. An extraordinary feature of these experiments was that at no time during the 5,025 trials did anyone appear to consider the possibility that the targets generated by Miss Ownbey could be influenced by her hearing Zirkle's calls, or even that she might make mistakes in her recording. A check could easily have been made. Miss Ownbey could have been provided with a list of symbols arranged in random order, and one of the faculty members could have recorded Zirkle's calls. The purely academic point whether Zirkle was displaying telepathy or clairvoyance could have been forgotten for the time being, and, in any case, Zirkle had already shown that he was unable to obtain above-chance results when tested for clairvoyance.

Looking at the results of the experiments and bearing in mind the pitfalls of the techniques employed, several features cannot but strike the critic.

It was reported that placing the subject away from the cards removed high scores, except when the PT technique was used. Since the obvious weakness of BT and DT lies in the possibility of the subject receiving sensory cues from the cards, it is to be expected that subjects would be unable to maintain high scores in the event of their using such cues when placed at any distance from the cards.

In the case of PT, distance would not affect the calling habits of the experimenter. The subject and agent could be a hundred yards away with a telephone link for the agent to hear the subject's call, and this would not remove the inherent weakness of the experimental technique.

Rhine commented after studying the results:

> These bring out the point of the difference between PT and BT results with distance, and their similarity at close range, suggesting that while PT can clearly be done at such distances, it may be that BT may not. It is still more strongly suggested that DT may be limited to close range.[5]

This observation fits precisely with what would be expected if the subjects utilized sensory cues with the BT and DT techniques. With the DT technique, these cues would be weakest, since only the sides of the cards, other than the top card, are visible to the percipient.

A LONG-DISTANCE EXPERIMENT

While BT and DT experiments with the subject at a distance from the cards showed no evidence for ESP, one other test was reported in which the result was of quite a different nature. This was a series of runs in which Miss Turner was situated 250 miles from the cards at Lake Junaluska, North Carolina, while the experimenter, Miss Ownbey, was at the Parapsychology Laboratory in Durham.

Each day, Miss Turner was to record 25 guesses at prescribed times and to send a record of her guesses directly to Rhine. The agent was likewise to send a record of her targets each day directly to Rhine. There were 3 series of tests. In the first, 8 runs of 25 trials each were completed. The first 3 made on June 30, July 5, and July 7, 1933, resulted in scores of 19 out of 25, 16 out of 25, and 16 out of 25; the probability that these scores arose by chance is fantastically remote. Rhine states in *Extra-Sensory Perception* that it was then discovered that Miss Turner's record had not gone directly to him as planned, but that it had been transmitted through Miss Ownbey. Twelve days later, tests were resumed and further runs were made on July 19, 20, 21, 22, and 24. On these days, both records were sent directly to Rhine, but the scores were not now significantly above the chance level.

Further tests, at a distance of 300 miles, were made on August 22, 24, 29, and 31, but again the scores did not differ significantly from chance expectations.

In spite of the lapse in the experimental conditions during the first three days and the remarkable scores that emerged, Rhine did not suspect either lady of duplicity. He commented that the subject's recordings were unmistakably in Miss Turner's handwriting and in ink with no evident changes. He then came to the conclusion that the young ladies had not been deceiving him. However, it should be noted that if Miss Ownbey had wished to deceive Rhine, she would merely have written out her record of the target series after seeing Miss Turner's guesses.

GENERAL OBSERVATIONS ON THE EXPERIMENTS

The scores obtained by each of the high-scoring subjects were such that no one could deny that some factor other than chance was involved. Rhine discussed 5 alternative hypotheses to ESP: chance, fraud, incompetence, unconscious sensory perception, and rational inference, and came to the conclusion that he had eliminated the possibility of each of them and that ESP stood without a serious opposing hypothesis. Even a superficial examination makes it difficult, however, to understand why the alternative hypotheses should have been so summarily dismissed.

It is clear that there can be little dispute about the inapplicability of the hypothesis that the high scores were the result of chance. Some criticisms have been made of Rhine's statistical treatment, but the result is undisputed. The method he employed was suitable for randomly distributed targets; that is, those that would arise if the card was returned to the pack after each guess and, after shuffling, a fresh card was selected as the next target. But since the packs of cards Rhine used contained exactly 5 of each symbol, a *closed pack,* the distribution of targets was not random. The use of a closed pack would not, however, affect the conclusions very much. Whether the odds of Pearce's result are 10^{100} to 1 or merely 10^{90} to 1 against chance is quite irrelevant.

The question of statistical analysis does arise when the results obtained from experiments where PT was employed are considered. Here, the subject guessed at 5 symbols arranged in a particular order, after which he was presented with 5 more targets consisting of a new order of symbols. If the experimenter merely produced the symbols in different orders for each run, the subject's chances of high scores would be considerably increased when compared with the possibility of high scores when guessing a randomly generated series of symbols.

The most remarkable feature of Rhine's discussion of the fraud hypothesis was that he made no mention of the first 3 runs in the Turner-Ownbey experiment. Whether or not he thought that there had been any tampering with the records, this case was highly relevant and should have been discussed.

Rhine considered two possibilities: fraud on the part of the subjects who tested themselves, and fraud by subjects and experimenters both. In the case of subjects who tested themselves, there was no check other than a comparison of scores obtained when they were alone with those made when witnesses were present. In most cases, the results agreed, but there was an exception in the case of Miss Ownbey, who tested herself using the down-through technique. She obtained most of her hits in the middle of the run, whereas all the other subjects who had been witnessed obtained most of theirs at the start and end of the run when this technique was used. Also, Miss Ownbey, who averaged 8.4 hits when unwitnessed, was unable to obtain a result that was statistically above the chance level when an observer was present.

When Rhine discussed the competence of the researchers and observers, he concluded that the experimental conditions had been steadily tightened up and pointed out that no adequate loophole had been discovered. His final conclusion was that the hypothesis of incompetence would find "few adherents and no justification"; but the critic cannot but be struck with the numerous occasions when a simple test on the part of an investigator would have saved a great deal of argument after the event. It is possible that the Pearce-Pratt experiment was intended to satisfy some of these criticisms, but that does not make it any easier to understand how the investigators could have gone on for week after week blindly trusting a rather weak experimental design. When, for example, it was found that Pearce could not obtain above-chance scores with the down-through procedure when more than a yard away from the cards, why was he not tested at close range, completely screened from the cards after he had entered the room until he had recorded all his guesses? If this was tried, no details are given. Pearce was tested with the cards held behind a screen, but in these basic-technique tests, it transpires that Pearce himself held the cards in this position and handled each card as he guessed it.

The manner in which normal sensory cues may be employed by subjects has already been touched on. Whether such cues are used unconsciously or consciously does not affect the argument very much. Rhine raised the point that Pearce did not usually look at the pack before he called his guess, although it seems that he occasionally glanced absent-mindedly at the pack. Rhine also mentioned that Pearce's favorite posture was with eyes closed, sometimes with his hand on his eyes or forehead. It should be noted that if anyone wished to look at the backs of the cards without making this too obvious, he could do so by half-shutting his eyes or by screening them with his hand. A person with half-closed eyes can be facing away from the cards with his eyes turned to them, and an observer would not necessarily be aware of the fact. A photograph of Rhine testing Pearce with the down-through technique shows that Pearce had every opportunity to study the top card and the sides of others in the pack.

Rhine also discussed unconscious whispering cues, and seemed to consider that to have a fan going or to be in a car with the motor running was sufficient safeguard against them.

The last hypothesis, that of rational inference, arises, for example, with the BT5 technique. Since the subject sees the targets after each 5 trials, he is in a position after the first 20 calls to know exactly which symbols are left in the pack. He will not know the order in which they will arise, but except in the case where exactly 4 of each symbol have come up in the first 20 cards, he is in a position to obtain extra hits. Thus if the wavy-lined symbol has arisen only 3 times in the first 20 calls, the subject has merely to call it for each of the last 5, and he is bound to obtain 2 hits. Rhine himself pointed out that the subjects obtained high scores in the last 5 trials when the BT5 technique was used. He also discussed rational inference in relation to PT, but the essential points were completely missed. It can easily be demonstrated that, by employing rational inference, it is possible for a subject to obtain extremely high scores in this type of experiment.

In view of the conditions under which most of the results reported in *Extra-Sensory Perception* were obtained, it is difficult to see how the experiments can be considered as other than exploratory. The final study with Pearce at a distance from the cards was, however, of quite a different order from those previously carried out. In these tests, since he was 100 yards or more from the cards, sensory cues were eliminated, and from the other details of the experimental conditions, it appeared that Pearce was at last having to perform under reasonably strict conditions. The Pearce-Pratt series, has remained to this day one of the few ESP experiments that the majority of parapsychologists agree to call conclusive; it will be considered in detail in Chapter 7.

CHAPTER 6

The Years
of Controversy 1934–1940

THE publication of *Extra-Sensory Perception* aroused enormous interest among the general public, and ESP became a household word; but at the same time, the book was criticized severely. It was natural that the main onslaught should come from psychologists and that some of those reading about the experiments should wish to see whether they could get the same results for themselves. Since, according to Rhine, 1 in 5 of the population could display ESP, a confirmatory test must have seemed a relatively simple matter to arrange.

ATTEMPTS AT REPEATING THE DUKE EXPERIMENTS

The first attempt to reproduce the results was reported in 1936 by W. S. Cox of the psychology department at Princeton University. Prospective subjects were told about the work at Duke, emphasis being put on the positive nature of the scores obtained there with the aim of putting the subjects in a favorable frame of mind for the experiment. Cox noted during the discussion that the majority of his subjects displayed a belief in extrasensory perception and that many of those who were skeptical about it eventually did not participate as subjects.

A total of 132 subjects produced 25,064 trials in which they attempted to guess the suits of playing cards; but there was no evidence for ESP. The data were then examined to see whether any persons displayed an aptitude for ESP. Cox's conclusion was:

> It is evident from the above results and computations that there is no evidence of extrasensory perception either in the "average man" of the group investigated or in any particular individual of

that group. The discrepancy between these results and those obtained by Rhine is due either to uncontrollable factors in experimental procedure or to the difference in the subjects.[1]

Other psychologists attempted to confirm Rhine's findings. E. T. Adams of Colgate University reported the results of 30,000 trials in which 30 subjects were individually tested; [2] J. C. Crumbaugh of Southern Methodist University tested over 100 subjects and recorded a total of 75,600 trials; [3] Raymond Willoughby of Brown University tested 9 subjects and recorded 41,250 trials; [4] and C. P. and J. H. Heinlein of Johns Hopkins amassed 127,500 trials.[5] The results obtained at Duke University were not confirmed in any of these investigations. On the contrary, it was found that subjects could not score significantly above the chance level when sensory cues were excluded.

Attempts to repeat the experiments were also made in England by Britain's best known parapsychologist, S. G. Soal.[6] Between 1934 and 1939, after testing 160 persons for telepathy or clairvoyance and recording 128,350 guesses, Soal obtained a score that was at the chance level, and only one of his subjects, Mrs. Gloria Stewart, produced a result that was in any way out of the ordinary. Her score had odds greater than 100 to 1 against chance occurrence, but as 160 persons had been tested, it was to be expected that at least one of them should produce such a score.

Further reports appeared in which Rhine's results were not confirmed, but on the other hand, several investigations were reported in which the subjects had no difficulty in displaying ESP. It is significant, however, that of the 36 experimental reports supporting the existence of ESP published in the period 1934–1940, only 5 were later assessed by members of the Duke Parapsychology Laboratory as being controlled sufficiently rigorously to provide conclusive evidence.

CRITICISM OF THE ESP CARDS

In 1936, ESP cards were put on sale to the general public in the United States. On the package was printed "ESP Cards for testing Extra-Sensory Perception, developed in Parapsychological Laboratory at Duke University, patent applied for by J. B. Rhine," It was soon noted by the psychologists R. H. Thouless, B. F. Skinner, and L. D. Wolfe, among others, that under certain lighting conditions the symbols on the faces of the cards could be seen by examining their backs. One prominent critic, J. L. Kennedy of Stanford, included a photograph to illustrate this point in an article he published in 1938.[7]

In a note published in the May 1938 *Journal* of the Society for Psychical Research, C. V. C. Herbert, who was then Research Officer of the Society, reported an investigation he had made of the cards.[8] He noted that they were of 2 types: the first consisted of playing-card blanks on which the symbols were impressed by means of rubber stamps or stencils; the second type was professionally manufactured. It seems that some 2 years before 2 packs of the first type had been sent to Thouless as examples of the actual cards used in the tests at Duke University. He found that with one pack it was possible to detect the symbol on a card's face by scrutinizing its back when it was held so that light was reflected from it. With the light from a window, 9 out of a pack of 25 cards were identified in this way, and with a 60-watt lamp hanging from the ceiling, 14 cards were so identified.

The second type was that made available to the American public. When these were held at a certain angle, it was found that the symbol on almost every card could be read easily from its back. It was further found that the pattern on the backs extended to the edges, so that the identities of some cards could be detected when the sides of the pack were inspected. Thus, 4 of the cards marked with a circle were identified by the white mark on their sides where the cutting machine had sliced through a particular part of the pattern printed on the back.

Replying to Herbert, Rhine commented that the cards used in the earlier years were cut from heavy, opaque stock and carefully inspected. He also stated that no conclusions about extrasensory perception were published unless supplementary tests had been made in which sensory contact with the backs of the cards was eliminated. But homemade cards cut from heavy stock are all the more likely to be recognizable from their sides, and it is difficult to see, after reading the account in *Extra-Sensory Perception*, how it can be said that sensory contact was eliminated. Screening cards with the hand, for example, hardly eliminates the possibility of sensory contact, since the back of the card that is to follow the one being held is visible.

The experiments in which subjects, after obtaining high scores when seated at a table with the cards in front of them, were moved away from the cards, merely demonstrated the manner in which ESP scores dropped to the chance level as soon as it was made difficult for the subject to utilize sensory cues. It is possible that the supplementary tests to which Rhine referred were of the pure-telepathy type, in which cards were not used, and the tests on Pearce at distances of 100 and 250 yards. These certainly excluded the possibility of the subject directly using cues from the cards, but it must be confirmed whether they were satisfactory in other respects. In the early experiments with Pearce, his scores certainly dropped in a remarkably consistent manner as soon as he could not see or feel the cards.

J. L. KENNEDY'S REVIEW OF ESP EXPERIMENTS

In 1939, Kennedy reviewed in detail the experimental work on extrasensory perception carried out up to 1938.[9] He started by listing and discussing the known sources of experimental error. These were:

1. Minimal and Subliminal sensory cues.
   a. Kinesthetic and Tactual cues
   b. Visual cues
   c. Auditory cues
2. "Mental Habits" and preferences.
3. Recording errors.

In a separate section he discussed the statistical methods used and the effects of selection of data on the experimental results.

Kennedy concluded his review by isolating those experiments in which the experimental conditions eliminated the possibility of all the above forms of error. He was left with 3 "inexplicable" experiments, about which he wrote: "Eventual explanation of these results appears to the present writer to rest on an entirely different basis than the foregoing ESP data."[10]

The first of these three experiments was an investigation by

Lucien Warner, a research fellow, assisted by Mildred Raible, a psychologist, both at Duke University.[11] The subject was in a ground floor room, and 2 experimenters were in a locked room on the first floor in an opposite wing of the same house. One of the experimenters selected the target at each trial by drawing a card from a pack that was shuffled after each trial. The subject signaled the experimenters when the next target was to be selected by pressing a key that operated a light in the experimenters' room. Only 250 trials were recorded, and the average score was 9.3 hits per 25 trials.

Kennedy noted 2 aspects of this experiment. First, the recording was not completely independent, since the flash of light in the experimenters' room could be varied in duration by the subject and thus provide a possible cue. Second, there were 5 different symbols in the target series, but the experimental record showed that 2 of these arose more frequently than the other 3. A test showed that the observed distribution would be expected to arise by chance in 1 out of 50 such experiments. In view of this fact, the method by which the targets were selected was suspect. For example, if after the pack was shuffled, it had been cut before each card was drawn, a bias easily could have manifested itself if there were variations in sizes of the cards bearing the different symbols. The report did not give full details of the parts played by the 2 experimenters, but it would appear that further tests could have been made with little difficulty, since 250 trials would take about 2 hours. Even so, further results were not reported, and the subject who displayed these remarkable powers of clairvoyance sank into anonymity.

The second experiment Kennedy isolated was reported in 1937 by B. F. Riess, Professor of Psychology at Hunter College, New York.[12] His subject lived about a quarter of a mile from Riess's home, and the experiment was conducted with each in his or her own home. Starting at 9 P.M., Riess exposed cards at 1-minute intervals from a freshly shuffled pack lying on his desk, and the subject recorded her guesses at the same times in her home. Two packs of 25 cards were exposed each day in this manner. The very high scores obtained startled even the parapsychologists. Thus, the score in 25 trials gradually built up over successive days until over 20 hits were being obtained, and scores were consistently high day after day. The hits per pack for the last 10 days were 17, 18, 19, 20, 20, 20, 19,

20, 21, and 21. Altogether, 53 runs were completed, yielding the most remarkable scoring ever observed in an ESP experiment. Then, after a break in the testing, further runs were made, and the scores dropped to the chance level. The next 10 runs yielded 2, 4, 7, 12, 7, 5, 4, 3, 5, and 4 hits per pack. Even so, the odds against the over-all score arising by chance have been assessed at greater than 10^{700} to 1. Since Kennedy made his review, further information about this experiment has become available. It appears that after Riess had been openly skeptical about ESP in discussion with his psychology classes, one of his students volunteered to produce a friend with high ESP. This friend turned out to be a young woman who had the reputation of being an amateur psychic, and it was she who had acted as the subject for the experiment. After it was over, she refused to take part in further tests under more strict conditions.

Riess kept his records of the card order in the drawer of a desk that was left unlocked during the day, and he did not receive the record of the subject's calls until the day after the session. A servant employed in Riess's home was known to the students, and the records were easily accessible to anyone in the house. Also, it seems that, at times, a period of a week or longer elapsed before the 2 lists were compared. Riess himself has written: "In view of the many uncontrolled factors, the data as presented are to be thought of as suggestive only." [13] Thus, this experiment cannot now be considered as in any way inexplicable.

The third inexplicable experiment noted by Kennedy was the Pearce-Pratt series, but here Kennedy was not satisfied with the information given about the method of checking the scores. At that time, very meager details of the experiment had, in fact, been revealed, and it was not until 1954 that a complete account was published.

Kennedy commented on Rhine's suggestions for experimenters as follows:

Attitudes of expectancy of good scores, playful informality and positive suggestibility in the subject seem best to help the un-noticed or unconscious use of sensory cues. But it is these condi-tions at work in the experimenter or recorder which seem to be most important in attempting to understand the production of ESP.

It should be noted further that the encouragement of playful informality by the experimenter involves the condition of split attention
which is a favorable if not an absolutely necessary condition for
unconscious error production.[14]

Kennedy suggested that the following controls should be present
in ESP experiments:

1. Distance or shielding sufficient to eliminate sensory cues.
2. Calls and cards should be recorded by 2 different persons and
checked by comparing the 2 records.
3. To produce a random distribution of targets, a tested method
should be used.
4. A limit to the number of trials should be established before
the experiment begins, and comparisons of records might well be
postponed until after the end of the experiment.
5. To assure objectivity, there should be no possibility of fraud
on the part of the subject. This might involve testing high-scoring
subjects in several different laboratories.

In classifying experiments as inexplicable, Kennedy had not
excluded the possibility of fraud: he merely implied that the
experiments were not explicable in terms of the sources of error he
had discussed in his article and that fraud was the only remaining
explanation other than ESP.

THE ESP SYMPOSIUM OF THE AMERICAN PSYCHOLOGICAL
ASSOCIATION

In September 1938, during its annual meeting at Columbus,
Ohio, the American Psychological Association held a symposium on
the methods of ESP research. Various criticisms raised in the past
were discussed, and the experimental methods in use at that time
at Duke University were considered. According to Soal and Bateman,[15] Professor Chester Kellogg, one of the most outspoken critics
of ESP, told Rhine that if he went on with the methods he was then
using, he would get no more extrasensory perception.

After the meeting, a committee was set up under the chairman-
ship of S. B. Sells, a psychologist at Columbia University, to review

and criticize reports of ESP experiments. A group of eminent psychologists formed the committee, including Lillian Dick, J. J. Gibson, E. R. Hilgard, J. L. Kennedy, and R. R. Willoughby.

APPRAISAL OF ESP EXPERIMENTS BY MEMBERS OF THE PARAPSYCHOLOGY LABORATORY

In 1940, the Duke parapsychologists published their own appraisal of ESP research in the book called *Extra-Sensory Perception after Sixty Years.*

The expressed aim of the authors was to survey the published reports and to assess them in terms of the criticisms that had been raised. Over the years, 35 counterhypotheses to ESP had been put forward to account for the scores obtained in the tests. The authors stated that the final step was to determine whether there was a remainder of evidence—an inexplicable portion of the summarized results of the ESP research—that could not be met by all the hypotheses combined.

Each of the experiments reported since 1882 was first considered in relation to each of the 35 counterhypotheses. Those that survived this examination were then listed, and it was pointed out how each of the counterhypotheses could be shown to be inapplicable. A total of 145 experiments carried out between 1882 and 1939 were assessed, of which the first 2 were the investigations of the Creery sisters and of Smith and Blackburn discussed in Chapter 4.

Only 6 experiments survived after being checked against the counterhypotheses, and these were then arranged in order of merit. Kennedy had, with reservations, included only 1 Duke experiment among the 3 he considered to be inexplicable. The Duke critics included 3 of their own experiments among their selected 6. These 3 were: the Pratt-Woodruff experiment (considered first in quality), which had not been published at the time Kennedy made his review (see Chapter 7); the Pearce-Pratt experiment (considered third best; see Chapter 7); the Rhine-Ownbey series (considered fourth best; see pages 54–55).

The other 3 experiments were the Warner experiment (second on the list; see pages 62–63); the Riess experiment (fifth on the list; see pages 63–64); and in last place, an experiment reported by Ernest Taves and Gardner Murphy, psychologists at Columbia University. This last experiment did not yield an above-chance score and will not, therefore, be discussed any further.

The presence of the Rhine-Ownbey series no doubt evoked some surprise in parapsychological circles, since no one had heard of it before. It is described in *Extra-Sensory Perception after Sixty Years* as follows:

> A fourth series meeting successfully all the requirements made by the combined counter-hypotheses is the following long-distance test on pure telepathy reported by Rhine and conducted by him in conjunction with Miss Ownbey (Mrs. George Zirkle) as co-experimenter. The shorter of the three distances that obtained in the three series was 165 miles. A total of 650 trials was reported in 1934 (238) under these conditions, with independent records turned over to (mailed or personally delivered to) Rhine by Miss Ownbey and the subject (Miss Turner or Mr. Zirkle).[16]

In Appendix 20, in which the scores for each session are given, it is stated only that the "Agent and Percipient mailed the records to Rhine."

From examination of the scores and dates on which the tests were made, it seems that the Rhine-Ownbey series consisted of the Turner-Ownbey series combined with a similar long-distance test in which George Zirkle acted as the percipient and Miss Ownbey as the experimenter. The tests on Zirkle consisted of 13 runs made during August and September of 1933 with a distance of 165 miles between the percipient and the cards, but the score achieved by Zirkle was not significantly above the chance level.

It will be remembered that the first 3 runs of the Turner-Ownbey series were sent to Miss Ownbey before being given to Rhine. The score of both percipients (Turner and Zirkle) combined in 650 trials was 177 hits as compared to the chance expectation of 130 hits; the odds are about 1 million to 1 against this result arising by chance. If, however, the scores obtained in the first three days of the Turner-Ownbey series are omitted, it is found that in 23 runs a total of 126 hits was obtained, compared to the chance-expectation score of 115 hits. Here the odds are 3 to 1, and it is unnecessary to invoke ESP to account for these scores. Thus, the result of the Rhine-Ownbey series is entirely dependent on the scores achieved during the first 3 days of the Turner-Ownbey series, when the conditions certainly did not eliminate the possibility that Miss Ownbey influenced the result of the experiment.

It is therefore of considerable interest to see how the authors of *Extra-Sensory Perception after Sixty Years* managed to cope, when discussing the experiments, with 3 of the counterhypotheses. Remarkably, no hint was given in the discussion of the unfortunate lapse in the conditions during the first 3 days of the experiment, although it would appear to be difficult to provide a full discussion of the counterhypotheses without mentioning that lapse.

The reply to counterhypothesis 21, "the data must have been tampered with by the subjects, assistants, or other persons," was:

> The short series which make up this work are the only ones of their kind and are sufficiently unique to be easily remembered by both E's [experimenters]. They were summarized in record books and all data reported by one E, both to the other E, and to the subject. The presence of two E's, together with the independent records, and the easy recall of such unique tests, is sufficient guarantee against these hypotheses.[17]

The two experimenters referred to are Rhine and Ownbey; the subject was either Turner or Zirkle. It is agreed that Rhine had no evidence that Miss Ownbey tampered with the records, but some mention might have been made of the fact that she could have done so, and that the experimental result was not inconsistent with her having done so.

The reply to counterhypothesis 27, "the results are due to loose conditions and poor observation by the experimenter," ran:

> Distance excludes a multitude of conceivable experimental weaknesses in telepathic tests. The only criticisms on this work bear on the questions (a) of its p-value, the probability of the result arising by chance, and (b) of possible pattern and preference similarity. Both are met by the data of Table 13, p. 127, giving back-check and cross-check averages on this work.[18]

The reply to counterhypothesis 30, "general untrustworthiness (moral or psychopathic) of the experimenters explains the results," was:

If over-enthusiasm or dishonesty are back of these results, *it is difficult to account for the striking decline in scoring level.* The main extra-chance results occurred during the first few days of the series . . . and the rest of the scores were but little above chance. *There was no change of instructions that might account for the decline:* only a shortening of the inter-trial interval from 5 to 3 minutes. *Any act of bad faith would of necessity have involved the collusion of one E with the other or with the S* [subject]. While an instance of this character is yet to be encountered in academic research, its possibility cannot, of course, be flatly denied. But again, to take the collusion hypothesis seriously throws the burden upon the group of confirmatory E's as a whole, and the mutual support of these must supply the answer needed.

That is to say, Ownbey and Turner, or Ownbey and Rhine, might be regarded as conspirators to deceive the world regarding ESP much more easily than could the combination of Ownbey and Rhine, Pratt and Woodruff, Warner and Raible, and Pratt and Rhine (to speak only of the above mentioned names). The notion of such wholesale conspiracy would be to most students more fantastic than the ESP hypothesis.[19]

These comments contain 3 statements, which I have put in italics, each of which is misleading.

1. "It is difficult to account for the striking decline in scoring level." If the readers of *Extra-Sensory Perception after Sixty Years* had been informed that the records were not sent directly to Rhine during the first 3 high-scoring sessions and that they were sent directly to him after this, there would have been no difficulty accounting for the decline.

2. "There was no change of instructions that might account for the decline." But there was a change in the *procedure* after the third day that coincided with the sudden decline in the score.

3. "Any act of bad faith would of necessity have involved the collusion of one E with the other or with the S." This statement would be true if the original instructions had been followed, but

in view of what happened during the first 3 sessions, it is not true. Miss Ownbey could have intercepted the mail and completed her record after seeing Miss Turner's record.

Subsequent published accounts of the Turner-Ownbey series make no mention of the unfortunate lapse during the first 3 runs. Thus, in *Parapsychology: Frontier Science of the Mind* by Rhine and Pratt, published in 1957, the series is described with reference to *Extra-Sensory Perception after Sixty Years*, rather than to *Extra-Sensory Perception*, which did note the one important point about the experiment.

The August before the ESP symposium of the 1938 meeting of the American Psychological Association, an experiment had been carried out as part of the requirements for a higher degree by J. L. Woodruff, then an undergraduate student in the psychology department at Duke. In this experiment, a significant above-chance score had been obtained by a group of 42 subjects. The experiment as it stood could not be considered other than exploratory, and it would certainly not have impressed the critics who were present at the Psychological Association meeting. In October 1938, immediately after the meeting, a further experiment based on Woodruff's work was started. It was called Series B, and Pratt participated as second experimenter, with much more effective control conditions in force. Both for parapsychologists and their critics, the Pratt-Woodruff experiment has been regarded as the best of the investigations producing evidence for ESP carried out in the United States. The other investigation, as has been noted, regarded as conclusive by members of the Parapsychology Laboratory, is the Pearce-Pratt experiment.

These are both of quite a different order from the earlier tests carried out at Duke University, and they will be discussed in detail in the next 2 chapters.

CHAPTER **7**

The Pearce-Pratt Experiment

HUBERT E. PEARCE, the divinity student, had been acting as a subject in ESP experiments for more than a year before he took part in the Pearce-Pratt experiment, or Campus Distance Series as it is also known, which was started in August 1933 and completed in March 1934. Rhine has stated that the aim of the experiment was to set up experimental conditions strict enough to exclude all factors, other than ESP, that could produce above-chance scores. The experiment has been described in several articles and books, but the most complete account was provided in a 1954 article in the *Journal of Parapsychology;* the description given here is based on this account of the experiment.

It was basically a clairvoyance test, in which Pearce guessed at cards in a pack controlled by Pratt, then a graduate student in the psychology department, while he was situated in another building on the campus.

THE PROCEDURE

The two men met in Pratt's room on the top floor of what is now the social sciences building on the west campus of Duke University. (At the time of the experiments this was the physics building, and the psychology department used a few rooms in it.) Both men synchronized their watches and fixed a time at which the test would start. Pearce then went across the quadrangle to the library, where he sat in a cubicle in the stacks at a distance of about 100 yards from Pratt, who from his window could see Pearce cross the quadrangle and enter the library.

71

THE TARGETS

Pratt sat down at a table, took a pack of ESP cards, and, after shuffling and cutting it, placed it face downward on the right side of the table. At the time fixed for the experiment to start, he took the top card and placed it, still face down, on a book in the center of the table. At the end of a minute this card was transferred to the left side of the table, and the second card in the pack was placed on the book. In this manner, each card was placed on the book at its appointed time and then transferred to a pile on the left side of the table. After a run of 25 cards, an interval of 5 minutes elapsed, and then the same procedure was followed with a second pack. Pratt did not see the faces of the cards until the end of the sitting when he turned them up to record their order. He then made a duplicate of his record, sealed it in an envelope, and later delivered it to Rhine.

THE PERCIPIENT

In his cubicle in the library, Pearce recorded his guess as to the identity of each card lying on the book. After recording 50 guesses, he made a duplicate copy of his record sheet and sealed it in an envelope that was later delivered to Rhine. The 2 sealed records usually were delivered personally to Rhine before Pratt and Pearce compared their lists and scored the number of successes.

THE EXPERIMENTAL CONDITIONS

The above procedure was followed at each of 37 sittings held between August 1933 and March 1934. The sittings were divided into 4 subseries: Subseries A consisted of 6 sittings, carried out under the above conditions; subseries B was composed of 22 sittings at which Pratt carried out his part of the proceedings in a room in the medical building, which would have put him about 250 yards away from Pearce; subseries C consisted of 6 sittings with the same conditions as subseries A; in subseries D, there were 3 sittings with the same conditions as subseries A, except that Rhine was with Pratt in the room in the social sciences building.

THE RESULTS

The scores at successive sittings obtained in each subseries are shown in Table 1.

TABLE 1

Scores in each run of the Pratt-Pearce Experiment [1]

Sitting	Subseries A (100 yards)	Subseries B (250 yards)	Subseries C (100 yards)	Subseries D (100 yards)
1	3	1, 4	9, 8	12, 3
2	8, 5	4, 4	4, 9	10, 11
3	9, 10	7, 6	11, 9	10, 10
4	12, 11	5, 0	5, 4	
5	11, 12	6, 3	9, 11	
6	13, 13, 12	11, 9	2, 7	
7		0, 6		
8		8, 6		
9		9, 4		
10		10, 6		
11		11, 9		
12		5, 12		
13		7, 7		
14		12, 10		
15		6, 3		
16		10, 10		
17		6, 12		
18		2, 6		
19		12, 12		
20		4, 4		
21		3, 0		
22		13, 10		
Total trials	300	1,100	300	150
Total hits	119	295	88	56
Average score per run of 25 trials (hits)	9.9	6.7	7.3	9.3

Something other than chance obviously was operating in each of the 4 subseries. The odds against the over-all result arising by chance are greater than 10^{22} to 1, and the result of each subseries is statistically significant.

ELIMINATION OF ALTERNATIVE HYPOTHESES

When discussing the experiment in 1954 in the *Journal of Parapsychology,* Rhine and Pratt stated that the only alternative to an explanation in terms of ESP would involve collusion among all 3 participants.

It is difficult to see how either Rhine or Pratt, unaided, could have cheated to bring about the result obtained in all 4 subseries; but, owing to the fact that Pearce was not supervised during the experiment, there are a number of ways in which he could have cheated to attain high scores.

Pratt saw Pearce disappear into the library; then, some time later, after the sitting was over, he met him and checked his scores. He had no confirmation, other than Pearce's word for it—if he ever asked him—that Pearce had stayed in the library. He could quite easily have walked back to where Pratt was conducting his part of the experiment. In view of this, the possibility that Pearce obtained knowledge of the targets must be carefully considered.

It would not have been necessary to obtain sight of the cards at every sitting, since the scores given in Table 1 only display scores higher than chance at some of the sittings. Ten or more hits would be expected to arise by chance once in each 52 runs. If such a score is considered high, it will be seen that one was not obtained at sittings 1 and 2 in series *A.* In subseries *B,* only 9 of the 22 sittings produced high scores; in subseries *C,* high scores were obtained only at sittings 3 and 5; and in subseries *D,* high scores were obtained only at each of the 3 settings of which it was composed. The distribution of scores shows a distinct bimodal characteristic— that is, having two maximi: one between values of 4 and 6, the other between values of 9 and 12—as if the cause of high scores was in operation on some occasions and not on others. At approximately half of the sittings, the scores reveal no evidence of the possibility of either ESP or cheating. Thus, if Pearce left the library, he need only have gained sight of the cards as Pratt was going through the run on those occasions when it was safe to do so.

An important point to note is that the experiment was conducted according to a strict timetable. If Pearce had chosen to cheat, he knew to the second—from the time he was supposed to start his recording to the time when he was supposed to make his last guess —what Pratt was doing. He knew that he had 55 minutes during which Pratt would be fully occupied and that at the end of that time Pratt would be busy making first a list of the order of the cards in the 2 packs and then a duplicate of his record. Provided it was possible to see into Pratt's room, Pearce could have left the library and observed Pratt, gaining sight of the cards when they were turned up for recording at the end of the sitting or, if they could be identified from their backs, he could have inspected them while they were on the book in front of Pratt for a minute. Clearly, it is essential to know something about the 2 rooms in which Pratt carried out his part of the proceedings and about the way in which he turned up the cards when recording their order.

From Pratt and Rhine's statement, the reader might assume that they had carefully considered every conceivable explanation other than a trick involving all 3 participants in the experiment. He may assume, since no description was given of the rooms in which the tests were carried out, that they were quite adequate for their purpose and that no one could possibly have seen into them. If he takes anything of the sort for granted, he may be led sadly astray. A first principle when assessing an experiment should be: never assume anything that is not stated in the experimental report.

THE ROOMS USED FOR THE EXPERIMENT

When I was at Duke University in 1960, Pratt showed me the rooms he used during the experiment. While doing so, he mentioned that since 1934 structural alterations had been made to both rooms. We first visited Pratt's old room, 314, in the social sciences building. I located the position of the table as shown in Figure 2. Pratt then pointed out that the wall beside the table had been further back in 1933. After its original position had been located, it was apparent that the room in its original state contained a large clear-glass window that would have permitted anyone in the corridor to see into the room at the time of the experiment. I judged the window to be about 2 feet square and to be about 5 feet 10 inches from the floor at its bottom edge. Anyone looking through this window from the corridor would have had a clear view of Pratt seated at his desk and of the cards he was handling.

There were similar windows leading into the offices on the other side of the corridor as well as clear-glass windows above the doors of all the rooms. Later, I went into a room on the opposite side of the corridor, 311, and found that the line of vision when looking through the transom above the door was through the window into Pratt's room and down onto his desk. It was impossible to be certain of this point since the wall in its new position hindered my view. However, there was a good possibility that Pearce could have returned to the social sciences building, locked himself in Room 311, and then observed Pratt with comparative safety by standing on a chair or table and looking through the transom above the door.

The room in the medical building had been changed drastically since 1934, and it was now used for making X-rays. There was a transom above the door and a window, but both of these were of ripple glass, and it is doubtful whether the cards could have been identified through them. In this room there was, however, a trap door in the ceiling, measuring about 4 feet by 1½ feet and situated immediately over the position occupied by the table at which Pratt sat during the experiment. Its cover had a large hole that looked as if it had been made recently. There was also a small metal plate on the trap door that could have covered another hole, and this plate looked as if it had been there a long time.

The room was on the top classroom floor of the building, and the main staircase went up another flight to a large attic, which extended over the floor the room was on. At the time of my visit, the attic was used for storage purposes, but I was told that most of the contents had been put there well after 1934. It would thus have been possible for an intruder to have positioned himself above the trap door to see the cards on Pratt's table.

I went to the architect's office of the university and asked to see plans of the rooms as they were in 1933. I also asked for details of structural alterations that had been made to the rooms, together

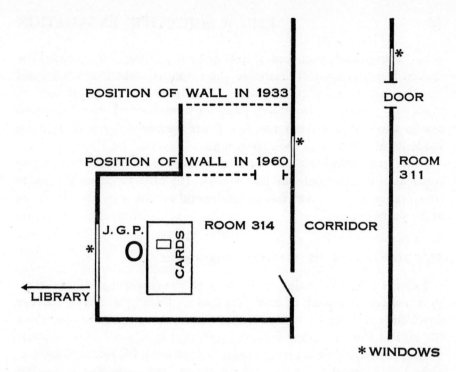

FIGURE 2. *Plan, not to scale, of the rooms in the social sciences building, Duke University*

with the dates on which they had been made, and the persons who had asked for them. These details were to be forwarded to me, but I never received them. I wrote again requesting them, but had no reply.

FURTHER DETAILS OF THE PROCEDURE

The day after we had seen the rooms, I asked Pratt to demonstrate to me the exact procedure he used during the experiment. I was particularly interested to see how he turned up the cards to record them, whether he shuffled the packs after use, and how he left them on the table.

From his demonstration it was clear that anyone looking into the room would have obtained a clear view of the faces of the cards when they were being listed. Each was turned on its back while an entry was made on the record sheet. Pratt did not shuffle the packs after noting down their order, and after recording the first pack he moved it to the top-left corner of the table. He told me that he did not lock his door during the sitting or after it was over and that he made his record on notebook paper. I also learned that the room across the corridor from the one Pratt had been in was used by students at the time of the experiment.

Pratt gave every assistance. He himself pointed out the structural alterations made to the rooms. He also emphasized, quite reasonably, that he was forced to depend on his memory of events of 26 years before.

THE POSSIBILITY OF VIEWING THE CARDS

Later, I asked W. Saleh, a member of the research staff at Duke, to run through a pack of ESP cards while I sat in an office further down the corridor. He was to record the cards on a sheet of paper at the end of the run using a procedure similar to that used by Pratt during the experiments with Pearce and to keep his door closed and locked. I slipped back to Saleh's room and saw the cards by standing on a chair and looking through the crack at the top of the door. I had a clear view of them and obtained 22 hits in 25 attempts. Saleh's desk was about 16 feet from the door, and he had no suspicion of what I had done until I told him.

In a second test, I asked him to record the cards in a room in which I had left a sheet of blotting paper on the desk to take an impression of what he wrote. I then read off the identities of the cards from the impressions of his writing on the blotting paper. But by this time Saleh was tired of having his leg pulled. He had carefully written out a second list, using the blotting paper for it, so that I was given false information. It was clear, however, from these tests that knowledge of the cards could have been obtained by the use of either method, provided other factors in the situation did not eliminate the possibility.

GENERAL FEATURES OF THE EXPERIMENT

Now that information has become available about the conditions in which the experiment was carried out, it is clear that it was far from foolproof, and the result could have been brought about in a variety of ways. The conditions were remarkably loose compared to those imposed on Smith and Blackburn, and it is difficult to understand how the experiment came to be designed in such a manner that any would-be trickster could fake his scores with comparative ease. It is thus of particular interest to know to what extent Pearce participated in the design.

In *New Frontiers of the Mind,* Rhine states that after Pearce had been relatively unsuccessful in earlier distance tests, the formality and fixed routine of experimental conditions were loosened, and Pearce was allowed to suggest changes himself. "He could say 'Let's try some D.T.' or 'Let me go over to the next room awhile. . . .' This broke the monotony and very probably contributed to his doing successful scoring." [2]

In the Pearce-Pratt experiment the distance of 100 yards was fixed from the start, although it was, "possibly, suggested by Pearce." Whether Pearce made other suggestions is not mentioned. It would be of interest to know, for example, who selected the rooms used for the experiment.

The experiment contained some 37 sittings in all. For sitting after sitting, Pratt sat in his room slowly turning over packs of cards and recording them at the end of each day's run. Pearce, after having failed miserably in earlier experiments as soon as he was moved more than a yard from the cards, was now suddenly obtaining very high scores at 100 times that distance or more. One would expect that anyone in Pratt's position would have examined the room carefully and have taken elaborate precautions so that no one could see into it. At least he might have covered the windows leading to the corridor. Also, the cards should have been shuffled after they were recorded, and the door of the room might well have been locked during and after the tests. These experiments were not a first-year exercise. They were intended to provide conclusive proof of ESP and to shake the very foundations of science. If Pratt had some misgivings, there is no evidence that he ever expressed them. He took no precautions to ensure that Pearce stayed in the library or to prevent the cards being visible to anyone looking into his room.

Again, Rhine might well have been wary of trickery, for neither he nor Pratt were novices in psychical research. Both of them were fully aware of its long history of trickery.

COUNTERCRITICISMS

I criticized the experimental conditions under which the Pearce-Pratt experiment was conducted in the *Journal of Parapsychology;* Rhine and Pratt made a joint reply in the same number of the journal. Their answer was that the subseries *D* experiment, in which Rhine was with Pratt while it was conducted, eliminated the possibility of Pearce cheating:

> In this series J. B. R., who had remained in the background previously, came into the test room with J. G. P. and sat through a series of six runs through the test pack (150 trials) for the purpose of scrutinising the entire procedure from that point of vantage, to ensure that it was faithfully executed. He, like J. G. P., *could see the subject from the window as the latter entered the library* (and, of course, could see him exit as well). He was in the experimental room at the end of each session to receive the independent records from both J. G. P. and H. E. P. immediately on the arrival of the latter at the close of the session. Thus the subject was obviously allowed no opportunity to enter the room alone and copy the order of the cards or the impressions left on the record pad. Even with the somewhat imaginative supposition that H. E. P. had a collaborator, there was no time for the latter, even if he had (unnoticed by J. B. R.) observed the card-turning and recording by J. G. P., to have communicated the knowledge of card order thus gained to H. E. P. as he arrived in the building for the check-up. H. E. P. had to have his duplicate record in his own handwriting, with one copy sealed in an envelope, ready to hand to J. B. R. on entering the room. J. G. P. had to do the recording of the last run of each session after the test was over and H. E. P. was already on his way to the test room. Yet these final runs of the session were, in themselves, independently significant statistically.[3]

However, what is important here is not whether Rhine could have seen Pearce leave the library if he had been watching for him, but whether he did actually see him leave at the termination of the experiment each day. Did Rhine stand by the window watching for Pearce to leave the library? If so, how did he know that Pratt was not busy faking his record? Rhine was with Pratt to see that he did not cheat, for it was assumed that a trick was possible only if both Pearce and Pratt were in collaboration, and Pratt need only have made about 5 false entries for each run to create scores such as those obtained by Pearce.

Rhine could not have been watching from the window leading into the corridor to see that no one was looking in while at the same time looking out the window on the opposite wall to see Pearce leave the library and also watching Pratt record the cards.

That Rhine saw Pearce leave the library, or the fact that he could have seen him had he been watching for him, now appears to be a most important control feature of the experiment. But even if Rhine or Pratt had watched to see Pearce leave the library, and there is no mention in any of the reports that this was done, it would have been a simple matter for Pearce to have deceived the experimenters. He could have returned to the library without being seen. He could have left a few gaps in his record, and worked with an assistant stationed in the corridor to see Pratt's cards and to note them as they were turned up. He could then have completed his list after entering the social sciences building. Only 10 entries, each a simple symbol, were required. The envelope addressed to Rhine could already have been prepared by Pearce while he was in the library.

It might be expected that Pearce would arrive at Pratt's room before the listing was completed, since he had merely to make copies of his record, whereas Pratt had to write down the order of the cards and then make a duplicate copy. What did Pearce do? Did he tap on the door and wait until he was called in? Did he peep through the window to see whether Pratt had finished? How long after the last run did Pearce make an appearance? Were his records checked to see that they were all in his own handwriting? He wrote down a list of symbols, not words or letters, and it would be difficult for even a handwriting expert to detect forgery.

THE FACTS OF THE EXPERIMENT

Up to this point, criticism of the experiment has been based on the account published in the *Journal of Parapsychology* in 1954 and on my viewing of the room used at Duke by Pratt. (I never saw the room used by Pearce; Pratt was unable to remember where it was located.) The 1954 version of the experiment has been used because it is by far the most complete, but when it is checked with the other descriptions provided from time to time since 1934, it is clear that it may have little resemblance to what actually took place.

The experiment was first mentioned, while in progress, in *Extra-Sensory Perception* (1934). Brief accounts were later given in the *Journal of Abnormal and Social Psychology* (1936), the *Journal of Parapsychology* (1937), *New Frontiers of the Mind* (1938), *Extra-Sensory Perception after Sixty Years* (1940), *The Reach of the Mind* (1948), and *New World of the Mind* (1954). Pratt has given further details in a recent book, *Parapsychology: An Insider's View of ESP* (1964).

Close examination of these sources indicates that while it is likely that some sort of long-distance test was carried out on Pearce in 1933–1934, the reports of the experiment may have changed with the passage of years. Completely contradictory statements appear in these various sources on the procedure adopted by Pratt, the recording of the targets, the number of sittings, and the actual scores obtained. For example, in *New World of the Mind*, the procedure adopted by Pratt when he moved the cards from a pile on the right of his desk, via the book, to a pile on his left is completely reversed. Also, there is doubt whether the experiment as reported constituted only a part of a larger series of tests.

The duplicate records made by both Pearce and Pratt were an essential control feature of the experiments. It is therefore surprising to find no mention of them in the 4 accounts of the experiment published before 1940.

The duplicates are first mentioned in *Extra-Sensory Perception after Sixty Years*, where the various counterhypotheses to ESP were being considered. After 1940, however, the duplicate records are mentioned in each of the 4 additional published accounts of the experiment.

In *New Frontiers of the Mind*, it is stated that there was to be no discussion between Pearce and Pratt until the records had been delivered to Rhine in sealed envelopes. In *New World of the Mind* the revised statement is that Pratt sealed his copy of the record in an envelope for delivery to Rhine before he met Pearce and that Pearce placed his copy in a sealed envelope before checking his duplicate with Pratt. The version in the *Journal of Parapsychology* is that the 2 sealed envelopes were delivered personally to Rhine "most of the time" before Pratt and Pearce had compared their records.

The *Journal of Parapsychology* article discusses the recording of targets as follows: "Over in his room J. G. P. recorded the card order for the two packs used in the test as soon as the second run was finished." *New Frontiers of the Mind* contains a similar statement. When replying to my criticisms of their experiment, Rhine and Pratt appeared to be implying that the recording of the targets in the first pack was made before the second run was started. "J. G. P. had to do the recording of the last run of each session after the test was over and H. E. P. was already on his way to the test room." In case there was any doubt as to the precise implication of these words, Pratt clarified the matter in his recent book *Parapsychology: An Insider's View of ESP*, in which he stated:

> When all the cards had taken their turn on the book, I made a record of the twenty-five cards in the order in which they had been used. As a rule, we went through this procedure again on the same day after taking a recess of five minutes to allow time for me to make the record and shuffle and cut the cards for the next run.[4]

This new procedure with the cards would invalidate a criticism I raised: that the 2 packs used in the experiment could have been inspected after the tests were over while Pratt was delivering his sealed record to Rhine.

Extra-Sensory Perception states that when the cards were moved 250 yards from the percipient, there was a low-scoring adjustment period at first.

But in *New Frontiers of the Mind*, it is stated that after increasing the distance to 250 yards in subseries B, there was no falling off in the score at the first sitting and that Pearce obtained scores of 12 and 10 in the 2 runs. Scores for the next 5 days are given as follows: second day, exactly chance; third day, two 10's; fourth day, a 2 and a 6; fifth day, a 5 and a 12; sixth day, a 7 and a 5. Similar scores are given in *Extra-Sensory Perception after Sixty Years,* but these are different from those given in the *Journal of Parapsychology* and reproduced in Table 1. Yet in *The Reach of the Mind,* we read: "For a time Pearce did as well at 250 yards as at

100; then something went wrong. . . ." Moreover, the scores published in the *Journal of Abnormal and Social Psychology* disagree with those in the *Journal of Parapsychology*. They give total hits for the 4 subseries as: *A*, 179; *B*, 288; *C*, 86; *D*, 56. The individual scores quoted are also in a different order for subseries *B* and *C* from those given in the *Journal of Parapsychology*.

In *New Frontiers of the Mind*, it is said that in 6 runs made on 3 successive days, Pearce 5 times made a score of 4 hits and that he scored 1 hit in the other run. This cannot be reconciled with the data given in the *Journal of Parapsychology*. According to the figures published in the *Journal of Abnormal Psychology*, there were 8 runs, the scores were obtained over 4 successive days and were 12, 4; 4, 1; 4, 4; 4, 7.

The *Journal of Parapsychology* article states that subseries *D* consisted of 6 runs, and the dates are given as March 12 and 13; but the scores for subseries *D* are given as 12, 3; 10, 11; and 10, 10; we are told also that the division between days or sessions is marked by the use of semicolons. Thus it appears that 2 of the 3 sessions must have taken place on 1 of the 2 days. But in *New Frontiers of the Mind*, Rhine says that he witnessed a 3 day series. Thus, either the dates in the table or Rhine's memory are at fault. Rhine has remarked about subseries *D:* "As a matter of fact, it is not easily overlooked and would be, for most readers, quite obviously, the climax series in the paper." As this subseries was the only part of the experiment in which Rhine actively participated, he might well be particularly aware of it. But in *New Frontiers of the Mind*, published 3 years after the experiment, Rhine completely forgot the subseries, saying that, after the tests in the medical building, "Pratt moved back to the Physics Building for another 300 trials." According to this account, "The next step involved a distance of two miles, and things went wrong from the start. The room arranged for was not open when it should have been and for several days there was frustration in the physical details of the experiment. After things were finally straightened out, there was no appreciable success." [5] In *New Frontiers of the Mind* further tests are also mentioned in which Pearce went in a car to different places in the country and recorded calls, but it appears that he was not hopeful, and there was no success. By 1954, however, the tests at a 2-mile distance had been forgotten. The *Journal of Parapsy-*

chology article, after reporting subseries *A, B, C,* and *D* comprising 74 runs, states: "The 74 runs represent all the ESP tests made with H. E. P. during this experiment under the conditions of working with the subject and target cards in different buildings done at the Duke Laboratory at the time." [6]

Shortly after the experiment was concluded, Pearce received a letter one morning that is said to have distressed him greatly. This incident was claimed to have been responsible for his loss of ESP. In fact, the last sitting of the Pearce-Pratt experiment appears to have been the last occasion on which Pearce displayed any supposed ESP ability.

SUMMARY

The Pearce-Pratt experiment cannot be regarded as supplying evidence to support the existence of extrasensory perception for the following reasons:

1. The various reports of the experiment contain conflicting statements so that it is difficult to ascertain the precise facts.

2. Essential features of the experimental situation were not reported, and readers have been led to assume that the experimental conditions were foolproof and that every possibility of trickery had been considered and guarded against.

3. A number of aspects of the experimental design were such as to enable the result of the experiment to be brought about by a trick. These features were: The subject was left unobserved; the rooms used by Pratt were not screened so as to make it impossible for anyone to see into them; Pratt recorded the targets at the end of each sitting in such a manner as to expose their faces to anyone looking into the room.

A further unsatisfactory feature lies in the fact that a statement has not been made at any time by the central figure, Hubert Pearce. The experimenters state that trickery was impossible, but what would Pearce have said? Perhaps one day he will give us his own account of the experiment.

CHAPTER **8**

The Pratt-Woodruff Experiment

THE Pratt-Woodruff experiment was carried out at Duke University between October 1, 1938, and February 28, 1939. It was originally intended as a test to determine the effects of the size of stimulus symbols on clairvoyance, but owing to the results obtained, the care taken in the experimental design, the precision of its execution, and the careful account of the procedure contained in the report,[1] it has remained as the classic ESP experiment. Rhine and Pratt, when discussing conclusive test methods some 15 years later, commented: "Those who wish to acquire a reading acquaintance with the highest standards of controlled psi testing may, for example, consult the Pratt and Woodruff report."[2] Rhine made even stronger claims: "The experiment was designed for the express purpose of meeting all the criticisms that came up in the years of controversy. In the entire history of Psychology no experiment has ever been carried out with such elaborate controls against all possible error."[3]

THE PERSONS TAKING PART

Three persons were present at each sitting: a main experimenter, J. L. Woodruff; a second experimenter, J. G. Pratt; and a subject. Pratt's task was to ensure that the experiment was carried out efficiently and that all the controls were observed; he will therefore be referred to as the "observer." In addition, one of the laboratory secretaries was responsible for seeing that all the score sheets, which were serially numbered in advance, were completed and included in the final analysis so that all tests would be contained in the final result and that only the predetermined number of runs would be made.

THE EXPERIMENTAL PROCEDURE

The experimenter and the subject sat at opposite ends of a table. Between them, across the width of the table, was a screen 18 inches in height and 24 inches in breadth. This screen had a gap 2 inches high and 20 inches across along its bottom edge so that 5 blank cards placed on the table beneath it were visible to both the subject and the experimenter. A smaller, sloping screen attached to the main one on the experimenter's side permitted the experimenter to see the 5 blank cards, but ensured that the subject could not gain sight of the experimenter or of a pack of ESP cards that he was handling.

On the subject's side of the screen, 5 "key cards," each bearing 1 of the 5 different ESP symbols, were hung on pegs above the gap at the bottom of the screen. Each card was then directly above one of the blank cards lying on the table. Before each run of 25 trials, the observer took the key cards from the pegs and handed them to the subject who changed their order and replaced them.

The experimenter, on the other side of the screen, could not see their positions on the pegs, and only the 5 blank cards were visible to him. He shuffled and cut a pack of ESP cards and then gave the signal to start. Thereupon the subject attempted to guess the top card in the pack. He indicated his guess by pointing with a pencil to the blank card beneath the key card with the appropriate symbol. The experimenter, seeing the end of the pencil through the gap at the bottom of the screen, laid down the top card from the pack, face downward, opposite the blank card the pencil pointed to. The subject made 24 more guesses in the same manner, and the experimenter put the cards in 5 piles in accordance with the positions indicated by the pencil. At the end of the run of 25 trials, with the screen still in position, the experimenter made a record of the cards in each of the piles on one of the serially numbered forms. At the same time, the observer recorded the order of the key cards, the subject's name, and the date of the sitting on a form bearing the same serial number as that used by the experimenter. When these 2 records were completed, they were clipped together and put through a slot into a locked box. The observer was careful to ensure that his record was not seen by the experimenter until the latter had recorded the 5 piles of cards.

The screen was then laid on its side. The cards in each pile were compared with the key cards, and the observer placed the hits together, next to the key card. The number of hits was counted and checked by the 3 persons present. It was then recorded by both the experimenter and by the observer in their personal notebooks. Thus, the scores as later determined from the serially numbered forms could be checked with these 2 other records.

Before the start of the next run, the screen was placed back in position. The key cards were "rearranged on the pegs," and the observer returned to his seat about 6 feet behind the subject and slightly to his right. The experimenter shuffled and cut his pack. He then gave the signal to begin the next run.

On the average, each run of 25 trials, including scoring, took 2 minutes. The experiment included 2,400 runs of which 2,000 were conducted in the above manner (called the STM procedure). In the remaining 400 runs, a modification was introduced: before each run the key cards were removed from the screen by the observer and replaced by him in different positions with their faces toward the screen (BSTM procedure).

THE RESULTS

The 32 subjects who took part in this experiment obtained a total of 12,489 hits in 60,000 trials. This constituted an excess of 489 hits over the score expected to arise by chance. The mean-scoring rate for the group was, however, only 5.204 hits per run as compared with the chance expectation of 5.0 hits per run. Thus, only 1 extra hit need have arisen in each 100 trials to account for the scores. Even so, the odds against the observed result arising by chance are greater than a million to 1, and this provides an example of the way in which a mean score, only slightly above the chance-scoring rate, can assume enormous significance provided it is based on a sufficient number of trials. Such a result must be treated with caution, since even the slightest laxity in the experimental conditions or the presence of weak sensory cues can make itself manifest.

Closer examination of the results of this experiment shows, however, that the explanation is unlikely to be in terms of such forms of error. The subjects varied considerably in their performance, but one subject in particular achieved scores at some sittings that, merely by inspection, can be seen to involve much more than chance. Even though the high scores of this subject, designated P. M. in the report, arose mainly in 3 out of 8 sittings, her over-all score of 947 hits in 4,050 trials had odds greater than 20 million to 1 against arising by chance. Four other subjects also obtained scores having odds greater than 20 to 1 against their arising by chance. Thus, there are clear indications that something other than guesswork or experimental error was involved in this experiment and also that its effects were by no means negligible in the case of at least one subject.

ANALYSIS OF THE EXPERIMENTAL CONDITIONS

If the experimenter had carried out his duties efficiently, it would have been extremely difficult for the subject to have achieved high scores in the absence of some manifestation of ESP. The following criticism of D. H. Rawcliffe should, however, be noted:

> When we hear that the screened touch-matching technique involves the personal handling of a face-down pack of cards by the experimenter who is sitting only a couple of feet away from the percipient, the claim to have imposed the strictest experimental controls must raise a smile.
>
> The only value of a screen between the percipient and the experimenter is that it probably prevents direct visual cues from reaching the percipient. If, in the absence of a screen, the possibility of direct visual cues reaching the *percipient* is admitted, then plainly the same possibility exists in regard to the experimenter; for he can not only see the backs of the cards but he can also touch the backs of the cards and probably the faces as well. Any information he may get from the cards, perhaps subconsciously, may be readily transmitted by unconscious articulation or *endophasic enneuoris*, by an auditory code of ideomotor movements, by intonations and variations in breathing, or by involuntary reactions to any tentative movements of the percipient's pointer over the exposed "key-cards." [4]

While it has been established that individuals are capable of responding to minute auditory, visual, and tactile stimuli as mentioned by Rawcliffe, it is unlikely that the result of the Pratt-

Woodruff experiment could have arisen in this way. The time taken
to make the 25 guesses during each run was about 20 seconds. The
experimenter was watching the fast-moving pointer and sorting the
cards into 5 piles. It would have been difficult for him at the same
time to have looked at the backs of the cards unless he was bent on
identifying them. In that case, he could quite easily have turned
them over and looked at their faces. It is difficult to understand why
the experimenter and the subject should have been placed in such
close proximity, particularly after Pearce's results at more than 100
yards, but if the experimenter carried out his duties efficiently, it is
unlikely that high scores could have arisen either through the
unconscious utilization of cues or by deliberate cheating on the part
of the subject. If, on the other hand, the experimenter had any
knowledge of the positions, or likely positions, of the key cards, and
wished to influence the result of the experiment, he was clearly in a
position to do so. He was completely screened from the other
persons present and had ample opportunity, either while distribut-
ing the cards or while recording them, to change the positions and
numbers of the cards in the 5 piles.

While at the Parapsychology Laboratory in October 1960, I
inspected the apparatus used in the experiments and found that,
when acting in the role of experimenter, it was quite a simple
matter for me to detect the positions at which cards were being
replaced on the pegs on the other side of the screen before the start
of a run. I obtained the assistance of Michael Sanders, who at that
time was a research fellow in the Parapsychology Laboratory, and
asked him to remove the cards from the pegs in order from left to
right and then to replace them in different positions. Having noted
the symbol occupying the left-hand position among the key cards
while the screen was turned on its side at the end of the previous
run, I was able to detect the position in which it was replaced.
Thus, in the role of the experimenter, I would have been able to
place cards in a position where they would secure extra hits during
the following run.

If the experimenter had wished to influence the results of the
experiment in this manner he could have adopted the following
procedure.

When the screen was turned on its side during the scoring at the
end of a run, he could have noted the symbol occupying position 1

(or position 5) in the row of key cards. After the screen was placed back in position, and when the key cards were removed from the pegs by the observer, he could have noted the order in which they were removed. When the subject changed their order and replaced them, he could assume that the last card replaced would be the one that occupied position 1 or 5 in the last run, depending on whether they had been removed from the pegs from left to right or from right to left. If, on the other hand, the positions of the key cards were changed by moving them about on the pegs, he could keep track of a particular card during this process, getting to know the position of one key card. He would allocate the cards to one of the piles during the run and then, after turning up the cards to record them at the end of the run, he would move cards bearing the appropriate symbol into the position where they would result in hits.

A trick of this type would cause a high score to arise frequently on a key-card symbol that had occupied one of the outside positions (1 and 5) during the *previous* run. The effects of such a procedure would also manifest themselves with the best possibility of being detected in the records of the highest-scoring subject (P. M.). The following preliminary analysis was, therefore, carried out to check whether this was so.

All runs made by the high-scoring subject yielding a score of 8 hits or more were considered. The symbol that secured the maximum number of hits in each run was noted. Where 2 or more symbols secured an equally high number of hits, that run was rejected for the purpose of the analysis. Having identified the symbol that secured the maximum number of hits in a run, its position was checked among the key cards in the previous run.

It was found that in 22 runs considered, the high-scoring symbol had occupied either position 1 or 5 among the key cards in the previous run in 17 cases. Most of the cases in which high scores involving preceding positions 1 or 5 did not arise were in the last 2 sittings. These were the 2 sittings in which the BTSM procedure was used and in which the key cards had their faces to the screen. When considering the first 6 sittings, in which the STM procedure was employed, it was found that in only 1 case out of 18 had the high-scoring symbol occupied a position *other* than 1 or 5. Thus, it was clear that something had happened during the

TABLE 2

*Positions that high-scoring symbols occupied
in the row of key cards used for the previous run*

(S = Star, R = Rectangle, P = Plus, W = Waves, C = Circle).   Subject P. M.

Date and type of sitting	Run	Score on run	Highest scoring symbol	Position of symbol in previous run
Nov. 21, 1938 STM	3	6	S	1
	5	6	P	1
	6	6	R	5
	12	10	W	5
	14	8	S	5
Nov. 28, 1938 STM	2	7	P	5
	3	8	W	5
	4	6	C	5
	5	6	R	5
	6	6	C	2
	8	9	C	3
	9	9	S	5
	10	9	W	5
	11	7	W	1
	12	11	R	5
	14	11	P	1
	15	6	P	2
Dec. 12, 1938 STM	6	10	S	5
	7	7	R	5
	8	11	W	5
	10	6	C	5
	12	10	C	5
	15	8	R	5
Jan. 9, 1939 STM	2	6	C	5
	3	7	P	1
	6	10	C	1
	8	7	C	4
	12	6	S	1

TABLE 2 (continued)

Date and type of sitting	Run	Score on run	Highest scoring symbol	Position of symbol in previous run
	18	6	C	1
	19	10	W	1
	20	7	C	5
	22	9	R	1
Jan. 31, 1939 STM	3	10	W	5
	4	6	C	3
	5	7	S	5
	7	8	P	1
	11	7	S	1
	13	6	W	3
	15	6	R	1
Feb. 3, 1939 STM	2	6	C	1
	7	6	P	2
	10	7	W	1
	15	7	R	1
Feb. 10, 1939 BSTM	2	7	S	4
	15	7	P	2
	16	9	S	2
	17	7	R	3
	22	8	R	3
	24	7	S	5
	27	10	S	4
Feb. 17, 1939 BSTM	8	8	R	2
	9	6	C	2
	11	12	P	1
	16	7	C	5
	25	7	W	4

experiment to cause hits to arise in this remarkable manner.

The analysis was then extended to include all runs in which more than 5 hits were obtained. The result is shown in Table 2.

The number of hits arising on a particular symbol should be independent of the position of that symbol in the key cards in the previous run. Thus, the highest score should arise on a symbol previously occupying positions 1 or 5, 40 per cent of the time, and it should arise on symbols previously occupying positions 2, 3, or 4, 60 per cent of the time.

However, of the 55 cases considered in Table 2, there are 39 in which the high-scoring symbol occupied positions 1 or 5 in the previous key-card order, and 16 where it had occupied positions 2, 3, or 4 during the previous run. The contingency table of Table 3 is obtained. A statistical test indicates that the numbers of cases observed in the 2 categories would be expected to arise by chance in only 1 in 100,000 similar experiments.

The high-scoring subject obtained 946 hits in 4,050 trials. Table 4 shows the number of *hits* arising on symbols that, in the previous run, occupied positions 1 and 5 among the key cards compared with the number of hits on symbols that occupied the remaining positions. The first run cannot be included in this analysis; therefore, it relates only to the remaining 4,025 trials in which 941 hits were scored.

Thus it will be seen from Table 4 that the above-chance scores are accounted for entirely in terms of hits made on symbols that occupied positions 1 or 5 in the previous run. The odds on the scores achieved on symbols that occupied positions 2, 3, and 4 in the previous run are nearly even, whereas the odds on the scores achieved for positions 1 and 5 are greater than 100 billion to 1.

TABLE 3

Positions occupied, during previous run,
by symbols securing maximum number of hits in present run

Position that highest-scoring symbol occupied in previous run	Cases observed	Cases expected
1 or 5	39	22
2, 3, or 4	16	33
Totals	55	55

TABLE 4

*Analysis of scores arising on symbols that occupied positions 1 and 5
on previous runs compared with scores arising on symbols
that occupied positions 2, 3, and 4*

Subject P. M.

Position of symbol in previous run	Trials	Hits obtained	Hits expected to arise by chance	Odds against score arising by chance
1 and 5	1,670	453	336.6	greater than 10^{11} to 1
2, 3, and 4	2,355	488	471.0	less than 2 to 1

THE RANDOMIZATION OF KEY-CARD ORDER

It would have been impossible for such a trick as described above to have been carried out by the experimenter if the observer had thoroughly shuffled the key cards before they were replaced on the pegs. There is no mention of the cards having been shuffled in the experimental report, but when I was at the Parapsychology Laboratory, Pratt told me that he remembered shuffling them. However, a study of the key-card order of many runs of the second highest-scoring subject (D. A.) shows little evidence of shuffling. At the first sitting, comprising 14 runs, the order of the key cards remained unchanged for the last 7 runs. At the second sitting, comprising 18 runs, the order of the key cards remained unchanged from one run to the next on 6 occasions. On 3 occasions the order of the cards was simply reversed; another time, 2 cards were interchanged and then put back to their original positions on the following run. These effects are confined to the first 2 sittings in which the STM procedure was used. In the third sitting, using the BSTM procedure, the order of cards appears to have been randomized effectively.

Unless the cards were systematically shuffled after every run, a trick could have been employed, and the experimental report makes it clear that the investigators had not seriously considered the necessity of such shuffling. It is stated that Woodruff shuffled the

TABLE 5

Positions occupied during previous run
by high-scoring symbols

STM procedure

Previous position of symbol	CC	DA	DL	HG	PM	Totals
1	13	2	2	13	16	46
2	3	1	4	5	3	16
3	6	2	2	5	3	16
4	3	0	3	6	1	13
5	5	0	5	3	20	33
Totals	30	5	16	32	43	126

pack of cards that he used, but the word "shuffle" is at no time used with reference to the key cards.

THE REMAINING HIGH-SCORING SUBJECTS

Five of the 32 subjects obtained scores significantly above the chance level, at odds greater than 20 to 1. The number of cases in which the high-scoring symbol occupied each of the 5 positions in the key-card order for these subjects, when the STM procedure was used, is shown in Table 5.

The total expected frequency is 25.2 for each position, and the observed values have odds greater than 1 million to 1 against arising by chance. When only subjects C. C., D. A., D. L., and H. G. are considered, their result is also significant, having odds greater than 100 to 1 against arising by chance.

As has been stated, in the last subseries of the experiment the BSTM procedure was used; that is, the observer removed the key cards from the screen and replaced them in different positions with their backs toward the subject. It will be seen from Table 2 that the scores under these conditions dropped markedly for the high-scoring subject P. M. and that there was no indication that hits were being obtained on symbols that had occupied one of the end positions in the previous run. The over-all score for all subjects under BSTM conditions was, however, above chance, and the scoring rate was about the same as under the STM conditions with odds of 20 to 1 against arising by chance. When the results of all subjects are analyzed to show the positions occupied in the previous' run by the high-scoring symbols, the figures shown in Table 6 are obtained. The distribution here is by no means random, although positions 5 and 4 are mainly involved, rather than 1 and 5 as was found with the STM procedure.

The BSTM series started after the first was completed, and a different technique was employed to change the positions of the key cards, since they were handled only by the observer. If a trick, as described above, was employed in the second series, a modification of the procedure by which extra hits were obtained was necessary. If, for example, the observer had a tendency to exchange cards in pairs on the pegs, a new technique could have been employed.

TESTING THE METHOD OF OBTAINING HIGH SCORES

After returning to Manchester, I made some tests with the help of 2 colleagues to ascertain the conditions under which it was possible for a person acting in the role of the experimenter to keep track of the position of a key card. A screen with a gap at the bottom and a second, smaller screen were arranged on a table in a

TABLE 6

Previous positions of high-scoring symbols
BSTM condition.   14 subjects

Position	Observed number of cases	Expected number of cases
1	8	14
2	14	14
3	5	14
4	22	14
5	21	14

manner closely resembling that of the original experiment. Five ESP cards were hung on pegs above the gap.

J. P. Anderson, a senior technician in the department, acted in the role of the subject of the original experiments. He was asked to replace the cards in random order on the screen after they were handed to him by the observer (myself). E. J. Dearnaley, lecturer in psychology, acted in the role of experimenter. Prior to each test, Dearnaley saw the previous order of the key cards. I then removed them and handed them to the subject, who was asked to replace them on the pegs at whatever positions he liked, and the experimenter was asked to indicate the position of any card.

The experimenter was tested under the following 4 conditions:

1. I removed the cards from the pegs in order from left to right, and Dearnaley attempted to identify the position of the first card replaced.

2. The cards were removed as above, but Dearnaley attempted to identify the last card replaced.

3. I removed the cards from left to right or right to left at my own discretion, without Dearnaley knowing which order was being used.

4. I removed the cards in random order from the screen.

The results of the 4 tests were as given in Table 7.

TABLE 7

Number of cards successfully identified
under four different experimental conditions

Subject E. J. D.

Test	Attempts	Cards successfully identified
1	10	8
2	10	9
3	10	9
4	10	9

A fifth test was then made in which condition 4 was used, and Dearnaley was asked to distribute cards from a pack as in the original experiment. He was informed that we would turn up the cards to record the symbols in each pile before the screen was lowered, and that he was to move cards to secure extra hits. Dearnaley was asked to write a report giving his observations on the tests and this is reproduced below:

REPORT MADE BY MR. DEARNALEY

Four methods were used to determine the position of a symbol:

1. I noted the symbol of the end key card on the left of Mr. Hansel and by watching the shadow cast by his hand saw that he picked up this card first. I assumed that Mr. Anderson would replace the same card first. By watching the shadow of Mr. Anderson's hand, and listening to the noise he made when placing the cards on their hooks, I was able to tell whether each card was placed to the left of the first one he replaced. I counted the number of placings to the left and right and was able to deduce the position of the known card.

2. I noted the symbol of the end card on the right of Mr. Hansel and, using the same cue as before, saw that he picked up this card last. I assumed that Mr. Anderson would replace it last. By listening, and watching the shadow of Mr. Anderson's hand, I counted the sequence in which each card was replaced to the left or right of the one before it. This count was not used to check my assessment of the position of the last card. This was more difficult than the first method, and I was less confident of success.

3. I noted the symbols of the two end key cards and using the same cues as before noticed which was picked up first; I memorized this symbol and assumed that it would be replaced first. Its position was then determined by the first method. This was easier than the second technique but not as simple as the first.

4. I noted the symbol of the end key card on the left of Mr. Hansel. By listening to the noise made in picking up each card, I counted the number of cards removed until I saw by the shadow that the card I knew had been taken. I assumed that the cards would be replaced in the same order. By this time I had learned the relationship between the shadows and the positions of the cards so that I knew immediately in which position each card was hung.

By counting the cards as they were replaced, I determined the position of the card I knew.

5. The position of the symbol determined by any of these methods was remembered during the 25 trials. The speed with which Mr. Anderson pointed to the positions during each trial was so rapid that I was fully occupied in laying the cards down in the places indicated. As this made a noise that might be heard by Mr. Anderson, they had to be put in their proper places. At the end of the run I first turned up the cards in the position for which I knew the correct symbol and then leisurely turned up the other cards. Whenever I found a symbol for the position I knew, it was exchanged with a card incorrectly placed in that position.

CRITICISMS RAISED BY PRATT AND WOODRUFF

When replying to my criticism of their experiment in the *Journal of Parapsychology*, Pratt and Woodruff objected that I selected the data used in my analysis. They stated that out of P. M.'s series of 4,050 trials I selected a relationship that depended upon only 55 observations. The data given in Table 2 included 55 runs, which were isolated from a total of 162 made by this subject in which an above-chance score was obtained; it was selected in this manner to save time and to give reasonably high sensitivity.

Pratt and Woodruff provided an alternative form of analysis in which the effect I had pointed out was confirmed. It should be noted that their own analysis also involved selection of data. They took all runs in which a score of more than 5 hits was obtained. They then counted the number of hits and misses secured by each symbol in relation to its position among the key cards during the previous trial. This form of analysis also involves selection, however, and is rendered relatively insensitive because attention is confined to those runs in which an above-chance score is obtained. If all runs are included, it becomes much more sensitive than my original analysis. Thus, the data given in Table 4, which was not included in my report published in the *Journal of Parapsychology*, shows how marked the effects become when account is taken of all the observations.

The second point raised by Pratt and Woodruff was the assertion that the effect present with P. M. was absent in the other high-scoring subjects. This is not so. It is only absent when the relatively

TABLE 8

Analysis of scores on symbols that occupied positions 1 and 5
on previous runs compared with scores arising on symbols
that occupied positions 2, 3, and 4

Subject D. A.

Position of symbol in previous run	Trials	Hits obtained	Hits expected to arise by chance	Probability of result arising by chance
1 and 5	491	126	98.2	0.002
2, 3, and 4	734	162	146.8	0.200

insensitive analysis that they used is applied to the data. When the data for subjects C. C., D. A., D. L., and H. G. are taken together (see Table 5), the effect is certainly present, and in the case of subject D. A., his results, given in Table 8, show an effect similar to that of the high-scoring subject P. M.

If the results of the 2 other high-scoring subjects, C. C. and H. G., were analyzed in a similar manner, it is likely that they would show the same effect.

Three alternative explanations were put forward by Pratt and Woodruff to account for the effects present in the scores of P. M. They wrote:

(1) Actually, one can offer a consistent and reasonable ESP hypothesis, as follows: For the subject P. M., the run began, in the psychological sense, when she rearranged and placed the target cards. The ESP task being a difficult one, she dealt with it by a "narrowing of attention" procedure. For her the task became one of attempting to identify only *some* of the cards in the deck: those with the particular symbols which had become salient because of their prominent end positions in the preceding run.

(2) There may be an alternative ESP interpretation, such as a differential rate of scoring on the five symbols, coupled with some habitual tendency in the placement of the symbols on the pegs.

(3) Finally, as stated above, this may be a selected, meaningless, statistical effect, for statistical oddities are a dime a dozen. To take

one seriously it is necessary to confirm it. The data of other subjects in our series fail to support this oddity, whereas they do support the significant scoring level of the experiment. Therefore
the Hansel effect is still unconfirmed and unexplained, and it certainly could not explain the Pratt-Woodruff result.[5]

Their first explanation is difficult to consider seriously. First, it
assumes ESP; moreover, it describes a new salience effect that
arises in more than one subject. It is difficult to see how the second
explanation works. While at the Parapsychology Laboratory, I did
investigate P. M.'s results to see whether they could be accounted
for in terms of the tendency of the subject to assign more cards to
one pile than another, coupled with a tendency to replace key cards
in particular positions. There was no evidence that any such effects
could account for the result. If this second explanation is to be
taken seriously, it must be described more clearly, and further data
should be provided from the record sheets.

The third explanation can hold no water whatsoever. The effect
in P. M.'s data is so definite that it emerges with any analysis that is
applied. The fact that it is not present with all the other subjects is
quite immaterial. If any of the subjects did shuffle the key cards
before replacing them a trick would not have been possible. If, in
an experiment of this type, just one of the subjects did not perform
this operation, the effects should then only appear in the records of
that one subject. If some subjects omitted shuffling the cards on a
small number of occasions before replacing them, the over-all score
for the experiment could easily give a result that was statistically
significant without the result for any single subject displaying any
evidence that a trick had been used.

Pratt and Woodruff assert that the lack of randomness in the
key-card arrangements for the subject D.A. may have arisen
because he decided to try out the effect of putting the key cards in a
particular order for a certain number of runs.

It should, however, be noted that there is evidence in the record
of the key-card arrangements of other subjects to indicate that the
cards were not shuffled between runs. Thus, when the position of
the symbol occupying each position among the key cards is
tabulated against the position of that symbol in the previous run, a
high degree of nonrandomness appears in the case of the subject

P. M. The odds against her arrangements arising by chance are greater than 100,000 to 1.

CONCLUSION

Since above-chance scores could have arisen in the Pratt-Woodruff experiment through the use of a trick, it cannot be considered as providing conclusive evidence for ESP. Whether or not a trick was used is a secondary matter. There is no reason why the experiment should not be conducted again under conditions similar to those used originally but with additional precautions to eliminate the possibility of a trick. It is remarkable that, in spite of the great claims made for the experiment and its relative simplicity, it was never repeated at the Parapsychology Laboratory itself.

CHAPTER 9

The Soal-Goldney Experiment

IN a position similar to that of Rhine in the United States is S. G. Soal, who, since 1930, has dominated research on ESP in Great Britain. Soal first became interested in psychical research through meeting Mrs. Blanche Cooper, a well-known medium, in 1922. He took part in Woolley's 1927 radio test of telepathy as one of the agents, and in 1929, together with Theodore Besterman, he repeated Ina Jephson's tests of clairvoyance. In neither of these early tests was any evidence found for ESP.

During the thirties, when Soal was carrying out extensive tests to check the claims made by J. B. Rhine, his attitude at the time was skeptical, and he was critical of the experimental conditions.

At first, Soal's investigations had revealed no evidence to support Rhine's claims, and only one of his subjects seemed to attain significantly above-chance scores. He has stated that until the autumn of 1939, he believed that it was practically impossible to find persons, at any rate in England, who could demonstrate extrasensory perception by guessing cards.

However, in November 1939, it was suggested to him that he should re-examine the record sheets of his unsuccessful ESP tests to see whether any of the subjects were scoring, not on the target card, but on the card one ahead or one behind in the trial series. After doing this, Soal found that his most promising subject in the early tests, Mrs. G. Stewart, displayed significantly above-chance scores, both for the target one ahead and for the target one behind. He also claimed that after checking the score sheets of the remaining subjects, a second subject, Basil Shackleton, a professional photographer, displayed similar scores.

Mrs. Stewart had been introduced to Soal in 1936, and in that same year Shackleton had first called to see him at the offices of the Society for Psychical Research. Shackleton had read an account of

Soal's investigations in a Sunday newspaper, and he declared that he had come, not to be tested, but to demonstrate telepathy. J. Aldred, a barber by profession and an old friend of Soal's, happened to be present when Shackleton called, and he acted as agent. Shackleton did not succeed, at the time, in convincing Soal of his ability to guess the card being seen by some other person. The high displacement scores that Soal alleges he found 3 years later were the first indications of any striking effects in Shackleton's score sheets.

THE SOAL-GOLDNEY EXPERIMENT

In 1941, with the collaboration of a Council Member of the Society for Psychical Research, Mrs. K. M. Goldney, Soal started a new investigation to test the telepathic abilities of Shackleton. The investigators aimed at designing a completely foolproof test, and the Soal-Goldney experiment of 40 sittings, held during the London blitz between January 1941 and April 1943, was to become the most extensive and best known of all English experiments on extrasensory perception.[1]

THE PROCEDURE

One basic procedure was used throughout the experiment, but it was not always enforced in full, and changes were introduced at some of the sittings. The first 38 sittings were held at Shackleton's studio on Shaftesbury Avenue; the remaining 2 in the rooms of the Society for Psychical Research.

Shackleton guessed the identity of cards bearing drawings of animals seen by only one other person, the agent, situated in an adjoining room. The door between the two rooms was slightly ajar so that Shackleton could hear an experimenter (EA) in the other room call out when he was to record his guess; but he was seated in a position where he could not see the agent.

THE AGENT

The agent and EA sat at opposite sides of a table. A screen, 31 by 26 inches with an aperture 3 inches square in its center, was placed across the table, and screened the agent from EA. Resting on the table, on the agent's side of the screen, was a rectangular box, about 16 inches wide by 10 inches high by 10 inches deep, with its open side toward him. Before each run of 50 guesses, 5 key cards, each bearing a different symbol, were shuffled by the agent or by an observer and placed face downward in a row in the box so that while they could be seen by the agent, they were screened from the view of other persons in the room. The key cards bore on their faces pictures of 5 animals: an elephant, *E*, a giraffe, *G*, a lion, *L*, a pelican, *P*, and a zebra, Z. The agent was instructed to lift one of the key cards, look at the symbol on its face, and then replace it during each trial.

The experimenter indicated to the agent which key card he was to look at by holding up a card bearing one of the numbers 1 to 5, so that it could be seen by the agent through the hole in the screen. Thus, if the number 3 appeared at the hole in the screen, the agent raised the key card occupying the position third from the left among the 5 cards that lay in the box before him, and after looking at the symbol on its face, he replaced it face downward in the box. EA also called out the serial number of each trial so that it could be heard by Shackleton in the adjoining room, thus indicating when he was to record his guess.

The number that EA displayed to the agent at the hole in the screen during each trial was decided by consulting a record sheet, which was composed of 2 columns of 25 entries each. Each column had 2 sections, *A* and *G*. Before each sitting, Soal entered one of the numbers 1 through 5 in random order 50 times in the *A* sections of the columns on a number of record sheets. These sheets were then kept under lock and key until brought to the sitting in a suitcase that was never out of his sight. At the start of each sitting, Soal produced these sheets of prepared random numbers, which were then serially numbered 1 through 50 to show the order in which they were to be used by EA. The same number of blank record sheets were serially numbered. These were to be used by the percipient, Shackleton, who recorded his guesses in pencil in section *G* of the columns. Shackleton's guesses were not of the number of the key card but of the letter identifying the symbol shown.

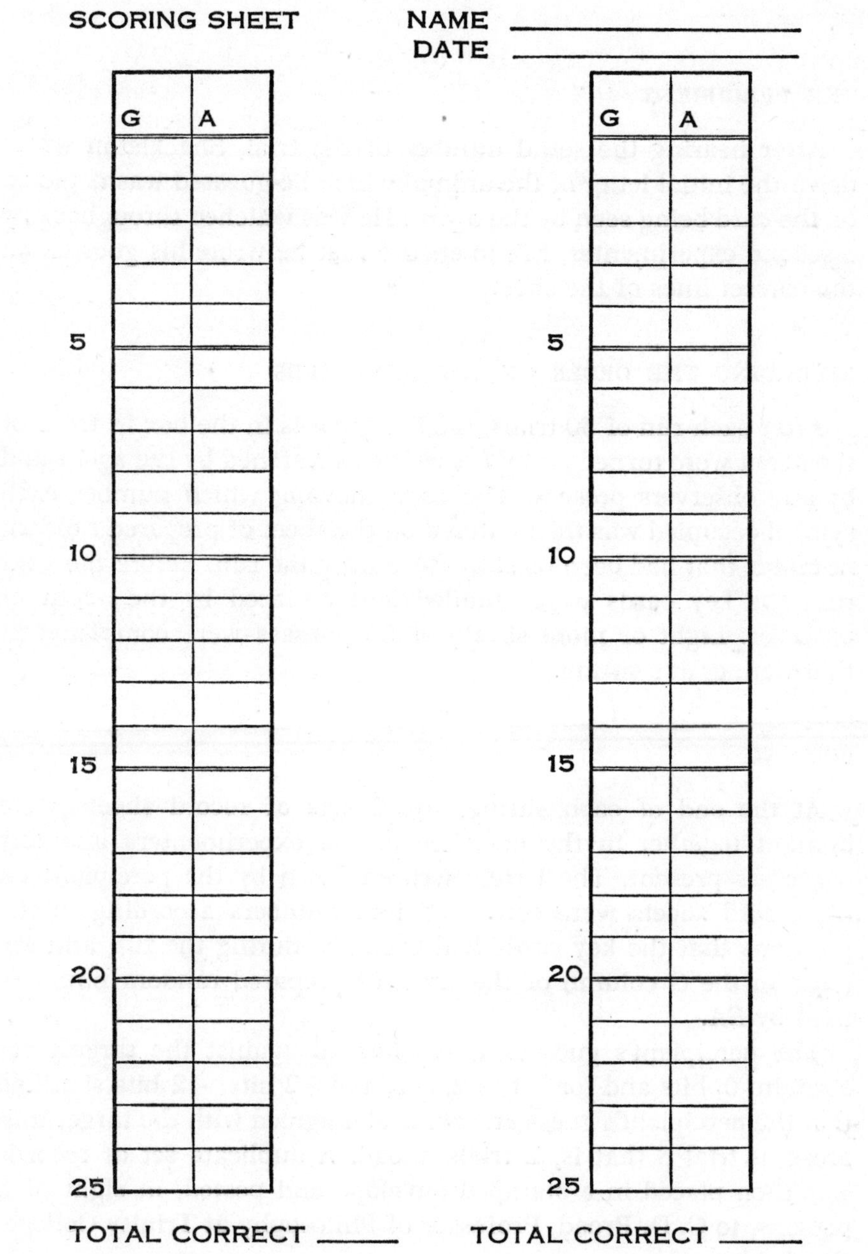

SCORING SHEET NAME _____
DATE _____

	G	A			G	A
5				5		
10				10		
15				15		
20				20		
25				25		

TOTAL CORRECT _____   TOTAL CORRECT _____

FIGURE 3. *Type of record sheet used in Soal-Goldney experiment*

THE PERCIPIENT

After hearing the serial number of the trial, Shackleton wrote down the initial letter of the animal which he guessed was depicted on the card being seen by the agent. He was watched throughout by a second experimenter, EP, to ensure that he wrote his guesses on the correct lines of the sheet.

RECORDING THE ORDER OF THE KEY CARDS

After each run of 50 trials, the 5 key cards in the box in front of the agent were turned up by EA who was watched by the agent and by any observers present. The code showing which number each symbol occupied was then entered on the sheet of prepared random numbers that had been used by EA during the run. Before the next run, the key cards were shuffled and replaced by the agent or observer. Eight or more sheets of 50 guesses were completed in this manner at a sitting.

SCORING

At the end of each sitting, the 2 sets of record sheets were brought together in the presence of the experimenters and any observers present. The letters written down by the percipient on his record sheets were converted into numbers according to the positions that the key cards had occupied during the run and entered in the G column of the sheet of prepared random numbers used by *EA*.

The percipient's guesses were checked against the targets for straight, 0, hits and for +1, +2, −1, and −2 hits; +2 hits signified that the percipient's guess at, say, trial 4 agreed with the target that arose at trial 6 that is, 2 trials ahead. A duplicate set of records was then placed in a stamped envelope and posted, in sight of 3 persons, to C. D. Broad, Professor of Philosophy at Trinity College, Cambridge.

The main modifications to the basic design used at some of the sittings can be classified as follows:

1. *Experiments with counters.* In some experiments, instead of using sheets of prepared random numbers to decide which key card the agent should look at, EA drew a counter from a bowl containing equal numbers of 5 different-colored counters. Each color denoted a position of one of the key cards. Soal, who acted as recorder, sat near the agent, where he could see the counters as they were displayed at the hole in the screen. After mentally converting the color into the appropriate number, he recorded it in the blank column of the record sheet. These records were later checked with Shackleton's guesses, using the same procedure as when prepared random numbers were employed to decide the targets. To carry out the above procedure, considerable skill is required, particularly when the calls are being made at a rapid rate.

2. *Clairvoyance experiments.* At some sittings, runs of 50 guesses were recorded under clairvoyance conditions. In these runs, the agent did not see the faces of the key cards either before or during the run; he merely touched the backs of the cards in accordance with the numbers that appeared at the hole in the screen.

3. *Prepared random numbers compiled independently.* At 3 of the sittings, to avoid any possibility that Soal was in collusion with either the percipient or agent, the sheets of prepared random numbers were prepared by someone other than Soal.

4. *Outside observers.* At some sittings, observers were present. They included C. E. M. Joad, a well-known philosopher, and C. A. Mace, Professor of Psychology, both at Birkbeck College, London University; H. Habberley Price of New College, Oxford University; and Sir Ernest Bennet, a member of Parliament.

FINDINGS OF THE SHACKLETON EXPERIMENT

Shackleton obtained high above-chance scores with 3 agents. In 3,789 of the +1 type trials with one agent, Miss Rita Elliott, in which prepared lists of random numbers were used, he scored 1,101 hits compared with the chance-expectation score of 776 hits. The odds against such a score arising by chance are greater than 10^{35} to 1.

In the 1,578 +1 trials with this agent, in which the random

series was obtained by drawing counters from a bowl at the normal rate, Shackleton obtained 439 hits compared with a chance expectation of 321. This gives odds against chance occurrence of 10^{11} to 1.

In experiments using counters at the rapid rate of guessing, Shackleton scored at the chance level on +1 targets but greatly exceeded the chance score on +2 targets. That is to say, he now scored on the card that the agent would be looking at two trials after he was recording his guess. In 794 trials at the rapid rate, with Miss Elliott as agent, Shackleton obtained hits on 236 +2 targets, compared with the chance-expectation score of 159. The odds against this score arising by chance are more than 100 million to 1.

The clairvoyance experiments in which the agent did not look at the letter cards gave scores that did not differ significantly from those to be expected by chance. Cross checks were also made by comparing the targets intended for the second 25 guesses on each sheet with the guesses made for the first 25 targets, and the targets intended for the first 25 guesses with the guesses of the second 25 targets. These cross checks in no case showed significant deviations from chance scores, thus showing that the results were not due to characteristics of the number series or the manner in which the percipient made his guesses.

Shackleton was also highly successful during 9 sittings in which Aldred acted as agent. With Aldred, he scored at above-chance levels both on the +1 and the −1 targets at the normal rate, and on both the +2 and the −2 targets at the rapid rate. Thus, in 720 trials at the normal rate he obtained 203 hits on +1 targets and, at the same time, 207 hits on −1 targets. The odds against this result arising by chance are greater than 10^{11} to 1. At the rapid rate, his scores on +2 and −2 targets were equally impressive. With this agent, Shackleton scored significantly below chance on 0 targets.

Significantly above-chance results were also obtained at 2 sittings in which Mrs. G. Albert acted as agent, and at sitting 5, at which Mrs. Goldney acted as agent. She was not, however, very much impressed by her own abilities as a transmitter and did not act as agent again until sitting 12, 2 months later. On that occasion, over 3 runs, scores were low, and Mrs. Goldney never acted as agent again.

Shackleton's rate of scoring with the successful agents was such that his result at most of the individual sittings had extremely large odds against arising by chance. He was, however, unsuccessful with 10 other agents.

After the experiments were over, Shackleton's powers waned. He emigrated to South Africa and was tested there for extrasensory perception, but he displayed no ability to obtain high scores. In 1961, he returned to England, but further tests again revealed no evidence for his precognitive abilities.

EVALUATIONS OF THE EXPERIMENT

In an extensive review of the experiment, Broad wrote:

> There was already a considerable mass of quite good experimental evidence for telepathy, e.g. in the work of Dr. Rhine and his colleagues at Duke University, but Dr. Soal's results are outstanding. The precautions taken to prevent deliberate fraud or the unwitting conveyance of information by normal means are described in great detail, and seen to be absolutely water-tight.[2]

G. Evelyn Hutchinson, an American Professor of Biology at Yale University, wrote concerning the experiments: "they appear to be the most carefully conducted investigations of the kind ever to have been made," and that "Soal's work was conducted with every precaution that it was possible to devise."[3] Rhine spoke of the experiment with approval, and compared it favorably with the best of the Duke experiments.

> A research can be so carried out that no errors can be made to favor any theory or mislead anyone. All such safeguards should be included in the design of the experiment. As already demonstrated, in the Pearce-Pratt and the Pratt-Woodruff series the experiment was so set up that these precautions were included. Similar provisions were made against error in the Soal and Goldney experiments.[4]

The public has to take statements such as those made by Broad, Hutchinson, and Rhine on trust. However, it is reasonable to ask whether all 35 alternative hypotheses to ESP discussed by Rhine and his colleagues in 1940 were adequately eliminated in the Soal-Goldney experiment, whether the precautions against fraud were absolutely water-tight, and whether the Soal-Goldney experiment, in fact, was conducted with every precaution that it was possible to devise as was claimed by the investigators.

By 1939, Soal had shown himself to be a careful and critical investigator. Unlike Rhine he had no overwhelming faith in the reliability of his fellows, and from the start it was stressed in the Soal-Goldney report that the investigators were aware of the necessity of adequate safeguards against trickery on the part of any participant. In their report, Soal and Goldney stated that they had given much thought and discussion to the question of making the conditions of the experiment "proof, so far as was humanly possible, against even the possibility of fraud, on the part of Percipient and experimenters alike." To decide whether the experiment supports the hypothesis of precognition, a critical examination must ensure that Soal and Goldney were successful in accomplishing their aim. In the event of some alternative explanation being found, the experiments cannot be regarded as providing *conclusive* evidence for precognition. They could then just as well be said to provide conclusive evidence for this alternative explanation.

SENSORY CUES

Any possibility of Shackleton's score having arisen through sensory leakage appears to have been eliminated by the fact that he scored on the symbol not yet seen by the agent and, in the experiments with counters, not yet decided by a process of random selection.

During the first 8 sittings, however, Shackleton called "right" immediately after he had recorded his guess. He was thus in a position to transmit information of what he had written back to the agent and others present. Thus, if Shackleton called "right" in a certain manner, such as by imposing a particular emphasis or delay, after he had written down one symbol, or even if the manner in which he said "right" was affected involuntarily by the symbol he had just written down, the agent could have been given information to enable him to move the appropriate key card for the following trial so that it occupied the position designated by the number card displayed by EA, thus securing a +1 hit. This possibility, however, was present after the eighth sitting on only 1 occasion.

It should also be noted that the speed at which EA had to manipulate the cards was such that he would almost certainly have had to look ahead to the next symbol on his list at the time he was displaying his number card at the hole in the screen. EA was thus in a position, consciously or unconsciously, to transmit information concerning the number series when he called out the serial number of the trial. The fact that the order of the key cards was unknown to EA ensured, however, that he could not provide cues relating to the target, but merely to the number shown at the hole in the screen.

A TRICK ON THE PART OF AGENT AND PERCIPIENT

It is clear that the percipient could not have brought about his high scores by means of a trick unless he was aided by either the agent or EA. In considering the possibility of Shackleton having been aided by the agent, it becomes quite clear that above-chance results could have been obtained and that this possibility was not eliminated in the experimental design. One such system was suggested by me in 1949.

The percipient memorizes a series of five symbols, say, P, G, L, Z, E, that he will write down on lines, say, 5, 10, 15, 20, and 25 of his record sheet when listing his guesses. The agent memorizes the same information. During the experiment, whatever random number comes up at trial 5, the agent places card P into the position designated by the number that appears at the hole in the screen. The percipient thus scores a hit on trial 5. On the tenth trial, the agent attempts to place card G in the position designated by the random number that appears at the hole in the screen. He may not always be able to do so as the same random number may arise as at trial 6. If the percipient and agent have memorized 5 different symbols, they can expect to obtain, on the average, 3.36 hits in the 5 trials by means of this trick. In the remaining 45 trials, they should obtain an average of 9 hits, thus giving a total of 12.36 hits in 50 trials. Higher scores can be obtained by memorizing more symbols, but the trick then becomes difficult to implement. In order to produce precognitive +1 hits in the above example, the percipient writes down his guesses one trial ahead, that is, on lines 4, 9, 14 and so on.

There has been considerable discussion over the possibility of such a trick having been used, and during it Soal has pointed out that it is impossible to account for the high scores achieved at some sittings by its application. In addition, it is difficult to believe that the percipient and agent would go to the effort of memorizing long lists of symbols and their positions on the score sheets for week after week. The fact that such a trick could have been employed constitutes, however, a weakness in the experiment, and it is difficult to see how Soal and Goldney could claim that their design completely eliminated the possibility of fraud.

THE CRITICISMS OF GEORGE R. PRICE

In 1955, George R. Price, a research associate in the Department of Medicine at the University of Minnesota, in a brilliant analysis of ESP research dealt with the problems of trickery in considerable detail. One statement that must have impressed parapsychologists and their critics alike was:

> Surprisingly, it is not only believers who are reluctant to imagine fraud, but virtually all skeptics as well will prefer almost any other type of explanation. It would be tedious for me to cite statistics to show that "the knavery and folly of men" are indeed "common phenomena," for everyone is aware of this—in an intellectual way. But when we try to imagine knavery and folly in connection with a particular individual, we encounter a surprising emotional blockage, and the possibility seems unreasonable. And thus we find skeptics searching for every other conceivable sort of explanation. While the one explanation that is simplest and most in accord with everyday experience is dismissed as inconceivable.[5]

Price pointed out that if Soal himself had wished to cheat and had got others to collaborate with him, he could have faked high scores in a number of ways. He then described 6 methods that could, he thought, have been employed. In the following quotation Price is assuming that he is taking the part that Soal had in the experiment, and that he is bent on trickery.

(1) The percipient and the agent are in the trick. The agent arranges the code as previously directed by me, and the percipient writes down a memorized sequence or takes a list from a drawer if no outsider is watching him. (This would be preferred procedure in most experiments except when an outsider determined the order of the code cards. It would succeed with outsiders as EA and EP.)

(2) The percipient and the agent (or the EA or an observer) are "in the trick." The code-card order is determined by an outsider. The agent (or the EA or an observer) notes this order, classifies it into 1 of 6 groups, and signals the group number to the percipient before or after the run. Only 2.6 bits of information are needed to designate a choice of 1 out of 6. For example, the agent glances at the backs of the cards and then says "Ready," "All ready," "Yes, I'm ready," "Yes ready"—and so forth. The percipient then takes from a drawer the designated guess sheet, which is already filled out in his hand-writing. (If the agent is an outsider, the EA or an observer can note the card order when it is recorded at the end of the run and signal it in the conversation then.)

(3) The percipient and the agent are "in the trick." The agent notes the card order and signals it (6.9 bits for the 120 possible permutations) before the start of the run. The percipient has memorized a number sequence, and he uses the card order to encipher each number mentally. (This can work with outsiders watching both the agent and the percipient and shuffling the code cards; or if the agent is an outsider, the signalling can be done by an observer who shuffles the cards.)

Next consider some of the procedures that could be used even when the number sequence was not known to me in advance:

(4) The percipient and the agent are "in the trick." They have copied or memorized the same lists of letter symbols. During the run the agent records (concealed by the box) the numbers corresponding (precognitively) to the letters that he knows the percipient is guessing, and at the end he rearranges the code cards to give the desired degree of success. For example, with a record like that shown in figure 1 [a contingency chart compiled by the agent showing the number of times each symbol arose in each position], the agent could see that card arrangement LEGZP will yield a large number of hits. (This procedure would be particularly useful when the EA was an outsider.)

(5) The percipient and the EA are "in the trick." The EA learns the order of the code cards and signals information to the percipient during the run. The percipient has memorized a random se-

quence of letter symbols. The EA, in calling out the serial numbers,
slightly alters his voice or timing a few times during each run (5
times per 50 trials to give 14 hits). Ordinarily the percipient is to
guess at random, but at each signal he writes down the next letter
on the memorized sequence. (I would use this method particularly
in experiments when an outsider who wore glasses served as agent.
Then the preferred experimental arrangement would be that in
which the cards are turned face up for 30 seconds, the screen
aperture would be located as it was in the Stewart sittings, and the
lighting would be so arranged that EA could see the cards by reflection in the agent's glasses.)

(6) The percipient plus the EA, the recorder, or the agent are
"in the trick." In runs where the number sequence is generated by
counters, I would have the EA draw counters of the needed color at
particular points, or the recorder could keep false records of counters drawn. And in some experiments, procedures 1, 4, or 5 could
be used. . . .

The procedures that could give the highest degrees of success,
and that thus would be chosen when I wanted simultaneous "−1"
and "+1," or "−2" and "+2" successes, are procedures 1 and 3.
Any of the others would be more than adequate for scores of 12.68
hits per run of 50, or 13.77 hits in 48 trials. For long-distance experiments, procedures 1 and 4 would work. Or I could employ
procedure 2 by telephoning the percipient after the sitting to tell
him which lists to mail in.[6]

Price pointed out that many other procedures were possible, but
the 6 chosen for description were selected as examples of what could
be done by simple means. He concluded:

. . . thus it should be clear that Soal's work was *not* conducted
with every precaution that it was possible to devise. The work
would have been enormously more nearly fraud-proof if Soal, instead of employing his highly complex arrangements, had simply
had many different agents send directly from lists prepared by
outsiders and given directly to the agent at the start of each run.[7]

Some time after Price's criticism of the experimental conditions,
it was revealed that Mrs. Albert, one of the 3 agents with whom
Shackleton obtained above-chance results, had stated after one sitting that when glancing through the hole in the screen, she had seen

Soal, while acting as EA, altering figures on the score sheet.[8] Whether Soal was in fact altering figures or merely tidying them up is immaterial. But looking back at the records of the experiment, it is clear that this incident had a considerable effect on the duties allocated to the experimenters during subsequent sittings. The allegations were made after sitting 16 held on May 25, 1941, and from the detailed list of sittings in the Soal-Goldney report, it is found that until sitting 16, Soal had acted as EA on all occasions when prepared random numbers were used to decide the targets. After that sitting, he never again acted as EA but, at all sittings where prepared random numbers were used, he took the role of EP. (There was one sitting at which Soal was not present, but then the regular agent was also absent and Shackleton scored at only the chance level.)

It would appear then, that the conditions of the Soal-Goldney experiment were such that Soal could have cheated, if he had wished to do so, in the following ways.

1. *Sittings 1–4 in which prepared random numbers determined the targets.* The percipient and, preferably but not necessarily, the agent would need to have been in the trick. At these sittings, Soal acted as EA, and he brought to the experiment the sheets of prepared random numbers and the blank record sheets to be used by the percipient. Soal could then have used Price's method 1. To avoid a great deal of memorization, however, at sittings 3, 7, and 8, when high scores were obtained with an EP present, the sheets handed to the percipient could have contained faint marks—for example, dots made in pencil—in 3 or 4 of the positions in each column. Thus, a dot in the top left corner of the space in which Shackleton was to record his guess would indicate that on that trial the letter P should be written down. Other positions of the dot would be used as a code for the remaining 4 letters. Shackleton, who recorded his guesses in pencil, could have written over the earlier marks when recording his guesses, thus ensuring that they would not be detected if anyone inspected the record sheets at the conclusion of the tests.

The agent would have been instructed to move the key cards to predetermined positions for each run, or, if the agent was not in the trick, Soal could have misrecorded the order of the key cards.

Alternatively, Soal could have entered the order of the key cards on some sheet of random numbers other than that later checked with the percipient's guesses. It would, for example, have been possible to have available a sheet of random numbers with gaps at suitable positions. The key-card order would be transferred to this sheet, behind the screen, and suitable entries made in the gaps. This trick would have been easy to manage since Soal kept all the records used before and during the experiment in a suitcase that never left his possession.

2. *Sittings 15 and 16.* Here, with a new agent not in the trick, Soal could have ensured that the key cards were recorded in a predetermined order on the score sheet at the end of the run. If he had had any difficulty doing this he could have altered the code when hidden behind the screen, or he could have entered the code on some sheet of random numbers other than that subsequently checked with the percipient's guesses.

3. *Sittings in which counters were drawn from a bowl.* At these sittings, Soal always acted as recorder. He could have handed the percipient serially numbered record sheets to be used by him during the experiment and marked in pencil as described in 1. Then he could have had a set of marked and serially numbered sheets, similar to those used by the agent, to be used by him as recorder. He could then have misrecorded so that the percipient obtained extra hits. Soal could have arranged that the agent should put the key cards in some prearranged code. Alternatively, since he sat where he could see the cards under the box in front of the agent, he could have carried out such a trick without the agent's help.

It would have been difficult to implement this trick if an observer were present to note the recording of the numbers, but according to the chronicle of the experiments, such an observer was present at only 2 of the sittings in which counters were used with a regular agent. The first of these, sitting 17, followed 6 sittings, 7, 8, 9, 10, 11, 13, at which counters had been employed, and at each of these high scores had been observed throughout. At sitting 14, counters were used and above-chance scores were not obtained, but at this sitting the regular agent was absent. Thus, at all the sittings previous to this one in which counters were used with the regular agents, high scores had been obtained.

At sitting 17, H. H. Price, Professor of Logic at Oxford University, was present as observer. He sat with Shackleton for the first 3 runs in which counters were used, and the scores continued to be high. For the next 4 runs he sat where he could observe EA, the recorder, and the agent. Scores now dropped to the chance level. It should be remarked that these 4 runs were, for the first and last time, made with counters at a "slow rate" (that is, 5 seconds per trial).

At the next sitting, 18, Dr. H. G. Baynes, a member of the Society for Psychical Research, was present as observer. He sat with Shackleton for runs 1–4 and during the last 2 runs, 5 and 6, he sat behind the agent "so as to check her selection of the cards as well as record the counters shown by (EA)." At this sitting, scores were at the chance level throughout.

At sitting 29, the next and last at which counters were used with a regular agent, an observer was not present, but scores were at the chance level throughout. No further experiments were carried out with counters, except at sittings 30 and 35 when a regular agent was not present and scores were at the chance level.

Thus, following 6 sittings at which high above-chance scores were consistently obtained when counters decided the targets, high scores were still obtained for the first 4 runs at the seventh such sitting. Then, as soon as an observer watched Soal recording the targets, scores dropped to the chance level. They remained there for 2 more sittings, and thereafter counters were no longer used to determine the target order—except at 2 sittings when the regular agent was not present and at which scores were at the chance level.

4. *Sittings 17–40 at which prepared random numbers were used.* Here, Soal always acted as EP, but in all but 3 sittings he was in charge of the prepared sheets of random numbers until the sitting began. When he had charge of these sheets he could have ensured that Shackleton's records were serially numbered to agree with those used by EA. The agent would have been responsible for getting the key cards into prearranged positions for each sheet. The percipient's sheet could have been marked as in 1, or Soal, who sat with the percipient, could have told him what to write down at appropriate positions in the run.

5. *Sittings where sheets of prepared random numbers were compiled by outsiders.* For 3 of the sittings, 27, 28, and 34 at which

the sheets of random numbers were prepared by someone other than Soal and sent directly to Goldney or to Mrs. Wooland, who acted as EA, the following method could have been employed.

At sittings 27 and 34, Soal was alone with Shackleton, and he could have looked through the partly open door to see the numbers displayed at the hole in the screen. He could then have told Shackleton what to write down. The agent, who would need to have been in the trick, would have arranged the key cards in a predetermined order.

For sitting 28, C. A. Mace brought to the meeting sheets of prepared random numbers that had been prepared for him by C. U. Blascheck, of Clare College, Cambridge. He handed these sheets to EA (Goldney) one by one as required, and they were not seen by either Shackleton or Soal until after the sitting. During runs 1 and 3, Mace was in the room with Shackleton and Soal, and during the remaining runs he was with the agent.

This sitting is of special interest, since the conditions were far more stringent than at any other. Here, an outside observer had been in charge of the sheets of prepared random numbers, and he had watched the percipient and then the agent during runs when high scores were recorded. Thus, it would have been impossible during those 2 runs for Soal to have looked through the partly open door to observe the number cards. During this experiment, however, the normal procedure was changed, as noted in the chronicle of the report.

> At B. S.'s own request an innovation was made in the method of recording guesses. B. S. and "EP" sat facing each other on opposite sides of the table. In front of "P" were five cards bearing pictures of the five animals. When "P" heard the serial number of the call, he spoke his guesses in a low tone, and S. G. S. recorded the initial letter of the animal's name in the appropriate cell of the G column.[9]

Thus, at this sitting, the only one at which cheating was impossible except by using the substitution method, the conditions were changed so that the agent heard Shackleton's calls.

The substitution method was thereby made possible without any effort of memory on the part of percipient and agent.

The only one of the tricks discussed above that might have presented any difficulty is the one in which EP was required to look through the partly open door and observe the number EA showed at the hole in the screen. But closer examination of the experimental report indicates that this trick need only have been used at sitting 34.

In the original report, the chronicle was reproduced for only three of the sittings, 8, 28, and 39, but it was stated that duplicated copies of the complete chronicle of the experiments could be obtained from the Society for Psychical Research. In that copy, which was obtained by me in September 1960, the accounts given for sittings 8 and 39 agree with those published in the Soal-Goldney report, but the chronicle for sitting 28 is different. The note about the new method of recording Shackleton's guesses is not present. It is merely reported that he spoke in a low tone. For the previous sitting a similar statement is also made, as well as for sittings 26, 25, and 24.

For sitting 23, at which Joad was present, it is stated that Shackleton sometimes registered his guesses by touching one of the cards in front of him and sometimes by saying the initial letter of the card. This is the first sitting at which there is any mention of Shackleton speaking his guesses aloud.

Thus it appears that Shackleton started verbalizing his guesses at sitting 23, and the substitution method of cheating could have been used at sitting 28 without involving the agent in any feat of memory.

At sitting 34, only Shackleton, Soal, Goldney, and the 2 successful agents were present. The rapid-rate type of test was used and Goldney acted as EA. Another innovation was introduced at this sitting. The screen in front of the agent was removed and the 5 number cards were laid in a row on top of the box containing the key cards. Goldney consulted the list of prepared random numbers and then pointed to a key card at each trial. Since she was fully occupied and had her back to the door between the 2 rooms, it would have been relatively safe for anyone to look through the aperture left by the partly closed door, opening it a little if required so as to see the number cards pointed at by EA. Alternately, the agent could have given a signal by moving his feet, according to a code. Such signals could not have been detected by Goldney, but they could have been observed by anyone in the other room standing at the door.

Using tricks such as those described above, it would have been possible for Soal, provided he had the assistance of 3 other persons —Basil Shackleton, Rita Elliott and J. Aldred—to have faked the result of the Soal-Goldney experiment. Thus, the experiment did not conform with the aim of its designers in that it did not eliminate the possibility of fraud.

If a team of independent investigators had been invited to test Shackleton and one of his successful agents first under conditions similar to those of the original experiment and then under conditions in which further safeguards were introduced, much tedious discussion might have been avoided.

It is impossible now to check on the methods of trickery that have been suggested as possible. If the records were marked in any way, it could not be detected, since the original sheets are no longer available. When visiting the Society for Psychical Research in 1956 to inspect the records, I saw only the duplicate copies. In correspondence, Soal stated on January 26, 1956, that the original copies had been lost, having been left on a train in 1946. This loss was subsequently reported in the March issue of the *Journal* of the Society for Psychical Research.

The loss of the records in 1946 is difficult to reconcile with a 1954 statement in *Modern Experiments in Telepathy*. There, when answering criticisms raised by the American psychologist B. F. Skinner, Soal stated: "Separate records were kept of card lists prepared before the experiment and of Shackleton's own guesses recorded by himself and these independent records could be rechecked at any future time." [10]

It is of interest to note that Soal appears to have come to the conclusion that lists of prepared random numbers might be used by the investigators themselves to bring about fraudulent results. Some 15 years after the Soal-Goldney experiment was over, when he carried out a series of experiments on 2 Welsh schoolboys, he stated: "We have eschewed the use of lists of random numbers prepared before the experiment, because, unless the most tedious precautions are taken, such lists definitely lend themselves to fraudulent manipulation by the regular experimenters." [11]

It would be valuable to know what tedious precautions were taken in the Soal-Goldney experiment. During most of the tests made on Shackleton, Soal alone was in charge of the lists from start

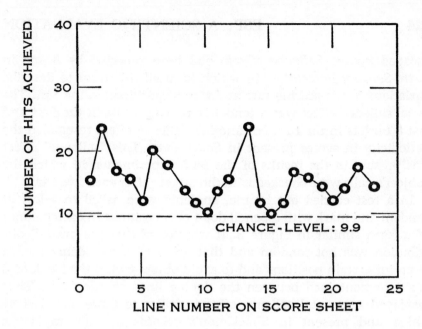

FIGURE 4. *Periodicity effect present in the scores on successive line numbers in the rapid-rate experiments*

to finish, and he was the one person whose presence was always necessary if Shackleton was to obtain a high score.

When Shackleton's hits are examined in relation to their place on the record sheet—which was ruled so that there was a double line after every fifth blank, a single line for the others (Figure 3)— it is found in the case of the rapid rate experiments that there is a marked periodicity effect (Figure 4). The odds are greater than 100 to 1 against the distribution of hits. Thus it appears that the subject's ability to score hits was in some way dependent on the position of his guess on the score sheet. It is difficult to explain the periodicity of the scores on the basis of any supposed precognitive ability, but it is quite consistent with the hypothesis that the subject was making prearranged "guesses" at predetermined positions of the form or with the hypothesis that the forms had been marked in some way to signify positions at which particular guesses had to be made.

When this effect was reported by me in *Nature* in 1960, Soal replied by pointing out that what had been brought to light was a most interesting "segmental salience" effect that had previously escaped notice. *Salience effects* had been reported by Rhine in *Extra-Sensory Perception,* in which he used this term to describe variations in the scoring rate at different positions in the run. The usual salience effect was a tendency to obtain hits in the first and last 5 targets in the run, but another salience effect resembled the periodicity in scores present in Soal's data. This "salience" effect was present in the results of the BT 5 experiments, in which the subject's calls were checked with the targets after each five trials.

In a test carried out by me, students were asked to select at random and mark with a pencil dot 4 or 5 positions in each column of a form similar to Figure 3. It was found that the over-all distribution was not random and that some of the students tended to prefer certain positions and to avoid others within the block of 5 positions contained between the double lines on the form. They displayed segmental salience effects similar to those observed by Rhine and present in Shackleton's records for the rapid-rate tests.

THE TESTS ON MRS. STEWART

In 1945, Soal started further tests on Mrs. Gloria Stewart, his other successful subject in the early experiments. A total of 130 experiments were carried out, 120 of which took place at her house.

The experimental conditions basically were similar to those of the Soal-Goldney experiment. Two rooms were used; the agent was in one and the percipient in the other, and the door between the rooms was left ajar. The screen and the box containing the key cards were employed, but the aperture in the screen was raised from 13 inches to 18 inches from the bottom of the screen. The system of synchronizing calls was changed. In the new experiments, Mrs. Stewart called "right" after each guess, whereupon EA displayed the next number at the hole in the screen.

Although the tests were similar in many ways to those on Shackleton, the control conditions were not as stringent. *Modern Experiments in Telepathy,* by Soal in collaboration with F. Bateman, a civil servant and former pupil of Dr. Soal's, stated:

The primary object of the new experiments was something quite different from a mere demonstration of the existence of telepathy; it was rather to find out something about it. . . . We have not, therefore, in these new experiments concentrated on ultra-rigorous precautions against fraud on the part of the *experimenters,* for, after all, if the experimenters (academic people) are not to be trusted, there is no point whatever in their doing experiments.[12]

THE RESULTS

Mrs. Stewart's over-all scores were no less impressive than Shackleton's. In a total of 37,100 trials, she obtained 9,410 straight hits. This represents 1,990 more hits than would be expected to arise by chance. The odds against such a result are greater than 10^{70} to 1. She also scored slightly, but significantly, below chance on both +1 and −1 targets.

The results of Mrs. Stewart's tests were similar in some ways to those of Shackleton, but in other respects they were markedly dissimilar. Her scoring rate was 25.4 hits out of each 100 guesses, which is identical to Shackleton's scoring rate on +1 targets when prepared random numbers were used. Both subjects were only successful with certain agents, but whereas Shackleton was successful with only 3 agents among 12 with whom he was tested, Mrs. Stewart had some degree of success with 15 out of 30 agents.

In the 1936 experiments, both Shackleton and Mrs. Stewart had made displacement hits, on +1 or −1 targets, but in the later experiments, Shackleton continued to give +1 hits with one agent and also produced −1 hits with another. Mrs. Stewart, however, scored a slight deficiency of hits on +1 and −1 targets and only obtained above-chance scores on straight hits.

The main types of experiment with Mrs. Stewart can be summarized as follows:

1. Experiments in which the duties of the agent were the same as in the Soal-Goldney experiment and also those in which the agent did not lift and look at the key cards while the percipient was making her guesses, but in which he had seen the positions of the

key cards under the box for a predetermined length of time before the run started.

Experiments in which the percipient had to choose between 2 letters instead of 5 when making her guess.

Experiments in which 2 or 3 agents took part, each agent having in front of him a different arrangement of the 5 letter cards.

Experiments in which the percipient had to guess the identity of playing cards.

In all the above types, Soal acted as EA, and he supplied the lists of prepared random numbers used in the tests. No precautions were taken to guard against a trick similar to the second possible trick in the Shackleton runs (see page 118).

2. Long-distance tests in which Soal did not act as EA or compile the lists of prepared random numbers. There were 2 of these. In the first, between London and Cambridge, I acted as EA and compiled the sheets of prepared random numbers; but during these tests, comprising 8 sittings, at each of which 200 trials were made, Mrs. Stewart displayed no telepathic abilities.

The second of the long-distance tests was between London and Antwerp. In this case, the sheets of prepared random numbers were prepared by outsiders, but they were handed over to Soal before the experiments. The main weakness in these tests was the fact that Mrs. Stewart's answer sheets were sent directly to Soal, and no precautions were taken to ensure that he could not determine the outcome of the experiment whether or not he was in collusion with Mrs. Stewart.

3. In split-agent experiments, 2 agents took part, one touching the backs of 5 blank cards as the numbers appeared at the hole in the screen, the other shuffling the 5 key cards, looking at them for a predetermined length of time before the guessing started, and then taking no further part in the experiment. During these tests, Soal always acted as EA, and he could have brought about high scores using the second type of trickery discussed in reference to the Shackleton tests.

4. In an experiment carried out on June 18, 1946, L. A. Rozelaar, Senior Lecturer in French at Queen Mary College, acted as agent. For sheets 2, 4, 6, and 8, the 5 cards were used inside the box in the customary fashion, but for sheets 1, 3, 5, and 7, blank cards were substituted for the key cards. Rozelaar was asked to keep in his

head an arrangement of the 5 letters that was easy to memorize, and no record of any sort was made of this order until the end of the run. At each trial, Rozelaar touched the blank card corresponding to the arrangement he had decided on. At the end of the run the order of the 5 symbols as memorized by Rozelaar was revealed to Soal, who recorded it on the sheet of prepared random numbers. In this experiment, the same type of trick again could have been employed.

Soal in collaboration with Mrs. Stewart could have brought about high scores without the help of any agent, since he either produced the lists of random numbers or had control of the score sheets on occasions when the tests were prepared by an outsider.

SECONDARY EFFECTS

In previous discussions of the Stewart series, considerable space has been given to what are called the secondary effects. These are the low scores observed on $+1$ and -1 targets and a tendency on Mrs. Stewart's part to score below chance on the first members of pairs of the same symbol in the target series and even lower on first members of longer runs of the same symbol. Any detailed analysis is useless unless it can be assumed that the sheets of prepared random numbers were in fact reasonably random.

It has since been revealed, however, that the random numbers used with Mrs. Stewart had a high degree of nonrandomness. Thus, if a run of 3 targets is taken at any position in a true random-number series, one expects to get a pattern of the type *ABA* (where *A* is any symbol and *B* some other one) about 16 per cent of the time. J. Fraser Nicol, the Research Officer for the American Society for Psychical Research, has pointed out that a deficiency in patterns of the type *ABA* was described as "very significant" by Soal and Pratt when they checked the target series used in the Stewart tests. In *Modern Experiments in Telepathy* it is called "a certain deficiency." Nicol pointed out that the expression "very significant" might be taken as meaning odds of 100 to 1 or 1,000 to 1, but that the actual odds were of the order of 10^{200} to 1. These are greater by a factor of 10^{130} than the significance of Soal's over-all result with Mrs. Stewart. This implies that if one generated true sets of random numbers and compared each set with Mrs. Stewart's guesses, by the time one obtained a set having *ABA* characteristics similar to those actually observed in Soal's prepared list of numbers, one would expect to have obtained a similar score to that obtained by Mrs. Stewart on 10^{130} occasions.

Nicol also stated, "The percentage deficiency of *ABA*'s *below* chance was, according to my understanding, almost the same as Mrs. Stewart's score *above* chance." [13]

SUMMARY

Looking back on Soal's investigations, it is seen that their meticulous experimental design was an illusion. They tended to be too complicated in design, and insufficient attention was paid to the really important point—the targets that were being guessed. While independent observers were invited to attend the experiments, they at no time had control of the arrangements, and as a check on the experimental conditions they were useless. If above-chance scores had been obtained when all the regular investigators were absent, or if a critical observer had been left free to change the experimental conditions imposing his own safe-guards, a positive result would have been vastly more impressive.

During the course of the experiments on Basil Shackleton and Mrs. Stewart, the experimental conditions rather than being tightened up became more lax. In Soal's next series of tests some 6 years later, this relaxation in test conditions is even more evident. As experimental conditions in the United States have been tightened up, so have the results become less impressive, until high scores have disappeared. In Britain, Soal started by testing 160 persons and producing no evidence for ESP. Thereafter, as the rigidity of his conditions relaxed, the evidence became more abundant and the results more impressive. Neither Mrs. Stewart nor Shackleton ever got 20 successes in 25 attempts. Such scores were, however, commonplace to Soal's next subject, a telepathic Welsh schoolboy.

CHAPTER 10

The Telepathic
Welsh Schoolboys

SINCE 1923, Soal had been in the habit of taking climbing holidays in the Snowdon area of North Wales, where he stayed each year with a couple named Jones. The Joneses and their 3 sons, Tom, Richard, and Will, lived in a small cottage near the village of Capel Curig. In 1936, Soal tested the telepathic abilities of the boys but found no signs of ESP.

Apparently, in 1955, Soal had an idea that unsophisticated children in rural communities might be telepathic and went to Wales to test Richard's son Glyn, and Will's son Ieuan. In *The Mind Readers*, he described how, over a period of 2 years, these 13-year-old schoolboys displayed extraordinary telepathic powers and earned large financial rewards for doing so under a variety of experimental conditions.

Before this book was published, considerable doubts were voiced in parapsychological circles over the experiment's merits. The Parapsychology Foundation of New York, which had helped finance the research, insisted that a note be included saying that it did not necessarily endorse the methods, findings, or conclusions of the authors. Rhine, who had been asked by Soal to comment on the page proofs, was enthusiastic about the research but called it "exploratory."

After the book was published, however, it received highly favorable reviews in leading British newspapers, including *The Times* and *The Observer;* the only unfavorable review appeared in the *Manchester Guardian.* It also received the longest and most enthusiastic review ever given an ESP experiment in a psychological periodical, the *Journal of Statistical Psychology.* In that review, Sir Cyril Burt, who at that time was an editor of the journal, declared, "Finally, it must, I think, be owned by every impartial reader that,

alike for their success and for the care with which they have been
conducted, the experiments here recorded are unrivalled in the
whole corpus of psychical research." [1]

It would take a great deal of space to consider in detail the long
series of tests. In *The Mind Readers* the experiments are split into
10 main groups. Six groups contain experiments carried out in the
homes of the Jones boys, while the remaining 4 consist of tests
conducted during their visits to London. Since the conditions under
which the experiments were conducted in Wales were far from
ideal, it is those carried out during the London visits that are of
principal interest. In the discussion that follows, therefore, only
brief details will be given of the work in Wales leading up to each
London visit.

THE EARLY EXPERIMENTS

In the initial tests carried out in Wales in August 1955, the boys
sat at either end of a 4¼ foot table, with a large suitcase placed
across the table between them to act as a screen. Soal sat with one
of the boys, the agent, and after shuffling a pack of cards he
showed them to him, one at a time, taking care that he himself
could not see the faces. He or the agent then tapped once on an ash
tray as a signal to the other boy, to call aloud his guess. Soal
recorded the guesses and after each 25 trials the order of the cards
in the pack was recorded in a second column. The targets consisted
of pictures of 5 animals, depicted in different colors: a lion (indian
red), a giraffe (pale brown), a penguin (dark blue), an elephant
(gray), and a zebra (darker gray). Each card also bore the initial
letter of the animal (*L, G, P, E,* or *Z*), and these letters were used
for recording purposes.

At first, results were disappointing, and no evidence for telepathy
was forthcoming; but on August 10, 1955, Glyn, acting as percipient, obtained a high score when his sister Rowena was agent.
Then, at the next sitting, on August 12, with Ieuan acting as agent,
Glyn secured the highly significant score of 59 hits out of 200
guesses as against a chance expectation of 40.

After this encouraging result, Soal decided to introduce an
incentive system. The approximate odds against a score of 9 or

more hits arising by chance in a run of 25 are 20 to 1; 10 or more, 60 to 1; 11 or more, 180 to 1; 12 or more, 650 to 1. Soal offered a shilling (a shilling was worth 14 cents in American currency) for every score of 9 out of 25 guesses; 2 shillings for a score of 10; 4 shillings for a score of 11; and so on, the reward increasing in geometrical progression. At this rate of remuneration, the boys would have earned between them 6,553 pounds (the pound was worth $2.80), 12 shillings for about 2 minutes' work on each of the 2 occasions when they scored 25 hits out of a run of 25, and Soal would have parted with about 80,000 pounds before the experiments were over. As it was, he owed the boys 15 pounds, 13 shillings each by the end of his first visit. The scale of rewards was thereafter changed to an arithmetical series, starting with sixpence (half a shilling) for a score of 9, a shilling for a score of 10, one and sixpence for a score of 11, and so on. It was, however, argued that a score of 18 was so remotely improbable that it was worth a pound, that 19 was worth 30 shillings, 20 worth 2 pounds, and so on. Thus, a score of 25 would earn the boys 4 pounds, 10 shillings apiece. In spite of this reduction in the rewards, the boys must have earned about 200 pounds each in prize money during the next 2 years.

The early experiments, during which the boys were seated at opposite ends of a table, can clearly prove very little, since they could have communicated by means of kicks or by touch under the table. This possibility seems to have occurred to Soal after the event, because it is later stated that the boys were too far apart to make contact with their feet and that, "For a boy of 13 Glyn had short legs." [2] Anyone who cares to carry out an experiment will find that most 13-year-old children can touch feet with ease under such a table, and Glyn must have had remarkably short legs if he was not able to make contact with Ieuan, who is described as being tall. It may be objected that Soal could have arranged for the boys to sit back from the table, but there is no mention of such an instruction; in fact, Soal stated that when he glanced behind the screen, which he did at intervals, Glyn was sitting close to the table.

At one of these early sittings, an observer was present who might have been in a position to observe the boy's feet under the table. But the observer, Mrs. Goldney, was seated at the side of the table alongside Soal, who was displaying the cards to Ieuan. At this sitting, H. T. Bowden, a schoolmaster who was recording Glyn's guesses, sat at a second table. Any chance he had of seeing any possible contact under the table was removed by the fact that he was seated with his back to Mrs. Goldney and, even if he had turned his head, his view was completely blocked. In a further test, Bowden sat closer to Glyn, who indicated his guess by pointing at a row of specimen cards. In the last case, even if he could have seen under the table, Bowden would have been occupied watching which card Glyn pointed at and then recording Glyn's guess.

At a sitting held on September 25, 1955, without giving the boys any warning, Soal moved Glyn from his position at the opposite end of the table from Ieuan and positioned him 15 feet away at a table in another room, but in line with Ieuan through a doorway. Glyn now obtained 159 hits in 325 guesses, as compared to the chance-expectation score of 65. Mrs. Goldney, who was present, paid special attention to Ieuan, watching his face and lips and listening for any signs of a code. No one appears to have paid any attention to Ieuan's leg movements, and these would have been visible to Glyn. In fact, the experimenters seem to have disposed themselves to the best advantage of the boys had they wished to signal by means of foot movements. Soal was behind the screen, seated at the table with Ieuan, so that he could not see the boy's legs. Mrs. Goldney was concentrating on Ieuan's face and lips. Bowden sat at a small table opposite Glyn and recorded his guesses. It might appear difficult for Glyn to have seen Ieuan's legs since Bowden was sitting opposite him blocking his view, but this difficulty had somehow resolved itself, for the table at which Glyn and Bowden sat had been rotated 90 degrees so that Glyn by looking sideways could get an uninterrupted view of the other boy's legs.

A few days later, Bateman arrived to assist with an experiment. He appears to have realized the possibility of visual cues being used, and after 4 runs in which high scores were observed with the boys seated at the table, he moved Glyn to the position 15 feet from Ieuan and shut the door between the 2 boys. Scores now dropped and were not significantly above the chance level. Soal observed that it was hard to draw any conclusions as to the cause of the decline in scores and that the boys were becoming tired.

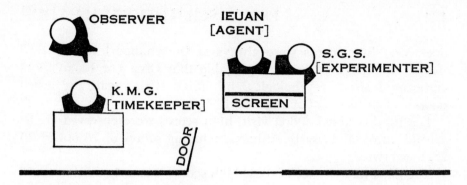

FIGURE 5. *Arrangement of tables* (above and below)
at first London visit

THE FIRST LONDON VISIT

On October 10, 1955, the Jones boys had their first test under anything approximating reasonable experimental conditions when they were taken to London to be tested in the rooms of the Society for Psychical Research. The boys were seated 24 feet or more apart in different rooms in line with and facing each other through a doorway (see Figure 5). Ieuan, acting as agent, sat at a table with a screen across it and index boxes piled under it, forming a screen to hide his legs. Neither boy, according to the account, could see any part of the other.

At the first sitting, Glyn made high scores in the first 3 runs of 25 guesses and scored at the chance level during the next 3 runs after he was moved just out of alignment with Ieuan through the open doorway. During subsequent tests, it was found that on occasions when the boys were out of alignment with one another or when the

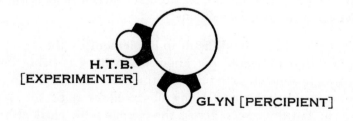

door was shut, scores were always at the chance level. As Soal wrote, "It soon became very probable that Glyn (or Ieuan) was suffering from a psychological inhibition with regard to closed doors and shifting out of alignment." [3]

During this first London visit, high scores were observed at the second, third, and fourth sittings, including scores of 18 out of 25 achieved twice.

The most likely cause of these high scores was a signal that could only be used when the boys were in alignment through the open doorway. In this position, removal of the screen above Ieuan's table and of the index boxes below the table would have left him in full view of Glyn. It is likely that signals could have been passed by Ieuan moving his knee or foot so that it became visible to Glyn. The edge of the table at which Ieuan was seated was in direct line with Glyn through the open doorway. If Ieuan had wished to signal, he could have done so by moving his toe or knee until it became visible to Glyn outside the edge of the screen formed by the pile of index boxes. Ieuan heard Glyn's calls and would have known when the movement he made was sufficient for it to be detected.

When answering this criticism after it was put forward in the *New Scientist,* Soal doubted whether Ieuan could have edged himself to the end of the table; but if a tall 13-year-old boy is seated together with an experimenter at one side of a small table, he will have to be careful to *avoid* extending some part of his body outside the line of the edge of the table.

A further point raised by Soal was that the agent would have been seen by Thouless, who was an observer in the experiment and who stood close to Glyn. But Thouless' letter reads:

> If your records show that when I attended the session in London the body of Ieuan was completely screened from Glyn, I have no doubt that this was the case. I thought that I's legs were visible to Glyn and that you would not regard that experiment as being done under completely rigid conditions.[4]

Such a trick might be difficult to implement by the agent owing to the fact that he would not know when he was being observed closely by someone standing in the same room as the percipient. He would know when he was being observed by a person standing beside him, but the screen across the agent's table blocked his view of anything that was happening in front of him. Under these conditions, however, the percipient would know when there was any danger of the agent being detected, and he could then stop the signals by calling his guess as soon as he heard the bell for the start of the trial. Obviously there would be no point in the agent signaling if the percipient had already made his guess. On occasions, when the boys were scoring at the chance level, the percipient was, in fact, calling in this manner:

> After he heard the single tinkle of the bell Glyn would normally wait a few seconds before making his call, but it was noticed that when he was bored and scoring badly his method changed and he would call out a letter in a drawling tone *immediately* the bell was rung. At such times he did not trouble to conceal his boredom.[5]

FURTHER TESTS IN WALES

After arriving back in Wales, the boys were tested on Guy Fawkes Day, November 5, 1955, in their old position, seated 15 feet apart, and in line through a doorway. It seems to have occurred to someone that Ieuan's legs might be a vital factor, for a rug was hung over the end of the table at which he was seated to screen his legs from Glyn's gaze. Telepathy was now absent. Then the experimenters noticed that Ieuan was coughing at fairly regular intervals. Later Mrs. Goldney noticed that Ieuan creaked his chair on 3 occasions when the lion card was shown to him and that Glyn got his guesses right. She then observed Ieuan sniffing when the penguin was shown. The boys admitted the attempt to cheat in this manner. Thus, it is possible that after having the means of visual signals blocked, the boys resorted to auditory signals, but without much success. After being caught cheating, the boys were given a good scolding and Glyn's father, Richard, suggested that the experiments should be carried out in his cottage so that he could supervise the proceedings.

Further tests were held in Richard's cottage in the afternoon. For the first 4 runs, the boys were again seated 15 feet apart and obtained impressive scores. Then the door between them was shut and the high scores were maintained. It was reported that there was a "tremendous" and "terrific" noise of exploding fireworks from the street outside, but this does not seem to have inhibited the Jones boys. It may, however, have made it difficult for the experimenters to stop them from using audible signals. It is puzzling that these sittings were the first and last time that the boys were able to communicate through a closed door. Oddly, on this quiet country road miles from anywhere in an isolated part of Wales the sounds of all hell were let loose. Agreed Guy Fawkes Day is one on which fireworks are set off, but it is usual to confine the celebrations to after dark.

By evening the inhabitants of Capel Curig appeared to have consumed their stock of explosives, and at sittings held after 5:30 no further noises were reported. Professor C. W. K. Mundle from the Department of Philosophy, Bangor University, and Mrs. Mundle had arrived, and they saw Glyn obtain high scores 10, 9, 9, and 11 hits over 4 runs of 25 each. During these runs, Ieuan's father, Will Jones, acted as a joint agent with his son and rang a bell once as a signal to Glyn to make his guess. The door between the two boys was either left just ajar or closed. Will Jones was in a position to communicate information by varying the manner in which he rang the bell. A slight emphasis or delay, for example, could have signified a particular symbol, and only 5 such signals need have been given in each run of 25 trials to account for the high scores. When Mundle took over the job of ringing the bell, the scores dropped to chance level. Ieuan was by now falling asleep and the tests were terminated.

During further tests the following morning, when Mrs. Goldney had the job of ringing the bell, scores remained at the chance level. The boys complained that they could not make good scores while she was around, and she felt compelled to stay away from the experiments until the following August.

A month later, the boys were tested in adjoining hotel rooms, but they produced no evidence for telepathy in that setting. The boys complained that it was a strange place and said that they could not make any better scores there. Everyone went to Glyn's cottage for a further batch of experiments, and it was again noticed that the boys were augmenting any ESP ability they had with coughs, creaks, and stamps. The boys were not told that they had been detected and went off to the cinema with Bowden. When they got back, they were given further tests, and it was found that they had managed to change the code during the recess. This was a relatively simple matter, since they spoke Welsh and none of the investigators could understand that language. Referring to the cheating episode, Mundle wrote, "I think this episode adds to rather than detracts from, the authenticity of the report." [6] Soal said, "We were perfectly aware that boys of the calibre of Glyn and Ieuan could never hope to deceive us for more than a few minutes." [7]

Up to this point in the investigations, the boys had failed to obtain high scores under certain, well-defined experimental conditions, but the investigators do not appear to have asked themselves why this was the case. Many times, after a successful run, a change in the conditions that eliminated a possible source of trickery caused their scores to drop. Thus:

1. They obtained high scores under clairvoyance conditions when seated at a table with a rather inadequate screen consisting of a suitcase and a firescreen. They failed as soon as the screen was covered with a cloth.

2. They obtained high scores when in alignment through a doorway, but failed to score when out of alignment.

3. They obtained high scores when Ieuan was seated at a table with his legs visible to Glyn. They failed to score when Ieuan's legs were screened by a rug and when the door was shut.

4. They obtained high scores while Will Jones, who was sounding a bell to signify the start of each trial, was seated where he could see the target cards, but their scores dropped to the chance level after he was relieved of this post.

THE REHABILITATION PERIOD

After having been caught cheating on the last occasion, the boys were left in disgrace for 4 months. When experiments were resumed, the first batch of sittings, held between April 6–13, was referred to as the rehabilitation period. Bowden was away at this time, and his place was taken by Bateman. During the 4 months' rest, the experimenters appear to have reconsidered their experimental arrangements, and the Jones boys had been given a good opportunity to improve their techniques.

The first test after resumption was made with the boys seated at a table with a cardboard screen between them. Tom Jones, the boys' uncle, was asked to sit near Ieuan to listen for sniffs and coughs, to watch his mouth, and to be on the lookout for foot movements. Over 6 runs, the boys averaged 8.9 hits per run. It is difficult, however, to see how Tom Jones was able to watch Ieuan's feet and mouth at the same time without the boy being perfectly aware of where the danger to any trick lay.

When Glyn was moved 8 feet away from Ieuan, whose legs were screened by a tablecloth draped over the end of the table, the scores rose to 30 hits out of 50 trials. Then, when Glyn sat with his back to Ieuan 10 feet away from him, high scores were still obtained. Thus, the Jones boys were now displaying a definite improvement in their performance.

At a sitting held on April 7, without warning the boys were tested with fresh cards bearing symbols that they had not seen before. They were now seated across a table from one another with a screen between them. Their score on the first run was 10 hits out of 25, and in the following 3 runs they obtained 8, 14, and 15 hits. They were then moved 16 feet apart, and the tablecloth was hung over the end of Ieuan's table. The scores continued to be high—14, 12, 10, and 7. From the result of this experiment, it was argued that the boys could not have been using a code of any sort, as the change of cards would render a code useless. But it would have been a simple matter for the boys to have established a code in the first trial. Both knew that new cards were being used and knew the symbols to be guessed. At the start of the first trial Ieuan could have kicked Glyn. Glyn would immediately call, say, "Policeman" and the code would be established. Other signals could be added. A score of 21 out of 25 is possible in the first run with new cards if this system is carried to its limit. Alternatively, since these new cards were colored, the old code could have been transferred to cards of the same color in the new set. During sittings held between April 9–12, 1956, the boys showed signs of succeeding under conditions that previously had beaten them. On April 9, Glyn and Bateman sat at a table in one room, and Ieuan and Soal sat at a table in another. The door between the rooms was open and the boys were in alignment with each other. The tablecloth was draped over the end of Ieuan's table to hide his legs from Glyn. Under these conditions, high scores were obtained. On April 10, under similar conditions,

"ESP was not functioning." But on April 11, under similar conditions, high scores again were obtained. After the tenth run a more efficient screen, consisting of a blanket, was suspended to hide from Glyn the whole table at which Ieuan was seated. The boys were again successful if the door was left open. They obtained a high score when Soal showed the cards to Ieuan as well as when this duty was taken over by Richard Jones.

On the following day, similar results were obtained, and then in 2 runs, 13 and 14, Soal investigated the possibility that Ieuan might be making sounds by asking him to place both hands over his mouth. Soal sat where he could observe Ieuan at close range. The scores during these 2 runs dropped to the chance level. In the following 3 runs, Ieuan was allowed to remove his hands from his mouth. The scores remained low. This test did not appear to increase any suspicions Soal might have had that auditory cues were being provided by Ieuan and does not appear to have been repeated.

The scores for successive runs during sittings held on April 11 and 12, 1956, are of particular interest since one variable was systematically varied. A curtain consisting of a blanket screened the boys throughout, but a door between them was shut in some runs and open in others.

After these tests, Soal came to the conclusion that a possible explanation for the drop in scores when the door was shut was that Glyn had developed a "psychological inhibition" for closed doors. He corresponded with Thouless, who said that he had experienced the same difficulty with one of his subjects and that he had been unable to overcome the inhibition.

When the boys were tested on their home ground, there were innumerable possible means by which above-chance scores might have been brought about. The results of the tests carried out during the rehabilitation period do, however, suggest that auditory cues might, for the first time, have been successfully used. The most likely source of such cues would be sounds made with the mouth, but the possibility also exists that Ieuan could have operated some device while he sat with folded arms. In such a position he could easily have operated a whistle blown by means of a bulb, and if he had been doing this, it is not surprising that scores should drop as soon as he had to sit with both hands over his mouth.

After these experiments, it was decided to shift the scene of operations to the field behind the house, and most of the tests carried out with the boys in Wales from then on were conducted outside. The next 2 sittings are of special interest as they constituted a dress rehearsal for the second London visit. Glyn and Ieuan sat from 50 to 60 feet apart with a screen between them consisting of a curtain pegged to a clothes line.

Soal and Richard Jones acted as experimenters. During these runs other members of the Jones family were indoors, and we know nothing of their activities. As the first floor of the house was well situated for observation of the test area, it was possible for Ieuan to have given signals with his legs or feet below the table at which he was seated, signals that could have been visible to someone in the house. Information could then have been passed on to Glyn in a variety of ways. However, as the boys had already shown their ability to obtain high scores when separated by a curtain, it is also possible that Ieuan could communicate directly with Glyn using a means that was not affected by its presence.

THE SECOND LONDON VISIT

The second visit to London took place between May 19–22, 1956. Soal intended to conduct the experiments on the playing field of St. Paul's School, but it was not available on the first day, so the tests were carried out in Birkbeck College, London University. These experiments at Birkbeck are mainly of interest because 3 scientists were present as observers. Soal, Bowden, and Richard Jones acted as experimenters. The first 10 runs did not yield above-chance scores, but during the next 2 runs, the scientist observers left the laboratory, and scores rose to 10 and 11. One of the scientists returned, and scores dropped to 8 hits on each of the next 2 runs. When the other observers returned, a score of 5 hits was observed. Soal now assumed the boys had a "psychological inhibition" for scientists.

On the following day, May 20, the first 2 sittings were held on the playing field, and a third was held there on May 21. Until the ninth run of the third sitting, telepathy lay dormant, but before this run experimental conditions were drastically changed, and thereafter the boys obtained high scores on every run. Since the experimental conditions of the first 2 sittings were similar to those of the first 8 runs of the third sitting, only this last sitting will be described.

Soal, Bowden, Richard Jones, Gareth Jones (Glyn's brother), G. W. Fisk, and a number of visitors were present. Only one of the visitors, A. T. Moakes, the Senior Mathematics Master of the school was present, however, during the latter part of the third sitting when high scores were observed.

The boys were seated at tables 50 feet or more apart. A canvas screen, 6 feet high and 14 feet wide was between them; Ieuan sat close behind this screen at a table with Bowden, who handled the cards, while Glyn sat at a table out in the field with Soal. Fisk acted as signaler and stood at the end of the canvas screen where he could see the card being displayed but could not see the symbol on its face, and where he could be seen by Glyn (Figure 6). During runs 1 and 2, Fisk held up his hand to indicate to Glyn when he was to record his guess. For runs 3 and 4 he shouted "next," and for runs 5, 6, 7, and 8, he waved a white handkerchief. Under these conditions, the boys were unable to obtain above-chance scores. It should be noted that visual signals could not be passed from one boy to the other past the large canvas screen. Auditory signals made by mouth would have been virtually impossible at such long range with observers present. If Fisk had been an accomplice, no doubt a method of relaying signals could have been devised, but he was in a position from which it would have been very difficult to see any movements on the part of Ieuan, since he was standing some distance to the side of the table at which the boy was seated, and Soal was at the same table in such a position that he blocked Fisk's view of Ieuan.

After run 8, Glyn and Ieuan exchanged places but not roles. Glyn was now seated with Soal directly behind the screen, and Ieuan was at a table with Bowden 69 feet away from Glyn. At this point in the proceedings, Gareth Jones took over the job of signaler, and he stood in front of the screen so that, while he was separated from Glyn by the screen, he was only about 9 feet from him (Figure 7). Gareth called out "Guess number one," "Guess number two," and so on, in a loud voice. Fisk now acted as observer and at the same time took some photographs. He watched Ieuan for a time, then he watched Gareth, and at the end of run 16 he departed. Moakes was also present, but his exact duties and whereabouts are not specified.

Before run 19, the table at which Ieuan was seated was moved farther back so that Ieuan was 99 feet from Glyn. The scores for runs 9–22 were as follows:

RUN	9	10	11	12	13	14	15	16	17	18	19	20	21	22
SCORE	9	8	6	6	8	11	9	8	13	11	10	12	14	12

As soon as the new experimental conditions had been introduced, the boys scored above chance and during runs 17–22, when Fisk was no longer present, the scores rose even higher.

There is good reason to believe from the result and description of the first London visit that the boys were able to communicate by means of signals given by movements or positionings of Ieuan's feet or legs. In the present experiments, Ieuan could not have signaled directly to Glyn, but when he was moved from behind the screen after run 8, hits immediately rose above the chance level. Ieuan was now visible to both Gareth and Richard Jones, and his

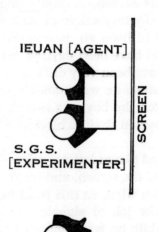

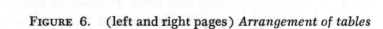

FIGURE 6.   (left and right pages) *Arrangement of tables*

feet and legs were fully exposed. The elder Joneses were in a position to observe foot movements and to pass on signals to Glyn. Gareth was in an ideal position, as he was standing just in front of the screen behind which Glyn was making his guesses and also was acting as signaler. The other signalers had merely called "next," but Gareth said, "Guess number one," "Guess number two," and so on. A slight accentuation of any word or syllable, or a slight delay, could have been a cue for Glyn, and as Gareth had a strong Welsh accent, such a trick would have been difficult for the other 5 to detect. Emphasis on either the first, second, or third words would have been sufficient to enable 3 kinds of signal to be passed, giving a score of 20 hits out of 25.

It is strange that after the eighth run not only was Ieuan put out in the field where he would be visible to other members of the family, but also that Gareth took over the duties of signaler. What is even more remarkable is the fact that no one present thought of getting someone else for that role, or of changing the method of signaling. There is ample evidence that the experimenters were well aware of the possibility of information being communicated to the percipient through the manner in which a person called for the next trial. In

H. T. B.
[EXPERIMENTER]

GLYN
[PERCIPIENT]

and screen with which scores were at chance level

earlier experiments, a bell or ash tray had been used with the aim of removing this possibility. To an observer such as Moakes, the mathematics master, it might appear difficult to see how inflections of the voice could be used to transmit information, but Soal was an authority on the subject. In spite of this, Gareth Jones was left to signal the next trial by calling out, and, moreover, he used a longish phrase with which he had every opportunity to use a code.

Soal discussed the possibility that Gareth might have relayed information by voice-inflection cues after observing Ieuan's foot movements and came to the conclusion that to have made scores of 12, 13, and 14 the same movements would have had to have been made many times. In fact, scores of 12, 13, and 14 were made only after Fisk left, when the sole outside observer was a schoolmaster quite unused to this type of situation, and his position during the runs in question is not certain. If he were on Glyn's side of the screen, he would have been unable to see Ieuan. To obtain an average score of 12 hits per run would require a signal on 8 or 9 of the cards in each run of 25. Only 2 different types of signal had to be used. Soal commented that any regular system of movements that was obvious to Gareth standing 60 feet away would be still more obvious to Fisk or Bowden at a distance of only 2 feet; but Bowden was certainly in no position to detect leg movements, since he was seated at a table close to Ieuan and busy displaying the

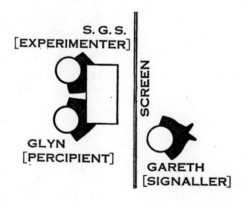

FIGURE 7.   (left and right pages) *Arrangement of tables*

cards to him. So far as Fisk was concerned, it would have been difficult for him to detect movements or postures unless he knew precisely what to watch for and was paying continuous attention. In his statement, Fisk reported that he was partially occupied taking photographs. Ieuan could see when he was being observed and could quite easily have stopped giving signals when in danger of being detected. The signal used could have been extremely slight. For example, for 3 different signals to be transmitted, the left foot could remain on the ground and the knee could be moved slightly to the right, remain in the vertical position, or be moved to the left. The vertical position would denote 1 of 3 cards, say *E, G,* or *L;* the knee to the left would denote *P* and to the right *Z*. If the gaps between the knee and the table leg were observed, a movement of 1 inch would be detectable at 60 feet. It is most unlikely that anyone not looking along the same line of view and not knowing the precise signal would detect anything. An alternative method that would be very difficult to detect would be for the agent to make some slight movement at a certain time interval after the signaler indicated the next guess, intervals of 1, 2, 3, and 4 seconds could each denote a card and the absence of a signal would then denote the fifth one. It would be difficult to be totally accurate using such a method, but such accuracy was neither required nor achieved.

IEUAN
[AGENT]

H. T. B.
[EXPERIMENTER]

and screen with which high scores were obtained

When outsiders act as observers, it is interesting to know what they expect to see if the agent is cheating. Do they expect to see a series of 5 different movements? If so, they are likely to notice nothing. The agent's signal may be any natural movement likely to arise over an interval of time. It may be one of several movements, or a very slow motion of, say, the knee towards the table leg. If this is practiced until it is only just detectable to someone watching for it and aware that it may take place, it is unlikely to be detected by anyone who knows nothing of it and who is having to watch for anything that may occur. Also, the agent can always stop signaling if he sees he is watched, and he need give only small signals in the hope that some of them may convey information to raise the score above the chance level.

THE THIRD SERIES OF EXPERIMENTS IN WALES

In the next series of experiments carried out 2 months after their second London visit, the boys started producing very high scores, and on 2 occasions they got 25 hits in 25 attempts. The first experiments were carried out in the field at the back of Richard Jones's house. The boys obtained high scores both when Richard was present and when he was absent. Glyn was behind a screen so that he could see only the experimenter who noted his guesses; the distance between the boys was 80 feet or more. When Richard was present, he stood where he could not see Glyn, but he was able to see the agent.

As high scores were obtained in the absence of other members of the Jones family, it would have been necessary either for Ieuan to produce a signal that could be detected by Glyn or for an intermediary in the house or near the test area to relay signals. He could have done this by watching the agent and receiving a cue from him, as described earlier.

In one experiment the boys were asked to perform in bathing trunks. Glyn said, before they started, that he was not going to try, and the score was only 11 hits out of 50 tries. The next day, the boys, fully clothed, obtained a high score with visitors present. At this sitting Ieuan turned out his pockets. On the following day the boys performed in bathing trunks, and the agent was closely examined to see that he had no apparatus concealed on his person.

It would appear that if the search of Ieuan was adequate, as no doubt it was, any signals reaching Glyn must have been given by an intermediary. It is not stated whether other members of the family were present in the field at the final experiment when Ieuan was searched, but if all the family were absent from the test area, it would have been quite possible for anyone concealed at an upstairs window to have observed the agent and give signals. In fact, the safest way for an intermediary to operate is at a distance and screened from others.

An experiment conducted in a schoolroom in the village at this time was similar in many respects to those carried out on St. Paul's playing field during the second London visit. Tests were made under 2 conditions: either the percipient was behind a screen at one end of the room and the agent was seated 40 feet away in the open room, or the percipient was behind the screen and the agent was out in the room. Soal's brother, C. W. Soal, acted as signaler. Significantly above-chance scores were obtained under the first condition but not the second. Again, high scores were only obtained when the agent was visible to some other member of the family. In this case, however, if Richard Jones was screened from Glyn as the report implies, he could only have relayed signals by auditory means. But as Richard did not speak during the experiment he could not have provided voice-inflection cues.

The important point to note about the experiments after the rehabilitation period, including those carried out in the open air, is that when the boys were on their home ground, high scores were obtained without any other member of the family taking part in the experiments; but, when they were away from home, as in the tests on St. Paul's playing field and in the schoolroom, high scores were obtained only in the presence of a member of the family who was in a position to see some part of the agent.

The outdoors experiments in Wales can prove very little as no attention was paid to the activities of members of the Jones family inside the house. In some of the tests, however, Glyn appears to have been relatively effectively screened, and if this was so, it is unlikely that visual signals could have been employed. Taking into account the fact that the boys had shown their ability to obtain high scores when separated by a blanket, an auditory cue would appear to be the only possible simple means of communication that could account for their improved performance. Earlier, the boys had been caught attempting to use auditory signals; it is possible that they had now perfected a more satisfactory method of communication using sounds and that, on at least some occasions, they were assisted by a third person, who relayed signals after observing movements made by Ieuan.

A POSSIBLE SOURCE OF TRICKERY

After reading *The Mind Readers,* I carried out some tests on two Welsh schoolgirls, aged 8 and 9 years, using an Acme "silent" dog whistle. I had purchased this in Cambridge in 1948 when I had considered its possible use in a fake demonstration of telepathy. The whistle was about 3 inches long, but the operative portion was only about 1 inch in length. After removing the superfluous parts of the whistle, it was attached by means of a length of rubber tubing to a bulb. It could then be suspended down one trouser leg and blown by the bulb which was kept in the trouser pocket.

In one demonstration I was standing between the agent and percipient who were 50 feet apart in the open air. The percipient was behind a screen and watched throughout by an observer. I arranged with the agent that on each trial I would sound pips on the whistle until she signaled me to stop by making a small movement of her foot when she had heard the requisite number of pips according to a prearranged code. The percipient also heard the whistle, and knowing the code, was able to state the identity of the card. After about 15 minutes' instruction and practice, my percipient was able to score 16 hits out of 25 attempts during her first run in the presence of witnesses. The agent and percipient were watched throughout and signed statements were obtained saying that no sounds or movements were observed. The girls were successful both when I stood between them, and when I was relaying signals from an upstairs window of a house near the test area.

In further tests using other children and carried out indoors, the agent and percipient were in different rooms with a doorway between them, and a blanket was hung over the doorway. I was in the room with the agent and gave signals according to a prearranged code. The percipient, a 9-year-old Welsh schoolboy, obtained 23 successes in 25 attempts. This percipient also obtained high scores when I both acted as agent and operated the whistle. The tests were observed by the boy's father, who detected no signs of trickery and had no idea of how the trick was carried out.

It was found that the whistle could be detected over considerable distances by young people while it was quite inaudible to elderly people standing a few feet away, even when they were listening for it. Since the average age of the investigators in the experiments on the Jones boys was nearer 70 than 40, such a technique could quite easily have been employed without fear of detection.

It is possible to improve on results obtained with the dog whistle by using a Galton whistle, which may be obtained from firms who supply apparatus for school laboratories. This whistle is formed from a tube of very small bore, tuned by a plunger. It can produce notes with frequencies extending through and well above the audible range. After removing the extraneous parts of this whistle, one is left with a small tube, about $\frac{1}{16}$ inch in diameter and $\frac{1}{2}$ inch long, which can be blown by means of the bulb from an eyedropper. Such a whistle can be adjusted so that it is completely inaudible to adults but audible to children over considerable distances. I found that my 9-year-old daughter could detect it at 150 feet in the open air, and a larger bulb extended the range to 500 feet. If a small reflector from a pocket torch was fitted to the apparatus, the range was further increased, and the whistle was then more directional. The 9-year-old child could detect the whistle quite easily through a closed door or in almost any room of a house when the doors were open. Thus, her performance was much more striking than that of the Jones boys. It is possible, however, that the boys communicated by making sounds with the mouth, such as whistling through the teeth in many of the short-range tests.

THE THIRD LONDON VISIT

After the sittings held in the summer of 1956, the boys made their third trip to London. The experiments during this visit are of particular interest because Soal was not present and Jack Salvin, a professional magician, took charge of the proceedings. Salvin, at the time Chairman of the Occult Committee of the Magic Circle, was said to be skeptical of ESP, although he was a member of the

British Society for Psychical Research. The sittings were held in the rooms of the Society, and Salvin was allowed to arrange the experiments in his own way. He supervised 6 sittings. In the first 3 of these, the boys obtained high scores. In the remaining sittings, they failed completely. This is of interest because *The Mind Readers* states, "Until the end of the third sitting the boys did not know who Mr. Salvin was or why he was there." [8]

The boys sat in the two rooms of the library of the Society for Psychical Research, more or less as in the first London visit. On this occasion, however, the only screen was a large, white blanket suspended from a line whose ends were fixed to bookcases. Glyn sat at a table behind this blanket with Bowden who recorded his guesses. At each of the successful sittings, the fathers of the two boys were present, but little is said about their precise whereabouts. The scores obtained at these 3 sittings are given below. Two unsuccessful runs are omitted. In one of these, clairvoyance conditions were used; in the second, Glyn and Ieuan had exchanged roles.

Sitting 1

RUN	1	2	3	4	5	6	7	8
SCORE	4	8	15	10	17	7	14	11

Sitting 2

RUN	1	2	3	4	5	7
SCORE	17	3	14	16	11	15

Sitting 3

RUN	1	2	4	5
SCORE	21	20	18	19

It will be seen that after the first two runs scores were high except in run 6 of the first sitting, and run 2 of sitting 2. These last 2 runs are the only ones in which Glyn and Bowden were not alone behind the screen. Salvin is reported to have gone behind the screen with Glyn during the first half of run 6, sitting 1, and to have sat beside Glyn throughout the second run of the second sitting. On that occasion, Glyn is reported to have made his guesses very rapidly.

After the first sitting, Salvin wrote in his statement: "I am completely satisfied, after making all the observations I desired and having permission to do what I wished, that no code or trickery took place, either on the part of the boys or on the part of anybody else (including the fathers of the two boys); and, in fact, that code or trickery in the experimental conditions I witnessed was impossible." [9] Similar statements were made by Salvin after the other two successful sittings.

It is difficult to place much reliance on Salvin's report, since it would have been almost impossible for him to detect trickery. He had established the fact that high scores ceased when he went behind the curtain with Glyn, but this did not raise his suspicions. One elementary precaution he might have taken would have been to have asked the boys' fathers to leave the room.

More than 2 years later, on March 21, 1959, Salvin supervised a sitting at which Mr. and Mrs. Christopher Scott took over the roles of the Jones boys. [10] Salvin took complete charge, and under similar conditions to those enjoyed by Glyn, Mrs. Scott obtained equally high scores. Mr. Scott, in Ieuan's role, had signaled to his wife by means of a Galton whistle. Salvin expressed himself as baffled and immensely impressed.

The next day, a demonstration was given to Alec Reeves, an acoustics expert who had been present at 2 of the sittings of the third London visit and who had been sure no auditory or visual signals could have been used.

In fact, almost any boys could communicate with one another, using a Galton whistle or a dog whistle in complete safety when supervised by most adults over 50 years of age. At the time he made his tests, Salvin was nearer 80 than 50.

It should be borne in mind that the Jones boys lived in a part of Wales where almost every child would have seen sheep dogs controlled by a whistle. They are likely to have attended a sheep dog trial, where the dogs appear to be controlled by some invisible influence. Their parents would also have known that as one grows older the whistle becomes increasingly difficult to hear. As Francis Galton commented when he first described his whistle, "there is a saying in Dorset that men over forty cannot hear the Bat's cry." [11]

The third London visit was the last real test for the Jones boys. Back in Wales, high scores were observed under a variety of conditions, all pitifully inadequate, until April 1957. After that month, no further experiments were reported and, it is understood, the boys' powers suddenly disappeared.

It is of interest to note that two books have been published since the conclusion of the experiments; each was written by a member of the Society for Psychical Research who attended some of the sittings on the Jones boys, and in neither case is any reference made to the experiment.[12]

Perhaps the most fitting judgment on the experiments was expressed by Soal: "What the investigation does demonstrate is the all-powerful influence on an intense motivation (in this case the love of money) in maintaining scores at a high level over a period of years." [13]

CHAPTER 11

Psychokinesis

EARLY INVESTIGATIONS

THE first attempt to test whether a person's thoughts could influence the movement of a physical object was made by the great English scientist Michael Faraday (1791–1867) in 1853. At that time, the American mediums had arrived in Britain and a cult of table turning was sweeping the country. Faraday, who had become involved in a controversy over spiritualism at the Royal Society, thought it likely that the tables were moved through the application of a force transmitted by the hands of those touching them rather than by any psychic influence. This, he decided, could be established experimentally.

Faraday found that there was no need to have a group of people sitting round the table; a single person could cause the table to move. Also, he observed that the table's motion was not necessarily circular but might be in a straight line. He then glued together 4 or 5 pieces of cardboard, one over the other, with pellets of a soft cement consisting of wax and turpentine. The bottom piece was attached to a sheet of sandpaper that was resting on the table. The edges of the cardboard overlapped one another slightly and a pencil line was drawn on their undersurface to indicate the positions of the cards before the test. The upper cardboard was larger than the rest, so that it covered the remaining sheets. The cement was strong enough to offer considerable resistance to mechanical motion and also to hold the cards in any new position they acquired. However, it was weak enough to give way slowly to a continued force. The table turner placed his hands on the upper card and results were awaited. Faraday found that when the table, hands, and cards all moved to the left together, the displacement of the cardboard sheets, as compared to the line showing their original position, showed that the hands of the table turner moved farther than the table. His hands had pushed the upper card to the left, and the under cards and the table had followed and had been dragged by it.

Faraday's subjects were all successful table turners who believed in their own abilities. Thinking that they moved the table as a result of a "quasi-involuntary" motion, Faraday next carried out tests in which the turner could become aware, by watching an indicator, when he was exerting any pressure. Under these conditions the table did not move. Faraday wrote:

> No form of experiment or mode of observation that I could devise gave me the slightest indication of any peculiar natural force. No attraction or repulsions, or signs of tangential power,—nor anything which could be referred to other than the mere mechanical pressure exerted inadvertently by the turner.[1]

Faraday had been investigating what is today called psychokinesis. A later investigation to determine the effects of thought on a physical system was carried out by Sir William Crookes using a delicate chemical balance, which, if there were powers of psychokinesis, might, he thought, be caused to move. He was, however, unsuccessful in moving the balance, and it is a remarkable fact that this rather obvious way of testing for psychokinesis has been ignored by later investigators.

At the turn of the century, a physical medium named Eusapia Palladino (see pages 209–217) claimed to be able to move a balance, or at least to get her spirit guide, "John King," to move it for her. She was tested by a committee in Paris that included the French physicist and codiscoverer of radium, Marie Curie (1867–1934), but it appears that on this occasion Eusapia was assisting "John King" by the use of a fine thread held between her hands. When suitable precautions were taken to screen the balance, it no longer moved.

THE EXPERIMENTS AT DUKE UNIVERSITY

The topic of psychokinesis was almost forgotten until Rhine began his investigations of it in 1934. He was interested in finding out whether subjects could influence the fall of dice by wishing for a particular outcome. The early tests carried out at Duke University were conducted under informal experimental conditions. Subjects were often tested in private homes or in dormitories. Some investigators used themselves as subjects, and the experiments were hardly more than exploratory.

The results of some 19 investigations carried out between 1934 and 1942 do not appear to have been very convincing at the time, since no mention was made of them in published reports of Rhine's work until after 1942. He has said that it was the discovery, in 1942, of a secondary effect in the old score sheets that convinced him of the reality of psychokinesis. Looking back at the records of the early experiments, he found that subjects tended to score higher in the first runs of a session than in the later ones and higher in early trials than in the later trials. He said: "The significance of these hit distribution data, found long after the tests had been made, was so great that we were at last fully convinced that the PK [psychokinesis] effect was a real one." [2]

In *Reach of the Mind*, published in 1949, Rhine reported the discovery of several new characteristics of psychokinesis. Subjects were more successful if they tried to influence many dice at the same time—the more the better; the distance of the subject from the dice did not affect the scores; metal dice produced above-chance scores whereas wooden ones did not; dice made of lead gave higher scores than those made of aluminum; rounding the corners of the dice so that they would roll more easily did not affect the scores. It is significant that techniques had developed to such an extent by 1949 that these detailed characteristics of psychokinesis could be determined, whereas in the first 8 years of research (1934–1942) the scores had been insufficient even to provide a convincing case for its existence.

J. Fraser Nicol, at a symposium held by the Ciba Foundation in 1955, criticized these claims:

On the strength of dice throwing said to have been performed at Duke University, it is recorded elsewhere that the psychokinetic force is more effective on heavy metal dice than on wooden ones; and also, from the same source, that the shape of the dice—sharp corners, rounded corners, or extremely rounded corners—makes no difference to the power of the human psychic force. Neither of

these strange claims can be validated in any of the published reports on psychokinesis. It is mainly on the basis of these and similar unverifiable assertions that the author concludes that "the
finding that *mass, number, and form* [of dice] *are not determining
conditions of PK tests*, takes its place, then, alongside the discovery
that time and space were not limiting factors in ESP."

Only a few of these rash pronouncements have been quoted in
the above paragraphs. Many others could be cited. One wonders
what the more objective but friendly type of scientist must think
when he is confronted with such highly adorned claims. He might,
one surmises, rather easily turn away from psychical research,
moved by the uncomfortable realization that a subject in which
scientific method and the need for careful reporting are so casually
pushed out of the way, is not a field of study in which he would
care to indulge.[3]

The experiments on psychokinesis carried out since 1934 have
been assessed in an extensive review made by the American
psychologist Edward Girden of Brooklyn College. He divided the
investigations into 4 categories:

1. The early dice tests carried out between 1934–1937 and
mostly published in the *Journal of Parapsychology* between 1943–
1946.
2. Later dice tests in which more care was paid to experimental
design.
3. Tests in which objects other than dice were used.
4. Tests in which subjects attempted to produce lateral displacement of an object.[4]

EARLY DICE TESTS

The main objections raised by Girden to the early dice tests
were:

1. They were "largely free-wheeling and off the cuff." Variations
of test conditions were a common occurrence.
2. When subjects attempted to obtain a particular face uppermost, they tended to attempt to throw a 6, and the dice were not
tested for bias.
3. Little or no attention was paid to accuracy of recording.

4. Adequate control tests were lacking. Thus, if the proportion of, say, 6's arising in 960 trials when the subject had attempted to obtain them had been compared with the number of 6's arising in an equal number of trials when the subject had made no effort to obtain them, any bias on the dice could have been allowed for. Trials of the 2 types could have been alternated or targets could have been decided by a series of random numbers (1–6).

Only one of the early experiments employed a control series. This was carried out by Frick, a graduate student at the Parapsychology Laboratory, in 1937. He tested himself when throwing dice from a cup under 2 conditions: (*a*) when wishing to throw 6's; (*b*) when wishing part of the time to throw 1's and part of the time *not* to throw 6's. When condition *a* operated, he obtained a positive deviation of 582 hits for the 6 face out of 52,128 trials, and under condition *b*, 576 hits for the 6 face out of 52,128 trials. Thus, the experiment provided no evidence for psychokinesis but clear evidence for bias of the dice, since the dice tended to fall with the 6 face uppermost whether it was being wished for or not. If the control series had been omitted, it could have been claimed that the experiment provided evidence for psychokinesis comparable to that provided by similar experiments reported at that time.

Frick's negative results indicated, according to Rhine and psychologist Betty Humphrey, then a research fellow in the Parapsychology Laboratory, that there was "no place in Frick's personal philosophy to accommodate the PK hypothesis. . . . It appears that Frick must have, as it were, completely deceived himself in the conduct of series B. He was not well unified in his motivational elements." [5]

Girden remarked:

On a number of interesting considerations, it is self evident that the most elementary requirement necessitated the equal representation of all six dice faces as targets in some randomised order and the tabulation of all dice faces in all trials. There is no need to make use of higher mathematics to conclude that biased dice could account for the obtained results. [6]

He also commented in his review that 19 early reports from the Duke laboratory were characterized by the presence of only one negative result, whereas 2 other experiments carried out at that time in other laboratories each gave negative results.

The first of these experiments, reported by Nicol and W. Carington, a well-known English parapsychologist, in England, was far better in design than any of the American tests. All throws of the dice were recorded and all faces were used as targets in systematic fashion. No evidence was obtained for psychokinesis, and detailed examination showed that decline effects were not present.[7] The second study, carried out by C. B. Nash of the biophysics department at St. Joseph's College, Philadelphia, in 1944, in which all 6 die faces were used as targets equal numbers of times, also provided no evidence for psychokinesis.[8]

Since the majority of the early Duke experiments were conducted in the investigators' homes or in dormitories by students, business people, and interested amateurs without professional supervision, the observed decline effects might well have arisen because of the way in which the tests were carried out. As such effects had not been envisaged at the time of the experiments, it is unlikely that any precautions were taken to guard against them. Similar decline effects were reported in the early experiments on clairvoyance carried out by Miss Jephson (see page 37). When her experiment was repeated, the result indicated that her original result was not due to extrasensory perception but to the fact that the subjects were not supervised. Whatever brought about high scores in her experiment also, presumably, produced the decline effect.

If a number of reports are collected together from people who have been left much to their own devices, such decline effects may be expected. Thus, for example, if an investigator tests a number of persons before finding one who gives high scores, and then goes on testing him, we should expect, in the absence of psychokinesis, the subject's record to show a decline effect across the record sheet. His scores would be high at the start, that being the reason he had been selected as a subject, but they would be unlikely to remain high. Also, if the number of runs in a test is not specified at the start, similar effects may be expected to arise. The initially successful subject may become discouraged and terminate the tests, after a run in which he has made a low score, but if he has made a number of hits in the last few trials of the run, he may feel encouraged to attempt a further run.

It is remarkable that the decline effects, when they were first noted, did not throw doubt on the experiments but were interpreted as providing convincing evidence for psychokinesis.

LATER DICE TESTS

These include investigations carried out after the development of the decline hypothesis. Following criticism of the earlier work, more attention was paid to experimental design and to effects such as bias on the dice. In some cases, all throws were recorded rather than only successes.

Among 30 of these later investigations listed by Girden, 13 supported the psychokinesis hypothesis. The remainder did not produce a significant above-chance score, and in only one case was there a decline effect.

The conditions for a conclusive test for psychokinesis as stated by Rhine and Pratt in their book *Parapsychology* are: (1) a two-experimenter plan; (2) randomization of targets or systematic variation of the targets with all faces of the dice acting as target equal numbers of times; (3) independent recording of targets, hits, and misses.

On these criteria, none of the 13 tests giving positive evidence for psychokinesis can be regarded as conclusive, whereas several of the remaining 17 investigations that failed to provide such evidence do satisfy the requirements.

EXPERIMENTS USING OBJECTS OTHER THAN DICE

Experiments using disks, coins, and other objects have been reported by 4 investigators. The first of the tests, reported by Elizabeth McMahon, a zoologist working at the Parapsychology Laboratory, was on children and college students; plastic disks were used, and the subjects wished for a particular face to fall uppermost. A decline effect was present, but the score in both cases was not significantly above chance.[9]

Thouless, who made the second of these investigations, used coins thrown 10 at a time off a ruler, and came to the conclusion, "It is obvious that the result is not of any value as independent evidence for PK."[10]

A third investigation, in which a subject tested himself by throwing a penny onto a rug for 100 trials per session over 10 sessions and also by throwing a die 216 times, was reported by Dorothy Pope, managing editor of the *Journal of Parapsychology,* with the comment that these attempts "offer suggestive data on the comparative success of dice and discs in PK experiments." [11] The odds against the combined score arising by chance were about 90 to 1.

The fourth and most extensive of these investigations was made by S. R. Binski, a government official, while working for his Ph. D. degree.[12] In one series, 117 subjects threw 100 coins at a time until altogether 153,000 coins had been thrown. In a second series, 123 subjects attempted to guess the winning number of roulette wheel spins. Neither series yielded evidence for PK.

Further tests were made by Binski with another subject whose scores, it was claimed, were highly significant. However, Girden has pointed out that these tests had no pre-experimental plan and involved no set number of runs. Gardner Murphy, when criticizing Girden's report in the *International Journal of Parapsychology,* pointed out that Binski's subject, using a coin, obtained 548 successes out of 1,000 attempts. Such a result is not very unusual —the odds are about 3 to 1—if one takes into account the fact that Binski had tested 240 subjects. It should also be noted that the 1,000 attempts represented only 10 throws of 100 coins. In such tests, where a large number of dice, for example, are thrown together, the greatest care must be taken with the randomization of the targets, otherwise the observations cannot be said to apply to independent events, and the statistical analysis may yield a misleading result.

LATERAL DISPLACEMENT

The best known of the experiments in which subjects attempted to produce the lateral displacement of objects by wishing it have been carried out by H. Forwald, of the Swiss Federal Institute of Technology at Zurich.[13] He not only claims that subjects have been able to obtain lateral displacement of objects, but also that he has been able to measure the psychokinetic force by observing the distance a cube slides sideways along a surface when dropped onto it from a height. His calculations are based on the assumption that if the object moved laterally a greater distance than the height from which it was dropped, then a psychokinetic force was present. For his work he was given the $1,000 McDougall Award, which is presented each year by the Duke Parapsychology Laboratory for outstanding research. Two objections have been raised concerning Forwald's research. The late C. C. L. Gregory, formerly Professor of Astronomy at London University, criticized the assumptions underlying Forwald's calculation of a psychic force in *Psychic News,* after having attempted without success to air his criticism in the *Journal of Parapsychology*. He pointed out:

> If anyone cares to perform the experiment of successively pushing wooden blocks from a child's building set over the edge of a low table on to a linoleum floor, he can easily satisfy himself that the cubes will scatter in a random manner equally in any direction up to a distance even greater than the height of the fall. *The reason for this scatter is not a sideways force, psychic or otherwise,* it is determined by the horizontal distance between the cube's centre of mass and the point of contact on striking the floor.
>
> Unless this distance happens to be zero, an impulsive couple will be imparted to the wooden block causing it to leap in a contrary direction to that of the point of contact with respect to the point below the centre of the cube. The sideways distance of the jump, roll or slide, will also depend on the friction, as Mr. Forwald found.[14]

The second objection was raised by J. Fraser Nicol. Forwald acted mainly as his own subject, and Nicol remarks:

> At what state in the difficult history of psychical research it became permissible for sensitives to report their own results and expect them to be accepted as serious evidence in psychical research, I do not know.[15]

As Girden has pointed out, Forwald's 1954 work began some 9 years after publication of *Extrasensory Perception after Sixty Years,* and yet by the standards of that book, all his data would be unacceptable.

In 17 reports on placement wishing, a result favoring the existence of a psychokinetic force was obtained in 4. Only 2 investigations other than Forwald's report positive findings. The first of these, conducted by W. E. Cox, a businessman and amateur magician associated with the Parapsychology Laboratory, gave a significant below-chance score, but the researcher recognized that the experiment involved unwitnessed observation and recording.[16]

The remaining investigation, that of Miss Elsie Knowles, lecturer in applied statistics at Birmingham University in England, suffered from the weakness that the experimenter and her brother constituted the only 2 subjects.[17] Miss Knowles acted as recorder for her brother and also for herself at 2 of the 3 sessions.

PSYCHOKINESIS IN EVERYDAY LIFE

A more general objection against claims for the existence of psychokinesis is that, if it were a real process, its effects might be expected to manifest themselves in many situations in everyday life. Thus, the American science author Martin Gardner writes:

> Another disturbing question comes to mind. For decades Chicagoans have played the "26 game" in their bars and cabarets. The dice are shaken from a cup, the player betting a certain number will show up at least 26 times in 13 rolls. Obviously the tired and bored dice-girl, who tallies each roll, doesn't care one way or another. Obviously the player is doing his damndest to roll the number. How does it happen that these tally sheets, year after year, show precisely the percentage of house take allowed by the laws of chance? One would expect PK to operate strongly under such conditions.[18]

It is also only natural that experts such as the American authority on dice, John Scarne, should be astounded by the claims for psychokinesis.

A further objection to the claims that such a force exists is the fact that, if PK really operates, a statistical analysis of repeated throws of dice should be unnecessary. As Gardner says, "There is an obvious and suggestive analogy between para-psychology's preoccupation with purely statistical evidence, with all its murky aspects, and the preoccupation of mediums with phenomena that for some odd reason take place only in darkness." [19]

This has always been the main objection to the claims for

psychokinesis. If such a force exists, its effects should be detectable by means of a sensitive instrument, such as a chemical balance. Parapsychologists have always found it difficult to reply to this objection and have not published details of research aimed at obtaining a direct measure of psychokinesis.

During a lecture given at Manchester University in 1950, Rhine was asked whether psychokinesis could not be measured directly with a sensitive balance. He replied that it was a good suggestion and that they might get around to trying it sometime. After 16 years of research and after the same question must have been asked countless times, such a reply is hardly satisfactory. The plain fact is that if a direct measurement is made of the psychokinetic force by any known means, it is found to be zero.

Why do these processes investigated by parapsychologists never manifest themselves directly? Why do they only manifest themselves under experimental conditions that are extremely conducive to error? These are questions that are difficult to answer. But a further question that arises is: Why does any prediction made on the basis of the data turn out to be useless? If Forwald can measure lateral displacement indirectly after an extensive statistical analysis, why cannot such a displacement be measured directly? A force applied over a period of time would more likely manifest itself to an increased extent; 100 "willers" would produce more push than a single one. A simple demonstration in which the effects of the psychokinetic force could be observed directly would be far more convincing than any number of experiments where the result can only be expressed after a statistical analysis or where psychokinesis is claimed to exist owing to the presence of a *post hoc* secondary effect in the data.

CHAPTER 12

Recent Developments in ESP Research

GROUP EXPERIMENTS

BEFORE 1934, investigators at Duke University had no difficulty in finding subjects who could consistently obtain high scores in ESP tests. Following each wave of criticism, however, such subjects became scarce. The criticism that arose after Rhine's first book resulted in a marked decline in the availability of subjects who could consistently obtain high scores. After the discussions at the meeting of the American Psychological Association in 1938 and Kennedy's criticisms in the *Psychological Bulletin* of 1939, high-scoring subjects became even more scarce and then disappeared completely from the United States, where not a single high-scoring subject has been discovered since 1939.

HUMPHREY'S EXPERIMENT

Since 1940, most of the experiments on ESP carried out in the United States have relied on a new type of technique used by Betty Humphrey of the Duke Parapsychology Laboratory to test the relationship between ESP and personality characteristics.[1] In her experiment, 96 subjects were first classified by means of a personality test into "compressive" and "expansive" types. After this, the subjects were given a test for clairvoyance, and the mean score of the compressives was compared with that of the expansives. It was found that the expansives scored significantly higher on the test, the odds being greater than 300,000 to 1 against the difference in scores arising by chance. The over-all score for the 96 subjects was, however, not significantly above the chance level, nor was the score of any one subject.

The personality test used in the experiments required the subjects to draw anything they pleased on a blank sheet of paper. Subjects who filled the area of the paper with a bold drawing were classified as expansives, while those who used only a part of the paper were classified as compressives. Thus, while ignoring any assumptions that relate the manner in which a person draws to other personality characteristics, Miss Humphrey's experiment seemed to indicate that people who fill a sheet of paper when drawing on it tend to obtain high scores in ESP tests, and people who make small drawings covering only a part of the paper tend to obtain low scores. A further remarkable result reported by Miss Humphrey was that when telepathy tests were used instead of clairvoyance tests, the result was reversed: the timid drawers now got high scores and the bold drawers low ones.

J. Fraser Nicol and Miss Humphrey (now Mrs. Nicol) have carried out 2 further experiments of the same type. The first of these gave scores that tended in the same direction but were not statistically significant.[2] It should be noted that the probability of the mean scores of 2 groups being identical is very small. Thus, in the absence of ESP, the odds against obtaining a result in the same direction as the original experiment are about even. The second experiment has not yet been published, but Nicol has informed me in correspondence that the result was "pure nullity," and that the whole affair needs to be re-examined. D. J. West of the Society for Psychical Research also repeated this experiment and found no difference in the scores of the groups and no signs of ESP.[3]

SHEEP AND GOATS

Since 1940, several investigators have divided their subjects into 2 groups, but they have used quite different criteria from those of Humphrey. In some of this research, the results have the same general characteristics as in her experiment.

The most extensive of these tests was that conducted by Gertrude R. Schmeidler of the City College of New York.[4] She divided her subjects into sheep and goats, a sheep being a person who believed in ESP and a goat being one who did not, and found that the flock of sheep scored above chance and the herd of goats below it. Again, the over-all score was not significantly above the chance level, and again repetition of the test by other investigators did not confirm the original result.[5]

EXPERIMENTS IN THE CLASSROOM

A similar technique has been employed in a number of experiments carried out in classrooms with the aim of seeing whether pupils who have good feelings toward the teacher will display ESP. Margaret Anderson of the Biophysics Department at the University of Pittsburgh, and Rhea White, a research fellow in the Parapsychology Laboratory, have employed a questionnaire to determine the children's attitudes toward the teacher and the teacher's attitude to the children.[6] The children were given a clairvoyance test, and it was claimed that where there was mutual good feeling between teacher and pupil, the scores tended to be above the chance level, while where there was not, scores were below it. Repetitions of these experiments by other investigators have again failed to confirm the original result, and a repetition by Mrs. White herself has also failed to achieve any confirmation.[7]

PRECAUTIONS NECESSARY IN GROUP EXPERIMENTS

Provided adequate precautions are taken in its design and administration, the group experiment has several advantages over those that rely on the scores of single high-scoring subjects. A high-scoring subject may stop obtaining the same level of scores, making it impossible to verify the original experimental result by further tests; but in the group experiment, subjects are selected at random from the population and no single one need display any significant signs of ESP. Anyone can repeat such an experiment by drawing a group of subjects from a similar population, and there would appear to be no reason why the original result, if it is genuine, should not be confirmed.

The type of group experiment in which 2 subgroups are compared does, however, introduce further hazards into the experimental situation. There are 2 new potential sources of error that need to be carefully guarded against. It is necessary to take as stringent safeguards against spurious high scores as in experiments with single subjects, but, in addition, extra precautions are necessary to ensure that the experimenter himself cannot unwittingly influence the result. In the earlier types of experiments, the main aim was to keep the subjects from getting any information about the targets; in the new group experiments, it is also necessary to ensure that the scoring of the tests and the classification into groups are completely independent and exact. In a split-group experiment, the lack of confirmation of a result in which one subgroup has scored above chance and the other subgroup below chance, while there is an over-all result at the chance level, at once points to some form of error in allocating individuals to their groups. Ideally, the grouping should be decided and the result made public before the ESP tests are carried out. There can then be no possibility that the original classification will be changed after the scores of the ESP test become known.

It is also necessary that the nature of the test and the number of trials to be given to each subject be standardized before any tests are made. It would be quite easy to obtain a spurious result when dividing people into believers and disbelievers in ESP if the number of trials to be given to each subject was not decided from the start. The skeptical goat might otherwise carry on with run after run until he had proved his point by getting a total score below the chance expectation. In this way he would influence the outcome of the experiment. If some goats, after obtaining high scores, decided that they did believe in ESP after all, and the experimenter changed their classification, this again would result in a lowered score for the goats and a higher one for the sheep.

One of the controls that Kennedy suggested should be present in ESP experiments was the listing of calls and cards independently by two different recorders. In the split-group type of experiment, it is also essential that the ESP scores and the classification into whatever categories are being investigated should be determined by independent investigators. As a major potential source of error in ESP experiments lies in the recording and checking of data, an obvious safeguard is the use of automatic data-logging equipment.

AUTOMATIC RECORDING

Although it is a simple matter to present targets and record data by automatic means, it is remarkable that few such attempts

appear to have been made. The electrical machine of G. N. M.
Tyrrell (see pages 37–38) represented an early effort, but apparently there has been no use of it in further tests or attempts to
improve on it after its defects were discovered. Another machine
designed by Dennis Parsons, a member of the Society for Psychical
Research, is described by Soal and Bateman, but they remark that
so far as they are aware no one has yet obtained any significant
results by its use.[8]

Tyrrell's machine introduced automatic presentation and selection of the targets and automatic registration of hits and errors.
When all three features were operating so that the testing was
completely automatic and the targets themselves were decided by
the randomizer, subjects' results were consistently at the chance
level. As soon as any human element was present—that is, when
Tyrrell compiled random numbers by using his randomizer and
then used these in an experiment—the subject was successful in
obtaining above-chance scores.

In recent years, relatively little interest has been shown in
automating the ESP test procedure. The two investigations that
follow are therefore of particular interest. In the first, carried out by
S. David Kahn, a medical student, in 1952, the scoring was automatic, but the remainder of the test procedure followed more or less
conventional lines. In the second experiment, carried out at the
United States Air Force Research Laboratories, the whole process of
displaying symbols and recording guesses was automated.

THE KAHN EXPERIMENT

In this experiment, the subjects made 300 guesses at targets
in which each could be 1 to 5 different symbols.[9] Standard cards
that could be checked on a computer were used, and the subjects
marked their guesses in pencil. The cards contained 150 rows of
5 spaces on each side of the card. A similar card had been prepared before the experiment to show the targets at which the
subjects were guessing. The pencil mark made by the subject
enabled the machine to score and count the hits automatically, thus
removing at least one possible source of human error.

A total of 43,278 guesses were obtained from 177 subjects and a scoring rate of 5.16 hits per run of 25 guesses was observed as against the expected scoring rate of 5.0 hits per run. The result for the group of subjects was statistically significant, having odds greater than 2,000 to 1 against arising by chance.

It should be noted that whereas the scoring system of this experiment was rigorous, other features of the test conditions were not entirely satisfactory. The test was carried out by a medical student on fellow students, but a condition that has generally been accepted as a requirement for a conclusive test is that there should be at least two experimenters with some postgraduate research experience.

The conditions were varied in 5 subdivisions of the experiment. In series 4, carried out under "rigid conditions," the subjects appeared in answer to an advertisement, and the testing was done on 2 different days using a different target sheet on each day and with the subjects assembled in a classroom. The results from this series gave a positive deviation from chance expectation of only +10 in 15,360 trials.

In 3 other subseries (1, 2, and 5), the subjects worked under "free conditions." They were given an answer sheet and then told to go away and fill it in during the next few days. These series produced an over-all deviation of +217.2 in a total of 21,364 trials. Thus, the looser experimental conditions produced the higher score.

A further unsatisfactory feature of the experiment was the fact that many subjects were guessing a common target series. Since subjects tend to fill in forms "at random" in a nonrandom way, the statistical test would not necessarily give a true assessment unless this was taken into consideration. The only satisfactory way of conducting an experiment of this type would be either to have different target series prepared by a randomizer for each subject or to have the subjects guessing at a standard target series and to ask the experimenter to predict the target series from an analysis of the subjects' responses before disclosing the guesses to the experimenter. When a single target series is employed, it is also necessary to take extremely stringent precautions to keep it secret, and preferably no one should know its order until all guesses are recorded.

The inherent difficulties of Kahn's experiment are eliminated in an experiment carried out at the United States Air Force Research Laboratories, in which the whole testing process was carried out on a machine.[10] The investigators, William R. Smith, Everett F. Dagle, Margaret D. Hill, and John Mott-Smith, approached their research with the idea that it was a waste of time to conduct further experiments merely to demonstrate the occurrence of ESP, and that it was more important to discover how ESP worked.

The apparatus they used was called VERITAC, and it automatically generated random targets, registered the subjects' guesses, compared them with the targets, and registered scores. There were 2 consoles, each in a different room: the subject's console, at which he sat and indicated his guess at each trial by pressing a button, and a control console on which the targets were generated (Figure 8).

The targets, consisting of the digits 0–9, were created by means of a random-number generator. The number selected by the generator at each trial appeared on an indicator tube on the control console.

The subject's console contained 2 electromechanical counters that indicated to him the number of trials he had made and his number of successes. In addition, a light flashed on the console each time he secured a hit. Thus, the subject had partial knowledge of the result after each trial.

Provision was made for the automatic recording of the targets, the number selected by the subject, and the time at which each trial was made. In addition, the total number of trials and hits was recorded. A record was also maintained to show the response time of the subject at each trial.

The rooms in which the consoles were situated were separated by a third room, and the doors between the rooms were kept closed during tests. VERITAC was checked for operational effectiveness, and several pilot studies were run to ensure that the apparatus was reliable in operation. The numbers generated by the randomizer were checked and found to meet rigorous statistical criteria for randomness.

Each subject had been given an indirect probing interview which classified him as a sheep or a goat. The 37 subjects each then completed 5 runs of 100 trials for each of 3 types of experiment:

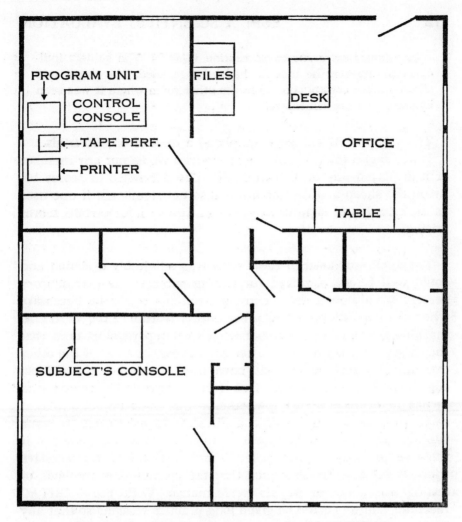

FIGURE 8. *Layout of rooms used with VERITAC*

1. *Clairvoyance.* At each trial the subject depressed the button representing the digit he thought had been selected and that was indicated but not seen by anyone on the control console in the other room.

2. *Precognition.* Here, the subject had to select the number he thought would be generated on the next trial. He started and stopped the random-number generator, and the numbers so generated were presented on the control console, but were not shown to the subject or to anyone else.

3. *General extrasensory perception* (*GESP*). The subject indicated the number he thought had been selected. The target was shown on the control console in the other room where it was seen by one of the experimenters.

The group of 37 subjects completed a total of 55,500 trials.

It was found that neither the group as a whole nor any member of it displayed any evidence of ESP. The difference in scores between the sheep and the goats was also not significant if one uses as the criterion of significance odds of 100 to 1 for certain scores arising.

The apparatus used in these tests was admirably designed and could well be standardized for testing subjects for extrasensory perception, although some extra precautions might be necessary when using it with the GESP procedure. A feature of the VERITAC machine that should commend itself to parapsychologists is that the subject learns the result after each guess. In most of the other experimental techniques that have been employed, the subject completes at least 25 trials before learning how he has scored, and he has no means of knowing whether he has made a hit or a miss at each trial. If ESP is possible and exists to an extent in some subjects, we should only expect them to improve with practice if they are given the chance to learn from the results in successive trials. It might even be argued that the conventional methods of testing are likely to impair performance. With the VERITAC machine, subjects could be given long practice sessions so that any ESP ability that might be present could be strengthened. Thus, parapsychologists would have both a testing and a training machine. It could also be modified to provide a reward after each hit and punishment, such as a mild electric shock, after each miss. It would then constitute a conditioning machine in which the subjects would try to avoid punishment and to secure rewards by making right guesses.

RESEARCH BEHIND THE IRON CURTAIN

In recent years, parapsychologists have discovered that ESP research is in progress behind the Iron Curtain. In Prague, Milan

Ryzl, a biochemist at the Institute of Biology of the Czechoslovak Academy of Science, has claimed extraordinary clairvoyant powers for his subject, Pavel Stepanek. Stepanek's act, for it can hardly be called more than that, is as follows:

An observer is given a pile of envelopes and cards. One side of each card is black, the other is white. The observer places the cards in the envelopes with either the black or the white side uppermost. The pack of envelopes is then sorted by Stepanek, and he is able to distinguish envelopes in which the card has its black side uppermost from those in which the card has its white side up. The envelopes are specially made and consist of two pieces of thin cardboard stapled together. Since Stepanek handles the envelopes, it is likely that he utilizes cues due to bending or warping of the cards.

Stepanek has been tested by several independent investigators. When tested by Pratt and J. G. Blom, one of Ryzl's colleagues, he produced very impressive results, but when the experiment was conducted by a psychologist, John Beloff, of Edinburgh University, he failed to display any clairvoyant ability. Beloff had supplied his own cards which were made of plastic.

Soviet research on ESP was started in the 1920's at Leningrad University, by the physiologist V. M. Bechterev, who is noted for his pioneer work on the conditioned reflex. Early experiments in which Bechterev collaborated with an animal trainer, V. L. Dourov, to investigate the effects of mental suggestion from a distance on a group of performing dogs, were mentioned by Rhine in *Extra-Sensory Perception*.

In the 1920's, considerable publicity was given to the theories of an Italian physicist, Ferdinando Cazzamalli, that telepathic communication was dependent on a type of electromagnetic radiation, "brain waves," a centimeter in wave length. In 1932, the Institute for Brain Research at Leningrad received an assignment to start experiments with the aim of finding a physical basis for telepathy. This research was put in the hands of L. L. Vasiliev, one of Bechterev's pupils, who is today Professor of Physiology at the University of Leningrad. Between 1932 and 1938, the experiments carried out by Vasiliev included tests in which an attempt was made to influence a person by telepathy while he was screened inside a metal chamber.

After 1938 no mention was made of telepathy in the Russian press until, in 1959, Vasiliev published a popular book, *Mysterious Phenomena of the Human Psyche,* in which one chapter was devoted to the topic.

At the end of 1959, an article appeared in the French journal *Constellation,* entitled "La Transmission de pensée—arme de guerre," ("Thought Transmission—Weapon of War") describing experiments said to have taken place on the American submarine *Nautilus.* This was followed by a similar article in February 1960, in *Science et Vie (Science and Life)* entitled "Du Nautilus" ("About the Nautilus"). Copies of the articles were sent to Vasiliev, who decided that the experiments showed it was possible to communicate by telepathy through sea water and the metal side of a submarine. He concluded that his own experiments, in which the percipients had been screened inside a metal box, were confirmed by the American tests. He commented later that such stories must be treated with caution, since authoritative sources in Washington disclaimed any such experiments; at the same time, he pointed out that the Parapsychology Laboratory at Duke University had received a financial grant from the United States Office of Naval Research in 1952 for experiments on ESP.

Vasiliev seems to have taken the French reports seriously, for he later stated, "This totally unexpected confirmation of our twenty-five year old experiments compelled me to make them known to a wide circle of scientific workers." [11] A symposium was then organized at Leningrad University in 1960, after which a special laboratory was set up for the study of telepathic phenomena under Vasiliev's direction.

Vasiliev's *Experiments in Mental Suggestion* was published in 1962, and an English translation was made available in 1963.[12] In this book, Vasiliev describes the experiments he carried out in the 1930's that, in his opinion, prove conclusively that human subjects can be put into a state of hypnotic sleep and wakened by an agent situated in another room.

Vasiliev's investigations are reported in four sections with the following chapter headings: (1) "Visual Images"; (2) "Mental Suggestions of Sleeping and Awakening"; (3) "Critical Evaluation and Improved Method"; (4) "Experiments in Mental Suggestion at Long Distances."

The main experiments in the first category consist of telepathy tests in which the subject had to guess whether an agent was seeing a black or a white disk at each trial. A simple randomizer utilizing black and white disks mounted back to back on a vertical rod rotating in a socket was used to select the targets. The disks were rotated before each trial and came to rest with one of the two colors facing the agent; the percipient then had to guess which was being seen.

Slightly above-chance scores were obtained both when the subject was in a metal-screened chamber and when he was unscreened. Under both conditions the over-all scores of groups of subjects were above chance and statistically significant. The experimental conditions were unsatisfactory, however, since the targets and subject calls were recorded by the one experimenter.

Vasiliev, himself, seems to have been dissatisfied with the tests, for at the end of the chapter describing them he wrote: "In order to substantiate our preliminary conclusion we were thus forced to employ another method of mental suggestion—one which yields far more significantly positive results; this turned out to be the procedure of putting to sleep, and awakening, by means of mental suggestion." [13]

Vasiliev's second type of test was one in which an agent attempted to induce sleep or waking in a subject positioned at a distance or screened in a metal chamber. The subjects used in these tests had taken part in conventional hypnosis tests and could be put to sleep or awakened by the agent with ease when telepathy was not involved.

In most of the experiments, the subject and agent were situated in different rooms. In some tests the subject was placed in a *Faraday Cage,* a metal-screened box that excludes electromagnetic radiation. In other tests, the agent was placed inside a lead chamber sealed with mercury.

The subject held a small rubber bulb and was told to press it rhythmically. This bulb was connected by tubing to a pen which the rhythmic pressure moved, and a record of the oscillations was made on a drum rotating at a constant speed. When the subject went to sleep, these oscillations ceased; they resumed when he woke up and proceeded to press the bulb again.

At a time unknown to the subject, the agent would move a switch that marked a second tracing on the rotating drum, and he would then attempt to induce sleep. Sometimes after the subject had fallen asleep, the agent would move the switch again, making another mark on the second tracing, and then attempt to wake the subject. The times between suggestion and the subject's falling asleep and between suggestion and waking up could then be determined from the record.

Since, however, a control group was not employed, this data can reveal nothing about the part played by the agent. To assess this effect it would, at the least, be necessary to know the length of time elapsing between mental suggestion and the subject's going to sleep or waking up and the time taken for the subject to fall asleep or wake up in the absence of any mental suggestion.

Vasiliev seems to have been aware of these objections, since in the next group of experiments, described under the heading "Critical Evaluation and Improved Method," he employed a control series in which mental suggestion was withheld. It is the experiments in this section that provide Vasiliev's main evidence for the possibility of mental suggestion at a distance.

In the new tests the subject was left alone in a room and requested to rhythmically press a bulb. The agent went to another room where he started the rotating drum and operated the black-and-white-disk randomizing apparatus. If the black disk showed, he immediately started trying to induce sleep (experimental series) until the oscillations of the pen tracing stopped, showing that the subject was asleep. If the white disk showed, he made no effort to induce sleep (control series). The agent is also reported to have noted with a stop watch the time elapsed between the start of the experiment and the subject's falling asleep.

A total of 53 tests of this nature were carried out, using 4 different subjects. The results for each subject are not given, but the pooled results gave 27 observations in the control series (without suggestion), having a mean time of 17.7 minutes (standard error 0.54 minutes), and 26 observations in the experimental series, having a mean time of 6.8 minutes (standard error 0.54 minutes). Standard error is a measurement of dispersion and in the case of the control series above signifies that if a large number of similar experiments were made, and the mean time was calculated for each experiment, we should expect 68 per cent of the experiments to produce a mean falling between 17.7 ± .54 minutes, i.e., between 17.16 and 18.24 minutes. The difference between the two means was significant with odds greater than 10,000 to 3 against arising by chance.

It should be noted that not much reliance can be placed on this final calculation, since each of the subjects fell asleep in the control situation when the agent did not try to induce it. If there were large individual differences in the times at which the different subjects tended to fall asleep, as appears to be the case from other data, a misleading result might easily be obtained unless each subject was tested an equal number of times in each condition.

The data given by Vasiliev in Table 12 of his book are unlikely to give one much confidence in the accuracy of the time measurements. Times were recorded both on the tracings and with a stop watch, and the 53 observations in this table are, with one exception, to the nearest 5 seconds. However, among the observations, 22 of them are to a whole minute, whereas the expectation would be that only about 4 would be of this type.

Taking Vasiliev's result as it stands, however, and accepting the difference in mean time between the control and experimental series, it is still doubtful whether this experiment can provide conclusive evidence for the possibility of suggestion at a distance.

It will be noted that Vasiliev's control series was necessary, since the subjects ultimately tended to go to sleep without any suggestion being given. His method of allocating tests between the experimental and control series by means of a randomizer is excellent, provided his rotation apparatus produced a random series.

The main weakness of the experiment lies in the manner in which readings were taken. It has long been known that it is essential in ESP tests that records of targets and of subjects' calls be maintained by independent observers. Thus, when a subject is guessing cards, the real order must be recorded by an experimenter who is unaware of the subject's calls, and the subject's calls must be recorded by someone who is unaware of the targets. Counting the number of hits with cards is a relatively simple operation, however, compared to deciding the exact point in time at which a wavy line on a drum comes to rest. In certain cases, there may be no doubt, but others are likely to arise in which there will be ambiguous features in the record. The decision as to the exact time at which the subject has gone to sleep must be made by someone who is unaware of whether he is dealing with a test falling into the experimental or control series, and having made his decision he must stand by it.

In Vasiliev's test, the agent was in the room with the recording apparatus; he also used a stop watch to determine the length of time elapsing before the subject went to sleep. To provide reasonable test conditions without completely automating the recording procedure, it would be necessary for the recording apparatus to be in a separate room with an experimenter who was completely unaware of the nature of the test to record the exact time at which the subject had gone to sleep. The agent would be informed by a signal from a randomizer whether or not he was to try to induce sleep, and this information would have to be kept secret from any other person until the test was complete and the time at which the subject went to sleep had been decided. It would also be essential to predetermine the exact number of tests to be carried out so that there could be no possibility of selection of data.

Vasiliev makes little attempt to control the human factor in his experiments, but a long history of research on hypnosis, with which he was familiar, shows the errors that can arise when such control is omitted. Also, insufficient information is given in Vasiliev's book about the precise conditions under which his experiments were carried out.

It would be of interest to know, for example, the exact order in which the tests were made; what information was given to the subject after a sitting in relation to what had transpired at that sitting; and whether the tracings were inspected by assessors who were without knowledge of the nature of the test.

The Soviet research reported by Vasiliev is similar in many ways to work carried out elsewhere in the 1930's; it is on much the same level of sophistication as the early work at Duke University. The chief weakness lies in the lack of precautions against errors in recording and against the experimenter being affected by what he knows about the experiment. With modern apparatus and techniques, it would be a simple matter to repeat the experiments and to obtain more conclusive information.

CHAPTER **13**

Summary of
the Experimental Work

DURING the 85 years of experimental research on extrasensory perception, there have been marked changes in the claims made for the results, but any analysis of these changes is complicated by the fact that the British and American investigators do not agree on the nature of the phenomena they are investigating.

In the United States, clairvoyance has been as easy to produce as telepathy, and most American research has been in clairvoyance. This makes the experiments relatively simple in design, since only one subject takes part, and difficulties arising from sensory leakage are easily overcome. In England, despite several attempts, no evidence has been produced for clairvoyance. Jephson's experiments failed as soon as the experimental conditions were tightened up, and Soal has failed to find evidence in any of his attempts.

Again, in America subjects have little difficulty in displaying ESP at a distance, provided the experimental conditions are not too rigorous. In Great Britain, subjects behave in a peculiar manner. Ieuan Jones's telepathic emanations were blocked by a single door, whereas one of Mrs. Stewart's agents successfully transmitted through the suburbs of outer London and Brussels.

In the United States, ESP has become more scarce and less pronounced in its effects during the past 35 years. High-scoring subjects who were easily discovered in the 1930's became impossible to find after 1939. Since then, groups of subjects scored above chance only in relation to subgroups who scored below it. In these group experiments, moreover, each successive test by the original experimenters tended to give a less impressive result, and repetitions of the tests by independent investigators have invariably failed to confirm the original result.

In England, subjects who manifested extrasensory perception in

179

the early days of the Society for Psychical Research were numerous, and then such people disappeared almost completely in the 1930's, when Soal was being most critical. They reappeared again in 1939, when Soal performed his about-face, and almost everyone tested by Soal since then has displayed remarkable telepathic abilities. Such manifestations became more and more pronounced, culminating in the remarkable scores achieved by the Jones boys.

American researchers have failed to find high-scoring subjects since 1939 because of the tightening up of experimental conditions. It is then reasonable to assume, whether ESP is possible or not, that the high scores in the early experiments were caused, not by ESP, but by factors not present in the later, better-controlled experiments. But if the early research gave fallacious results, studies such as the Pearce-Pratt and Turner-Ownbey experiments cannot be supposed to provide conclusive evidence for ESP. If the scores obtained were not due to extrasensory perception, something else must have been responsible for them.

English experimental work has always resembled, to some extent, the type of investigation made in the early days of the Society for Psychical Research. This situation may be due to the fact that the research has been carried out mainly by lone individuals working outside the universities. Although Soal received some support from the Department of Psychology at Birkbeck and University Colleges of the University of London, his "successful" research was almost all carried out in the homes or places of work of his subjects.

The success of the percipients in the early British studies was due to their deceiving the investigators. In the 1930's, at the same time that American research became lax, Soal tightened up English research. After the Soal-Goldney experiment, Soal loosened experimental conditions until, by 1955, the investigation of the Jones boys had become similar in many ways to the first investigation of the Society for Psychical Research on the Creery sisters. For sitting after sitting, the investigators pitted themselves against their wily, adolescent subjects; numerous changes were made in the experimental conditions, often at the instigation of the subjects; extraordinary feats were performed; the genuineness of the phenomena was stressed with great vigor by the investigators and by their supporters. The experimental report was persuasive, but the investigators invariably missed obvious weaknesses in the conditions. The one piece of evidence sought for by the critic was lacking; there was no confirmation of the effects by independent investigators. In the case of both investigations, the subjects were caught indulging in trickery, and in both cases it was argued that, in spite of this, they had not been cheating all the time.

The experiments reported from both sides of the Atlantic do however, contain many points in common. These can be summarized as follows:

1. *Inadequacy of experimental design.* Little attempt has been made to devise experimental conditions acceptable to critics. Human errors in recording could be removed easily by employing automatic recording devices. Targets could be randomized and presented by means of a machine. Even those studies that aim at being conclusive show a lamentable lack of care in their design.

2. *Lack of criticism during the experiment.* If high scores begin to appear during an experiment, it is then that the possibility arises of eliminating all normal explanations. During the Pearce-Pratt experiment, for example, the various possible alternative explanations could have been eliminated successively.

In many of the experiments, a simple test at one point could have established whether a subject or experimenter was cheating. Such tests, if they were ever made, were not reported.

3. *Inadequacy of the experimental report.* The Pearce-Pratt experiment provides a case in point. After noting the numerous discrepancies in the different accounts of the experiment, the authenticity of the final report may be questioned.

Soal's reports are detailed, but owing to his habit of continually introducing changes in the experimental conditions, he produces, not one experiment containing a reasonable number of observations under precise experimental conditions, but a mass of studies made under a variety of conditions.

4. *Excessive claims made by experimenters.* Both Rhine and Soal appear to display excessive confidence in their experiments and in the results they obtain. They often make statements that are extremely naïve. For example, Rhine and Pratt have written: "Only

at such a time, however distant it may be in the future, can the standards of parapsychology be lowered to those of the other psychological sciences." [1]

Other statements, too, indicate that the investigators considerably overestimate their own experiments. In a survey carried out by Lucien Warner, an opinion analyst who was at one time a research fellow at the Parapsychology Laboratory, and published in 1952, American psychologists did not react well to the claims for ESP. Rhine and Pratt noted this in their account of the Pearce-Pratt experiment.

> If, then, as the Warner survey revealed, these results, along with all the other researches on extrasensory perception, failed to establish a convincing case for ESP for the majority of the members of the American Psychological Association responding to Warner's questionnaire, it can safely be said that the issue is not a matter of scientific evidence. The series contributed all that an experiment can do towards establishing the ESP hypothesis. The rest is a question of receptivity on the part of the professional group. [2]

No psychologist could be expected to change his views after reading about the Pearce-Pratt experiment. It should be borne in mind that a full account of the experiment had not been provided at the time of Warner's survey. There were available only a number of incomplete statements, each conflicting with the other. No one was likely to have accepted Pearce's performance on trust unless either the investigation was fully reported or the statement had come from a laboratory noted for the reliability of its reports. The Duke laboratory has never been noted for the high standard of its pronouncements, and psychologists have not easily forgotten Rhine's telepathic horse or his ESP cards that could be read from their backs.

5. *Failure to report essential features of the experimental conditions.* This is exemplified again in the Pearce-Pratt experiment. Anyone reading that report might assume that the rooms used by Pratt were suitable for such an experiment, but less fitting rooms could hardly have been chosen. In the Pratt-Woodruff experiment, the essential feature turns out to be—a posteriori—the shuffling of the key cards. If the importance of this feature was realized at the

time of the experiment, it should have been mentioned in the report.

6. *Inability to survey the evidence impartially.* Surveys of the experimental work pay little attention to investigations that have failed to provide evidence for ESP or of criticisms that have been raised.

7. *Inability to confirm a result.* Neither Rhine nor Soal has ever taken the advice of critics and handed over a high-scoring subject to an independent laboratory for confirmation of his findings. They must be well aware that this is a necessary procedure, but they have made no attempt to obtain such information. In the Pearce-Pratt experiment, the only change made in experimental procedure was the introduction of an observer (Rhine) during the last subseries. This change was made at the suggestion of McDougall; it does not appear to have occurred to the experimenters themselves. The presence of Rhine during the 2 (or 3) sittings of subseries *D* was to be an assurance that Pratt did not cheat. Surely he could have sat with Pearce for a further subseries.

8. *Inability to predict.* Inability to confirm an experimental result is one aspect of a wider problem—the inability to make any sort of prediction from the experimental findings. In science generally it is possible to predict what will happen in new experimental circumstances from what has already been established. But predictions made from the results of ESP experiments invariably fail.

The simplest case of prediction arises when an experiment is repeated. If the phenomenon is real, it is predictable that it will occur again in similar experimental circumstances. Rhine found that at least 1 in 5 of the population could display ESP. If this is a fact, an experiment could be designed in which some subjects possessing ESP would be bound to turn up, since from a sample of 100 people the odds are greater than 1 million to 1 against there not being at least 1 subject who displays ESP. But even better results should be possible, if predictions based on findings from other experiments are considered. If subjects are screened and those who disbelieve in ESP are removed, according to the sheep-goat experiments, the proportion of subjects in the sample who can display ESP should be increased, and if suitable personality tests are applied, subjects with ESP should be found even more exactly. It should be a fairly simple matter to get together, say, 100 subjects with really good ESP ability with whom it should be possible to display ESP to a skeptic without relying on any statistical measures.

The skeptic would think of a Zener card and each of the 100 subjects would be provided with 5 pushbuttons, one for each symbol, on which to select his guess at each trial. The outputs from these buttons would be connected so that the symbol obtaining most votes from the 100 subjects at each trial would be indicated to the skeptic on a display panel. A hundred subjects with nothing like the ability of Glyn Jones or Hubert Pearce would be able, in this manner, to convert any skeptic on the spot, since on a high proportion of trials they would indicate to him the symbol of which he was thinking. Again, using a similar technique, given a set of 25 cards in a sealed envelope, it should be possible with sufficient subjects, all believers in ESP, making guesses as to the order of the cards in the pack, for some to make an accurate prediction of the order. The inability to make predictions is most evident with psychokinesis. Here, tests that could detect forces far more minute than those required to move dice fail to provide evidence supporting psychokinesis.

SPONTANEOUS DATA

While all the years of research into ESP have failed to provide a clear demonstration for its existence, this does not necessarily imply that it does not exist. It could be argued that the techniques used in the experiments are completely on the wrong track and that ESP would not be evident in them even if it did exist. Some parapsychologists argue that the weight of evidence from spontaneous cases is sufficient in itself to establish the case for extrasensory perception. This evidence is primarily of 2 types: first, reports of strange experiences from everyday life; and second, investigations of people having special powers, such as mediums and clairvoyants. Such evidence will be discussed in the following 3 chapters.

CHAPTER 14

Accounts of
Strange Experiences

ACCOUNTS of unusual experiences that appear to contradict accepted ideas of what human beings can and cannot do are continually being reported in the popular press. It is frequently claimed that these accounts provide proof of telepathy, clairvoyance, precognition, and other processes. Any such story may be examined to decide how closely it checks with what is known to have actually happened and how far it has been elaborated or distorted. If it is decided that the event did take place, it is then necessary to decide how likely or unlikely its occurrence would be in the ordinary run of events. If the happening still appears unusual after such an examination, an explanation may then be sought to account for it.

Anecdotal data tend to be unreliable, since what is reported is dependent on a person's memory and on the observer's interpretation. It is known that various observers may give quite different accounts of what they have seen or heard in the same situation, even when they make their reports at the time of the experience. Also, with the passage of time, accounts may show progressive changes and become increasingly less accurate when checked against the original events.

When the account is that of a single person, it is often impossible to know whether his report relates to an external event or whether he is reporting experiences that had no outside physical cause. Thus, if a man says he saw a pink elephant, it cannot be assumed that a pink elephant actually existed that other observers would have seen and that could have been photographed.

THE APPARITION SEEN BY SIR EDMUND HORNBY

An early case reported by Gurney and Myers was thought at the time to provide irrefutable evidence for the appearance of an apparition. It concerned Sir Edmund Hornby, formerly Chief Judge of the Supreme Consular Court of China and Japan at Shanghai. He had been in the habit of allowing reporters to come to his house in the evening to get his written judgments for the next day's papers. On January 19, 1875, he wrote out these judgments in his study an hour or two after dinner. His report concerning subsequent events, as taken down by Gurney and Myers, was as follows:

I rang for the butler, gave him the envelope, and told him to give it to the reporter who should call for it. I was in bed before twelve. . . . I had gone to sleep, when I was awakened by hearing a tap on the study door, but thinking it might be the butler—looking to see if the fires were safe and the gas turned off—I turned over . . . to sleep again. Before I did so, I heard a tap at my bedroom door. Still thinking it the butler . . . I said "Come in." The door opened, and, to my surprise, in walked Mr. ————. I sat up and said, "You have mistaken the door; but the butler has the judgment, so go and get it." Instead of leaving the room he came to the foot of the bed. I said, "Mr. ————, you forget yourself! Have the goodness to walk out directly. This is rather an abuse of my favor." He looked deadly pale, but was dressed as usual, and sober, and said, "I know I am guilty of an unwarrantable intrusion, but finding that you were not in your study, I have ventured to come here."

I was losing my temper, but something in the man's manner disinclined me to jump out of bed to eject him by force. So I said, simply, "This is too bad, really; pray leave the room at once." Instead of doing so he put his hand on the foot-rail and gently, and as if in pain, sat down on the foot of the bed. I glanced at the clock and saw that it was about twenty minutes past one. I said, "The butler has had the judgment since half-past eleven; go and get it!" He said, "Pray forgive me; if you knew all the circumstances you would. Time presses. Pray give me a précis of your judgment, and I will take a note in my book of it," drawing his reporter's book out of his breast pocket. I said, "I will do nothing of the kind. Go downstairs, find the butler, and don't disturb me—you will wake my wife; otherwise I shall have to put you out." He slightly moved his hand, I said, "Who let you in?" He answered,

"No one." "Confound it," I said, "What the devil do you mean? Are
you drunk?" He replied quickly, "No, and never shall be again; but
I pray your lordship give me your decision, for my time is short." I
said, "You don't seem to care about my time, and this is the last
time I will ever allow a reporter in my house." He stopped me short,
saying, "This is the last time I shall ever see you anywhere."

Well, fearful that this commotion might arouse and frighten my
wife, I shortly gave him the gist of my judgment. . . . He seemed
to be taking it down in shorthand; it might have taken two or three
minutes. When I finished, he rose, thanked me for excusing his
intrusion and for the consideration I had always shown him and
his colleagues, opened the door, and went away. I looked at the
clock; it was on the stroke of half-past one.

[Lady Hornby awoke, thinking she had heard talking; and her
husband told her what had happened, and repeated the account
when dressing the next morning.]

I went to court a little before ten. The usher came into my room
to robe me, when he said, "A sad thing happened last night, sir.
Poor ———— was found dead in his room." I said "Bless my soul!
Dear me! What did he die of, and when?" "Well, sir, it appeared he
went up to his room as usual at ten to work at his papers. His
wife went up about twelve to ask him when he would be ready for
bed. He said, 'I have only the Judge's judgment to get ready, and
then I have finished.' As he did not come, she went up again, about
a quarter to one, to his room and peeped in, and thought she saw
him writing, but she did not disturb him. At half-past one she
again went to him and spoke to him at the door. As he didn't
answer she thought he had fallen asleep so she went up to rouse
him. To her horror he was dead. On the floor was his notebook,
which I have brought away. She sent for the doctor who arrived a
little after two, and said he had been dead, he concluded, about an
hour. I looked at the note-book. There was the usual heading: "In
the Supreme Court, before the Chief Judge: The Chief Judge gave
judgment this morning in the case to the following effect'—and
then followed a few lines of indecipherable shorthand."

I sent for the magistrate who would act as coroner, and desired
him to examine Mr. ————'s wife and servants as to whether
Mr. ———— had left his home or could possibly have left it without their knowledge, between eleven and one on the previous
night. The result of the inquest showed he died of some form of
heart disease, and had not and could not have left the house without the knowledge of at least his wife, if not of the servants. Not

wishing to air my "spiritual experience" for the benefit of the press
or the public, I kept the matter at the time to myself, only mentioning it to my Puisne Judge and to one or two friends; but when
I got home to tiffin I asked my wife to tell me as nearly as she
could remember what I had said to her during the night, and I
made a brief note of her replies and of the facts.

[Lady Hornby has kindly confirmed the above facts to us, as
far as she was cognizant of them.]

As I said then, so I say now—I was not asleep, but wide awake.
After a lapse of nine years my memory is quite clear on the subject. I have not the least doubt I saw the man—have not the
least doubt that the conversation took place between us.

I may add that I had examined the butler in the morning—
who had given me back the MS. in the envelope when I went to the
court after breakfast—as to whether he had locked the door as
usual, and if anyone could have got in. He said that he had done
everything as usual, adding that no one could have got in even if
he had not locked the door, as there was no handle outside—which
there was not. . . . The coolies said they opened the door as usual
that morning—turned the key and undid the chains.[1]

The following November, the *Nineteenth Century* contained a
letter from a Mr. Frederick H. Balfour pointing out certain discrepancies between the account and the facts:

1. Mr. ————— was the Rev. Hugh Lang Nivens, editor of the
Shanghai Courier. He died not at *one* in the morning but between
eight or nine A.M. after a good night's rest.

2. There was no Lady Hornby at that time. Sir Edmund's second
wife had died two years previously, and he did not marry again till
three months *after* the event.

3. No inquest was ever held.

4. The story turns upon the judgment of a certain case to be
delivered the next day, January 20, 1875. There is no record of any
such judgment.

Before publishing Balfour's letter, the editors of the *Nineteenth
Century* had sent it to Judge Hornby, who commented:

My vision must have followed the death (some three months)
instead of synchronizing with it. At the same time this hypothesis
is quite contrary to the recollection of the facts both in my own

mind and in Lady Hornby's mind. . . . If I had not believed, as I still believe, that every word of it [the story] was accurate, and that my memory was to be relied on, I should not have ever told it as a personal experience.[2]

The late John E. Coover, one of the greatest critics of psychical research, in discussing this case wrote:

All these discrepancies are concordant with the results of psychological research on testimony, and are to be attributed to psychological law rather than to either dishonesty or culpable carelessness.

The readiness of metaphysics to rely upon observations of séance phenomena, their insistence that illusion can be avoided, and their quick condemnation of the competence of an observer who is tricked, clearly indicate that they do not understand that error is inevitable. Consequently the psychologist remains incredulous in the face of all the accumulating "evidence." [3]

Gurney and Myers stated when introducing their report that its evidential value depended on the high authority on which it came. But the story illustrates that an eminent judge is no less liable to errors of memory and recall than anyone else.

SOME OTHER STRANGE HAPPENINGS

In 1886, Gurney, Myers, and Podmore published *Phantasms of the Living*. Its 2 large volumes contained accounts of more than 700 unusual happenings, many of a type to make the flesh creep. The accounts were based on reports received from members of the public about their own unusual experiences. Since that time, thousands more such cases have been collected together by various societies and groups interested in psychical research in the effort to provide conclusive proof of ghosts, apparitions, telepathy, clairvoyance, and precognition. None of the stories investigated has withstood critical examination.

The journals and files of the Society for Psychical Research must contain thousands of these accounts of spontaneous occurrences. In his *The Personality of Man*, written in 1947, G. N. M. Tyrrell gave a few examples drawn from those investigations. He was a firm believer in the supernatural, and it is reasonable to assume that the cases he reports are the best ones he could collect to demonstrate the reality of extrasensory phenomena. But it is necessary only to read them to see how trivial and unsatisfactory they are. Anyone who says, "That may be so but I know of a case far more difficult to explain," should remember that Tyrrell had at his fingertips all the data that could survive any sort of investigation. He reported the first case as

A certain Canon Bourne and his two daughters were out hunting, and the daughters decided to return home with the coachman while their father went on. "As we were turning to go home," say the two Misses Bourne in a joint account, "we distinctly saw my father waving his hat to us and signing us to follow him. He was on the side of a small hill, and there was a dip between him and us. My sister, the coachman and myself all recognised my father and also the horse. The horse looked so dirty and shaken that the coachman remarked he thought there had been a nasty accident. As my father waved his hat I clearly saw the Lincoln and Bennett mark inside, though from the distance we were apart it ought to have been utterly impossible for me to have seen it. . . . Fearing an accident, we hurried down the hill. From the nature of the ground we had to lose sight of my father, but it took us very few seconds to reach the place where we had seen him. When we got there, there was no sign of him anywhere, nor could we see anyone in sight at all. We rode about for some time looking for him but could not see or hear anything of him. We all reached home within a quarter of an hour of each other. My father then told us he had never been in the field, nor near the field in which we thought we saw him, the whole of that day. He had never waved to us and had met with no accident. My father was riding the only white horse that was out that day.[4]

Tyrrell comments on this story:

The cause which set the telepathic machinery in motion in this case is obscure. No accident had happened to Canon Bourne. It more often happens that the vision coincides with some accident or peculiar event happening to the agent. . . . Canon Bourne unconsciously imposed the pattern or theme of his presence in that

particular field, with details of horse, etc., on the minds of his
two daughters and the coachman.[5]

If the definition of telepathy is to be extended so that it includes
cases where the percipient has information that does not accord
with any actual happening, it would appear that normal means of
verification do not apply. In this case, certain people thought they
had had a telepathic communication but on checking found that in
fact they had not had one. If, on the other hand, an accident had
occurred it would no longer have been a case of telepathy but of
normal observation. The feature of the story that appears to require
an explanation is why three people simultaneously saw—or
thought they saw—a figure on a horse in a distant field. Thus, the
explanation is likely to be psychological rather than parapsychological.

To investigate the story fully, it would have been necessary to
question the three witnesses independently, but as they had had the
opportunity of discussing the matter among themselves, their
statements could not be independent. It would appear likely that
the witnesses saw something they thought was Canon Bourne
although, in fact, it was not Canon Bourne—that is, if his
statements about where he had been that day were truthful or if he
had had no lapse of memory. They reported that the horse looked
dirty, but at a distance they would not recognize dirt as such; they
would only infer its presence from the appearance of the horse.
They apparently saw a horse that was similar, but not identical, in
appearance to Canon Bourne's; they assumed it to be the Canon's
and that its changed appearance was due to dirt.

That one of them should see the Lincoln and Bennett mark
inside the hat is not unusual. Any psychology student who has
worked with a *tachistoscope* encounters many instances of this sort
of thing. In the tachistoscope, a drawing is exposed very briefly to a
subject so that he sees it for, say, $\frac{1}{50}$ of a second. He is then asked
to draw exactly what he has viewed. Under these conditions, most
subjects tend to introduce changes and add details in their repro-
ductions that were lacking in the original. They draw what they
think they should have seen based on their identification of the
drawing with some known object. In a real life situation, much

more striking effects of this nature would appear than in the laboratory.

If the statements of the witnesses and of Canon Bourne are reliable, it would appear possible that some other person was present in the field that day whom the sisters mistook for their father. Identification of the father is supported only by the mark inside the hat, which the witness states was too far away for such recognition.

If these people made a false recognition of this nature, particularly if they were emotionally disturbed—as they could have been in this case because of the coachman's remark about an accident—and if they were able to converse together so that each could influence the others by suggestion, it is quite possible that they would feel convinced they had seen Canon Bourne, regardless of the fact that he later told them he was not in the field that day. There is no reason why the witnesses should have been greatly affected by the incident, but no one else in reading about it should suffer any perplexity.

An announcement by the Society for Psychical Research discussed *Phantasms of the Living* in these words: "The conclusion drawn is that the coincidences of the type in question are far too numerous to be accounted for as accidents; and the establishment of some cause for them, beyond chance, is the proof of Telepathy." [6] However, stories of this nature, however numerous, cannot provide evidence for ghosts or extrasensory perception unless they are backed by corroborating evidence. Without such evidence, they merely indicate the generality of well-known psychological phenomena. The more of them that are gathered together, the better the chance of finding a really extraordinary coincidence.

The accounts constitute a selected sample from millions of experiences that have arisen in the countries concerned; they are selected because they are unusual and, therefore, one would think, experiences that people would write or talk about. Members of the various societies who have reported these experiences in journals must be aware of the importance of supplying supporting evidence, but so far, these surveys have failed to provide a single story that is conclusively supported by ample confirmatory data.

Stories purporting to demonstrate supernatural processes are liable to be distorted by the personal characteristics of the witnesses. The following extract from the 1911 confession by Douglas Blackburn, which was discussed earlier, summarizes his impressions after acting as an investigator.

> I am convinced that this propensity to deceive is more general among "persons of character" than is supposed. I have known the wife of a bishop, when faced with a discrepancy in time in a story of death in India and the appearance of the wraith in England, to deliberately amend her circumstantial story by many hours to fit the altered circumstances. This touching-up process in the telepathic stories I have met again and again, and I say, with full regard to the weight of words, that among the hundreds of stories I have investigated I have not met one that had not a weak link which should prevent its being accepted as scientifically established. Coincidences that at first sight appear good cases of telepathic rapport occur to many of us. I have experienced several, but I should hesitate to present them as perfect evidence.
>
> At the risk of giving offence to some, I feel bound to say that in the vast majority of cases that I have investigated the principals are either biased in favour of belief in the supernatural or not persons whom I should regard as accurate observers and capable of estimating the rigid mathematical form of evidence. What one desires to believe requires little corroboration. I shall doubtless raise a storm of protest when I assert that the principal cause of belief in psychical phenomena is the inability of the average man to observe accurately and estimate the value of evidence, plus a bias in favour of the phenomena being real. It is an amazing fact that I have never yet, after hundreds of tests, found a man who could accurately describe ten minutes afterwards a series of simple acts which I performed in his presence. The reports of those trained and conscientious observers, Messrs. Myers and Gurney, contain many absolute inaccuracies. For example, in describing one of my "experiments," they say emphatically, "In no case did B. touch S., even in the slightest manner." I touched him eight times, that being the only way in which our code was then worked.[7]

CAUSES OF "INEXPLICABLE HAPPENINGS"

It is likely that many people have personal experiences that puzzle them and appear inexplicable. In daily life certain types of events may appear strange if a cause cannot be ascribed to them.

This inability may arise in a number of ways, some of which are described below.

A common link in two casual sequences. I once was walking along a country road and a tune was running through my head, but I was not whistling or humming it. A boy approached on a bicycle, and as he passed, I heard that he was whistling the tune precisely in time with me. As I walked on puzzling over this occurrence, I passed a house and through the open window heard the radio playing the same tune. I therefore assumed that the boy and I had both started thinking of the tune through having heard it on different radios in houses we had passed. If I had not reached another house after passing the boy, I might have been very puzzled and, if there had been a series of similar experiences, might have started believing in ESP.

Seeming coincidences may often arise in this manner. A common stimulus in the pasts of two persons may set similar trains of thought going. The cause is no longer apparent when, some time later, one of the persons concerned says something about which the other is thinking.

Another experience of mine may make this clearer. After returning to England from the Duke Parapsychology Laboratory in 1960, I was driving through Manchester with my wife. While in the car, I recalled how I had expected to find laboratories with white-coated researchers turning over packs of Zener cards but had seen little activity of this sort. I also recalled the regular morning meetings at which there was considerable discussion over coffee. I then thought that it would be of interest to know whether more cups of coffee were drunk than runs made with Zener cards. At this point my wife spoke, saying how much she would like some coffee.

In this case, as far as I could see, there was no common stimulus to make my wife and me both start thinking of coffee. However, unless the incident was pure coincidence, it is possible that such a stimulus had been present a few minutes earlier, although no longer apparent at the time. We might have passed a billboard with an advertisement for coffee, or a café, or the aroma of coffee may have been in the air, or a word sounding like coffee might have set going a string of common associations for both of us. It is in fact possible that we had been talking about coffee some time earlier and that I had forgotten about it.

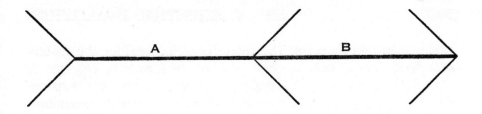

FIGURE 9. *Which of the two lines* A *and* B *appears to be longer? After deciding, place the edge of a piece of paper against that line and mark off its length. Then compare the length marked off with the length of the line that was judged to be the shorter.*

Even if only pure coincidence could be involved, its possibility should not be dismissed. In a world of more than 3 billion people, each person having hundreds of experiences each day, there must, every day, arise numerous coincidences having odds of the order of 1 million to 1 against chance expectation.

The elusiveness of memory. Most people are aware of visual illusions. When looking at the figure, most people will say that line *a* looks longer than line *b*. If the lines are measured it will be found that, in fact, *b* is longer than line *a*.

A visual illusion of this nature is puzzling, but its existence cannot be denied, since lines can be measured with a ruler. Illusions of memory are, however, much more intangible, since there is seldom an opportunity to compare our memory of events with what actually happened. When events from the past are recalled, a single fleeting incident that occurred once and was gone is all that can be relied on. In addition, when something happens in everyday life, one is not usually expecting it to happen. It may be necessary to remember something that was quickly over, which at the time no effort was made to remember. The memory of an incident may be vague or startlingly clear, but in both cases there usually is no way of checking its accuracy.

The elusiveness of dreams. Remembering some event from one's waking life of a few years back is a relatively clear-cut process compared with recalling a dream of last night. Many people recount dreams with the greatest of confidence, but since a dream is a private experience there is no way of checking its factual content. It is not surprising that a large number of so-called psychic experiences involve them. The great danger in recalling the content of a dream is not only the ease with which it may be changed or embellished, but that the dating of a dream presents extreme difficulty. If a person after hearing about some event, remembers having dreamed some days before that it would happen, no one can check this fact. He may be remembering something that really happened, or the dream may have been produced and placed at a suitable position in his past at the time he hears the story.

Most memories of past events can be located at some point in time by virtue of the fact that they arise in a context; there are events before and after them. If this context is lacking, it will be difficult to place the memory in time, and it will lack reality. A dream largely lacks this context, and when it is recalled, there is little to guarantee that it happened last night, some other night, or that it was not primarily generated at the time of recall. Just as perception is affected by memory, recall is affected by contemporary conditions, and when the memory is vague, as when a dream is recalled, the amount of material added to it may be large.

The effects of past experiences. Reactions to a situation are influenced by expectations. If a superstitious man is roaming around a house he believes haunted, he is likely to encounter a ghost at the slightest opportunity. A man who does not believe in ghosts, but who has been told that the house is infested with rats, is more likely to see rats. A relevant past experience can be recent, or it can be in the remote past of a person. Early events of childhood are particularly likely to affect a person's response in a "psychic" situation. Most children encounter fairy stories, ghost stories, superstitious beliefs, and religious ideas that are more compatible with the world as seen by parapsychology than by science. These ideas all embody principles that form the content of psychic belief.

The adult may have discarded them and no longer believe in ghosts, but the fact that he once believed in them is likely to affect him. He may still get a chill down the spine when reading a good ghost story. Early beliefs would be expected to manifest themselves at times of emotional arousal, stress, fatigue, sickness, and old age. Even the most hide-bound skeptic of the paranormal is likely to find himself having what appears to him irrational thoughts at times.

But most people are not skeptics. They are only too eager to believe anything that will take them further from the harsh world of reality toward the world of superstition. It is not surprising that so many extraordinary experiences are reported, or that they bear little critical examination.

The above discussion has considered events in the lives of normal human beings. When allowance is made for abnormal conditions as, for example, those elaborated by D. H. Rawcliffe in his *Psychology of the Occult,* it is even more to be expected that remarkable things should sometimes be reported as having happened. Another explanation for the wide currency of stories of psychic phenomena lies in the fact that newspapers have to attract readers in order to maintain sales. For that reason, their accounts tend to be sensational, and a simple account be embroidered by both reporters and editors in order to liven it up. Such stories are often presented in a manner calculated to make the reader feel convinced of their authenticity. The distortions may not be intentional on the part of the reporter. He is looking for news and will notice anything of value. He usually has little time to make a thorough investigation and has to rely on what he is told. Those he interviews will be no less eager to impress him than he is eager to impress his readers.

An article, "Crime Busting with ESP," by Jack Harrison Pollack appeared in *This Week* magazine on February 26, 1961. It described the work of W. H. C. Tenhaeff, Director of the Parapsychology Institute of the University of Utrecht, Holland, who claims to assist the police in solving crimes. He has assembled a group of people, whom he calls *paragnosts*, alleged to have clairvoyant powers. Pollack's report read, in part:

An early success in this case I checked in the Parapsychology Institute and Dutch police files. On December 5, 1946, a pretty, blond 21-year-old girl was returning home at 5.45 P.M. along a quiet country road near Wierden, Holland. Suddenly, a man *leaped out from behind a stone storehouse,* and assaulted her, hitting her on the *neck and arms* with a hammer. Before he disappeared into the dark, she was able to wrench the hammer away from him.

Police contacted Dr. Tenhaeff, who came to the station, bringing Gerard Croiset, one of his team of paragnosts. Because the *girl was in the hospital,* Croiset didn't see her. Instead he picked up the

hammer, his large hand squeezing the handle as *police* watched
sceptically. Croiset concentrated.

"He is tall and dark, about 30 years old, and has a somewhat deformed left ear," said the paragnost. "But this hammer doesn't
belong to him. Its owner was a man of about 55 whom the criminal
visits often at a small white cottage . . . near here. It is one of a
group of three cottages, all the same."

The deformed left ear was a key clue. Several months later the
police picked up a tall, dark 29-year-old man on another morals
charge. *His badly scarred and swollen left ear* led to questioning
about the first attack. Finally, he admitted assaulting the girl with
the hammer. He said he had *borrowed it from a friend, who, the
police discovered, lived in a white cottage on the edge of town, with
two others just like it on either side.*

Dr. Tenhaeff's files bulge with such cases. Each is documented
with a recording or stenographic transcript of the prediction, and
with statements confirming its accuracy from witnesses and
police.[8] [Italics added by C. E. M. H.]

I sent this account to the police at Wierden asking whether they
could verify that the account agreed with data in their files. I
received in reply the following letter from the burgomaster, E. D.
Maaldrink.

Wierden, March 22, 1961.

Dear Sir,

With a great interest and even still greater astonishment, I
read your letter of March 9th. How is it possible that a simple
story can be mutilated in such a way! Maybe the answer is simple:
when someone desires to see something special, after a certain
time he will see it, even if it is not there.

Your letter was directed to me, as in Holland the burgomaster
is normally also head of the local police, and so I'll try to answer
it. My English grammar being rather poor, I do beg you to take the
freedom of interrogating me about questions which are not described clear enough.

When the story began on December 5th, 1946, I was already
burgomaster of the town of Wierden, Overijessel, Holland.

The whole community at whose head I have the honour and
the pleasure to stand, has about 15,000 inhabitants, and contains
two villages: Wierden with 6000 inhabitants, and Enter with

4000, the rest of the people living as farmers round about in the country.

So the young girl, indeed good-looking, lived with her family in a farm, about three kilometers from the village of Wierden.

In the evening of the fifth of December she returned home on her bicycle by a sand-road, with a big box of cardboard held in one hand, with a sugar-cake, as it was the evening of the national homely feast of Santa-Claus.

Being about 700 meters from her house she was indeed assaulted by a man. He did *not* leap from behind a stone storehouse. In the neighbourhood there is not any building to be found.

The man hit her twice with a hammer on the head, *not* on the neck and arms.

Then he saw the light of another bicycle, which was nearing and fled away on his own cycle, leaving the wounded young girl and his hammer.

The girl was transported to her home and it was *not* necessary to bring her to an hospital.

The policemen of course did all their best to find the man, but without any result in the beginning.

After a few days there circulated the name of a certain young man, called K. Who called the name first, is not clear.

He was married since a year and a few months and his wife had a first baby.

It seems the name was mentioned because some people had noticed that he had committed or tried to commit exhibitional acts.

The truth hereabout we could not find out. As you know most people don't like to talk about such facts.

The only spur was the hammer. To find the owner it was showed behind the window of a grocer's shop in the midst of Wierden, but nobody seemed to recognise it.

Then after several weeks, perhaps even six, I received the visit of an elderly sort of landlord, who lives at a country place, not far from the spot where the assault was committed.

The family had as a girl-servant the sister of the attacked young girl and this girl did not dare to turn home when she was not guided by the landlord.

The last was of course rather annoyed about these trips every evening and asked me if I would allow him to take the hammer to Mr. Croiset and ask him information.

So happened. I don't know yet exactly who belonged to the party which visited Mr. Croiset, then living at Enschede.

And unhappily I don't neither know if the visit was beforehand announced to him. The last thing is in this kind of matter very important as later turned out.

About the hammer Croiset told that it had been behind a big window. In fact it had been behind the window of the grocer.

Further that the owner of the hammer or the owner of the window had a disease of the aerial ways. Indeed the grocer has bronchitis.

About the performer of the assault he told that he lived in a small house, rather similar to the houses of the two neighbours, with a stone well behind it.

When you believe in Telepathy, you can imagine that the policeman, who was present, thought at that moment about the rather likely house of Mr. K. and that Mr. Croiset felt this!

Further he told that it was a young person, but anybody will give young men greater chance to do such silly things than elder men. Mr. K. was born December 16th 1919.

And the man would have a deformed ear and a ring with a blue stone in it.

The police could do nothing with these communications. Mr. K. had two normal ears and when he might possess a ring with a blue stone, he seemed never to wear it.

So one month after another passed on without any result for the Wierden police.

Then in the early springtime 1947 Mr. K. was arrested near the town of Almelo (which lies only 5 Kilometers from Wierden) while committing the act of exhibitionism.

He was tried for several hours by our police and at the end he confessed.

We even yet don't know who was the owner of the hammer. This morning one of my policemen asked him, but Mr. K. refuses to tell us, so we suppose he has stolen it.[9]

Pollack said that he had checked the case in the Dutch police files. I wrote to *This Week* pointing out discrepancies in the account and asking that details of the police files consulted should be stated. My letter was not published, but from the reply received from Pollack, it would appear that the nearest he got to a police file was to see the burgomaster's original letter to Tenhaeff in the files at the Parapsychology Institute. Unless he read Dutch that would have meant little to him.

I received two further communications about this story, the first from a Dutch parapsychologist, P. B. Otterwanger, who for years has cast a critical eye on the activities of parapsychologists in Holland. He confirmed what the burgomaster had told me and stated that other cases reported by Pollack in his article were equally misleading.

Croiset lived at Enschede, less than 17 miles from Wierden and at one time worked as delivery boy for a grocer there. It is possible, therefore, that he knew of the grocer in whose window the hammer had been displayed and that he had heard about the crime. Thus, if all the information he gave had turned out to be true, it need have surprised no one.

It is of interest that the newspaper account introduced details that were lacking in Tenhaeff's account. Tenhaeff's report was accurate, but he did not mention that Mr. K. was suspected from the start by the police or that some of Croiset's remarks turned out to be wrong. He reported that the girl was hit on the head. He did not note the stone storehouse. He made no mention of the girl being in the hospital. And did not mention that Croiset could say nothing of value until after he had been told that the hammer had been used in a case of attempted murder.

The Wierden story appeared again in a 1961 article in *Maclean's* magazine, "First Report on Extra-Sensory Powers among Canadians," by Sidney Katz. It had by then undergone further changes.

> One of Dr. Tenhaeff's most gifted psychics, it is said, described the unknown assailant of a pretty blonde as a tall, dark man of thirty with a deformed left ear. He went on to state that the weapon used was a hammer borrowed from a friend who lived in a small white cottage, which is one of a group of three white cottages. This information, according to one report, was enough for the police to make an arrest.[10]

Katz's account is typical of the type of story that emerges after a series of repetitions. At the present time, mediums or clairvoyants claim to assist the police in the detection of criminals, and in some countries the police have utilized their services and made decisions as a result of their advice.

Dr. F. Brink, who, as a Dutch Police Inspector, investigated the activities of parapsychologists in their attempts to assist the Dutch police in solving crimes, has sent me an article he published in the *International Criminal Police Review*. It is of great interest to see how a trained investigator reacted to the artfulness of the mediums and the tests he applied to test their claims. His conclusion was that while such persons were sporadically consulted, the police had, to his knowledge, never derived any help from their supposed powers of clairvoyance.

Brink described investigations he made of 4 clairvoyants, one of whom was very well known. These tests involved handing photographs to them of objects or people. Some were from police files and others were of persons or things with no connection with the police. Letters of an abusive nature, anonymous letters, and such things as weapons, knives, and keys were also handed to the clairvoyants. Such objects are referred to as "inductive material." Of them, Brink said:

> The several tests were marked by a diversity of procedure and circumstances. Those made during a period of over one year have not evinced anything that might be regarded as being of actual use to police investigation. Whether the relevations made by the clairvoyants had been inspired by any of the things, transmitted by way of inductive material, or by photos, of which as many as twenty-four had been occasionally given to them for the same purpose, the results invariably proved to be nil. . . .
>
> Another remarkable feature of the clairvoyant's manner of performance—which is bound to strike anyone who is listening in to the reproduction of their revelations, registered by a tape recorder—is that clairvoyants appear to favour the habit of expressing the greater majority of their remarks, communications and conclusions in the interrogative form. Even though they should know, or at least presume, that they cannot expect a direct answer from the experimenter addressed in that manner, they persistently indulge in this habit.
>
> In this connection it is worth noting that in the event of any of their feelers, in the form of tentative questions, such as, "May it be possible that ————" being answered in the affirmative, they will instantly make the experimenter feel that they have scored a hit, by saying "I told you so, didn't I?" thus creating the impression that their particular mode of speech should be regarded as an instance of knowing, really, and not of probing.
>
> In those cases where the experimenter is not responsive to this

form of enticement, it will nevertheless be hard to control involuntary reactions produced by the sensorimotor process, and showing emotional effects, such as mimic gestures, muscular contradiction, etc. It is practically impossible to restrain these unconscious reactions, especially in the case of a person who is confronted with a continuous flow of questions.[11]

Recently, a case was reported in the fortieth *Annual Report* of the American Civil Liberties Union (ACLU), in which a medium in the United States was responsible for the wrongful arrest of a man. This extract is taken from an article about the case by a psychiatrist, S. H. Posinsky:

> The bizarre chain of events began when a local government hospital psychiatrist offered police the services of a . . . [European] telepathist to help clear up the unsolved murders of Mr. and Mrs. Carroll V. Jackson and their two young daughters early in 1959. Accompanied by state troopers, the savant went to the Virginia grave where the bodies had been found and advised police to search for a man whose business was "either junk or garbage." Police then arrested a trash collector John Tarmon, and interrogated him extensively. Unable to obtain any evidence linking him with the crime, they induced his wife to sign a commitment petition, resulting in a hurried lunacy hearing being conducted at 3 A.M. with the psychiatrist sitting as one of the three members of the lunacy commission. As a result, Tarmon was found insane and whisked two hundred miles away to a mental institution for the criminally insane. He was released after a lawyer provided by the ACLU filed a habeas corpus petition which prompted the hospital to concede that he was not insane.
>
> Later it appears another man was arrested by the F.B.I. for the crime after more conventional police work.

Posinsky concluded:

> In a tragicomic time when superstition and psychiatry alike pass as science, while science itself is invoked like a primitive deity, the case of John Tarmon requires the satirical genius of a Jonathan Swift.[12]

CHAPTER 15

Spiritualism

THE FOX SISTERS

SPIRITUALISM in its modern form apparently originated in 1847 because of the pranks of two girls, Margaret, aged 8, and Kate, aged 6, the daughters of John D. Fox, who lived with his wife in an isolated farmhouse in Hydesville, near Rochester, New York. For night after night, when the girls had been put to bed and were assumed to be fast asleep, raps were heard coming from the wall of their bedroom.

At this time, Mrs. Leah Fish, an elder sister of the girls, visited Hydesville. She promptly organized a Society of Spiritualists and encouraged people to come to the house to see the children. The affair received considerable newspaper publicity, and Mrs. Fish then took the children to Rochester and arranged meetings at which an audience paid to hear their questions answered from the "spirit world." The girls were later taken to New York and then toured many cities in the United States.

The remainder of their story is best told as it appeared 40 years later in a statement by Margaret Fox in the *New York World* of October 21, 1888, part of which is reproduced below.

> My sister Kate and I were very young children when this horrible deception began. I was only eight, just a year and a half older than she. We were mischievous children and sought merely to terrify our dear mother, who was a very good woman and easily frightened.
>
> When we went up to bed at night we used to tie an apple on a string and move the string up and down, causing the apple to bump on the floor, or we would drop the apple on the floor, making a strange noise every time it would rebound. Mother listened for a time to this. She could not understand it and did not suspect us as being capable of a trick because we were so young.

At last she could stand it no longer and she called the neighbours in and told them about it. It was this that set us to discover a means of making the raps more effectually. I think, when I reflect about it, that it was a most wonderful discovery, a very wonderful thing that children should make such a discovery, and all through a desire to do mischief only.

Our eldest sister was 23 years of age when I was born. She was in Rochester when these tricks first began, but came to Hydesville, the little village in central New York where we were born and lived.

All the neighbours around, as I have said, were called in to witness the manifestations. There were so many people coming to the house that we were not able to make use of the apple trick except when we were in bed and the room was dark.

And this is the way we began. First as a mere trick to frighten mother, and then when so many people came to see us children, we were ourselves frightened and for self-preservation forced to keep it up. No one suspected us of any trick because we were such young children. We were led on by my sister purposely; and by my mother unintentionally. We often heard her say "Is this a disembodied spirit that has taken possession of my dear children?"

Mrs. Underhill [Mrs. Fish later remarried], my eldest sister, took Katie and me to Rochester. There it was that we discovered a new way to make raps. My sister Katie was the first to observe that by swishing her fingers she could produce certain noises with her knuckles and joints, and that the same effect could be made with her toes. Finding that we could make raps with our feet—first with one foot and then both—we practised until we could do this easily when the room was dark.

In Rochester Mrs. Underhill gave exhibitions. We had crowds coming to see us and she made as much as $100 or $150 a night. She pocketed this. To all questions we answered by raps. We knew when to rap "yes" or "no" according to certain signs which Mrs. Underhill gave us during the seance.

Katie and I were led around like lambs. We drew immense crowds. We went to New York from Rochester and then all over the United States.

There followed three more pages of confession, in which Margaret described her career as a spiritualist during the ensuing 40 years.

During their long career, the Fox sisters had started a cult of spiritualism that swept the United States and rapidly spread to England and Europe. Margaret had appeared at séances for Queen Victoria, and Kate had performed before the Czar of Russia.

The story of the Fox sisters is important in showing how belief in the supernatural can outweigh all rational argument. The source of the raps was questioned almost from the start. E. P. Longworthy, a Rochester physician, investigated them and reported in the New York *Excelsior* on February 2, 1850, that the knockings always came from under the girls' feet or from objects such as doors or tables with which the girls' dresses were in contact. His conclusion was that Margaret and Kate themselves made the noises and that they voluntarily produced them.

John W. Hurn of Rochester, whose articles were published in the New York *Tribune* during January and February 1850, had come to a similar conclusion. In the same year, the Reverend John M. Austin of Auburn wrote to the *Tribune* to state that he had reliable information that the noise could be made by cracking the toe joints without any movement being visible. In December 1850, Reverend D. Potts demonstrated before an audience that he could produce raps in this manner.

By January 2, 1851, Reverend C. Chauncey Burr reported in the New York *Tribune* that he could produce the raps by cracking his toe joints and that he could produce sounds of such volume that they could be heard in every part of a hall large enough to contain a thousand people.

In February 1851, Austin Flint, Charles E. Lee, and C. B. Coventry of Buffalo University reported the results of an investigation they had made of the raps produced by Margaret Fox and her older sister Leah, who it seems was also by now participating in the act. Having studied Margaret's facial expression during the performance, they concluded that the raps were made by voluntary effort. They believed that the sounds were created by dislocation of the bones at the joints of the toes, knees, ankles, or hips; for they had observed that when the girls were placed on a couch with cushions beneath their feet the raps were no longer heard.

On April 17, 1851, Mrs. Culver, a relative by marriage of the sisters, admitted in a signed statement before witnesses that she had assisted Kate by touching her to indicate when the raps should be made. She declared that Kate had shown her how to make raps by snapping her toes and that Margaret had told her that she could produce raps with her knees and ankles when people insisted on seeing her feet and toes.

Professor Page of the Smithsonian Institute reported an investigation he had made in 1853. He concluded that the raps were produced by the girls and that every one was accompanied by a slight movement. He remarked that he was surprised to notice how the scrutinizing powers of the most astute fail as soon as they entertain the remotest idea of the supernatural.

In June 1857, the Boston *Courier* offered a prize of $500 to any medium who could pass an investigating committee. The Fox sisters were the first to try for the prize. Three Harvard professors were on the committee, whose report was unfavorable to Margaret and Kate; it suggested that the raps were produced by movements of the bones of the feet.

In spite of the criticisms and explanations that had been advanced, and even in spite of the statement by Mrs. Culver, belief in the Fox sisters grew. As the years went by, the sisters started introducing new tricks into their act, and they also took over many devised by other mediums.

The last official investigation of the raps took place in America under the auspices of the Seybert Commission. Henry Seybert (1801–1883), a mineralogist, philanthropist, and a keen believer in spiritualism, had donated a sum of money to the University of Pennsylvania to endow a chair of philosophy, and he had added the condition that the University was to appoint a commission to investigate "all systems of morals, religion, or philosophy which assume to represent the truth and particularly of Modern Spiritualism." The Commission, established in 1884, consisted of members of the faculty of the University.

In a preliminary report published in 1887, it was stated that it had investigated a number of mediums, including Margaret Fox. It reported that raps were heard close to her that could easily have been produced by normal means. Moreover, while the raps were sounding, Professor Furness, the chairman of the Commission, had placed his hand upon one of Margaret's feet and felt pulsations in her foot. It was also reported that Margaret knew when raps other

than her own were produced, no matter how similar they were in
sound to hers.

It was not only the uneducated that were impressed by the Fox
sisters. The renowned William Crookes, who in 1871 held séances
with Kate in London, was so impressed by her performance that he
wrote:

> With a full knowledge of the numerous theories which have
> been started, chiefly in America, to explain these sounds, I have
> tested them in every way that I could devise, until there has been
> no escape from the conviction that they were true objective occur-
> rences not produced by trickery or mechanical means.[1]

After their confession, the Fox sisters once more toured theaters
together—this time to denounce spiritualism and demonstrate
their tricks. They continued touring until 1889, when Kate's
drunkenness caused cancellation of their bookings. Kate died in the
street near her home in 1892, and Margaret, by this time also an
alcoholic, died the following year. The Fox sisters' confession and
numerous exposures of mediums at this time had little effect either
on the public or on the zeal of the psychical researchers.

Remarkably, the Fox sisters are still discussed in the parapsychological literature without mention of their trickery. Thus, a recent
book by Renée Haynes, a Council member of the Society for
Psychical Research, after relating how strange knocks were heard
in a farmhouse in 1847, continues:

> A cumulative wave of interest in these happenings swept over
> America and into Europe, generating more phenomena in its
> course, some genuine, some the work of ingenious persons seizing
> the opportunity to make money and fame, some genuine at first
> but eked out by legerdemain as the unknown power to produce
> them waned.[2]

The account given in the *Encyclopedia Britannica* (1963 edition) is rather similar, and a striking feature of both reports is that
the reader is given no reason to believe that the Fox sisters were
anything but perfectly genuine.

EUSAPIA PALLADINO

The year that the Fox sisters made their confession marked the rise to prominence of the greatest medium of all time. Eusapia Palladino was born on January 21, 1854, in Minervino Murge, southern Italy. Uneducated and illiterate, she was employed as a servant at the age of 13 by a family who indulged in spiritualism. One day she was asked to make up a "circle" at a séance. Surprising manifestations of psychic activity were observed, and she declared herself to be a medium. In spite of her affiliations with the spirits, Eusapia remained very much a woman of this world. "An unlettered peasant, retaining," as one writer put it, "a most primitive morality and of such a decidedly erotic nature that it was said she thought of little else." [3]

After a long apprenticeship in the mediumistic circles of Naples, Eusapia came under the influence of Ercole Chiaja, a keen student of the occult. He was so impressed by her that in 1888 he published an open letter to Cesare Lombroso (1836–1909), the famous Italian criminologist and psychiatrist, inviting him to investigate the phenomena that arose in Eusapia's presence.

Eusapia was introduced to Lombroso in 1888, and by 1891, she had convinced him of her supernatural powers. This, it should be noted, need not have presented her with as much difficulty as might appear. Lombroso was no hidebound skeptic. In 1882, he had reported the case of a patient who, having lost the power of seeing with her eyes, saw as clearly as before with the aid of the tip of her nose and the lobe of her left ear.[4]

An idea of what went on during one of Eusapia's séances may be gleaned from the detailed report of an investigating committee. Two curtains were hung across the corner of the séance room to form a small triangular space, called the *cabinet*. A small table was placed inside the cabinet, and around and on it reposed a number of objects, including a tambourine, a guitar, a toy trumpet, a flageolet, a toy piano, and a tea bell. Eusapia sat at a light table, the *séance table*, with her back to the cabinet so that the curtains were just behind her chair. The investigators sat at the sides of the séance table.[5]

The scene during the séance, discreetly veiled by the dim light, must have been remarkable. The voluptuous Eusapia sat in the clutch of two very serious gentlemen: "One of us sat on either side of her, holding, or held by, her hand with his foot under her foot, his leg generally pressing against the whole of hers, often with his free hand across her knees, and very frequently with his two feet encircling her foot." [6]

In the dim light, the table in front of her rose from the floor, objects floated from the cabinet, the curtain bulged, sounds were heard from the musical instruments inside the cabinet, and spirit hands touched the investigators. Great thumps were heard. The curtains suddenly blew out over the séance table. Eusapia was in communion with her spirit guide, John King.

In 1892, sittings were held in Milan for the benefit of a committee containing many eminent scientists, including Lombroso and the French physiologist Charles Richet, then Professor of Physiology in the University of Paris. The conclusion, reached with some reserve owing to the unsatisfactory way in which Eusapia's hands were held—the one thing that really mattered—was that none of the phenomena produced in "good light" could have been due to trickery.

A further series of 14 sittings was held in Warsaw in 1893–1894. Among 23 investigators, 10 were convinced that trickery was not used, and 3 considered that the whole performance was fraudulent. One claimed to have detected, among other tricks, the substitution of hands and feet. He maintained that 2 persons who thought they were holding the left and right hands of Eusapia were, in fact, both holding one hand.

In the summer of 1895, Eusapia visited Cambridge, England, where she gave 21 sittings. Here, suspicions were again aroused, owing to the fact that the conditions imposed on the experimenters were such that fraud would have been difficult to detect had it been present. The investigators were not allowed to feel about in the darkness, and they were forbidden to grab at the hand that floated around, touched them, and played various tricks.

After the Cambridge sittings, Eusapia was classified as a fraudulent medium by the Society for Psychical Research. However, belief died hard. Although her repertoire was such as to invite suspicion, and though she had been detected indulging in trickery, she still had many supporters. During the next few years, many leading European scientists, including Sir Oliver Lodge, visited Eusapia and became convinced of her supernatural powers.

Several further investigations took place, including one series of 43 sittings under the auspices of the Institute General de Psychologie ("Psychological Institute") of Paris. These experiments extended over 3 years at a cost of 25,000 francs. They were attended by the great French scientists Pierre and Marie Curie, D'Arsonval, the physicist; the philosopher and psychologist, Henri Bergson; Richet, the physiologist; and numerous other scientists and savants. The French committee detected many signs of trickery on Eusapia's part, but they were clearly puzzled by some of the phenomena.

In 1908, 3 members of the Society for Psychical Research, the Hon. Everard Fielding, a barrister, W. W. Baggally, and Hereward Carrington, went to Naples to investigate Eusapia. They obtained the services of Albert Meeson, a stenographer of the American Express Company, and their 11 sittings were reported in considerable detail.

The general arrangement of the curtain and tables at these sittings has already been described. Fielding, Baggally, and Carrington sat at the séance table. The stenographer sat at another table, some distance away and facing Eusapia, where he could witness the whole performance. His job was to record the remarks of the investigators and any visitors who were present.

During the séance there was considerable movement. Eusapia would twist and contort in her chair. The investigators, trying to maintain contact with her feet and hands, would follow her like marionettes. Extraordinary things happened. On one occasion, Baggally even managed to get himself kissed through the curtain, although he decided that there was an element of fraud as the head resembled a closed fist and the sound of the kiss resembled the clicking together of a thumb and finger. Psychic manifestations often followed one another at such a rate that the stenographer must have had difficulty compiling his record as the investigators called out anything they thought should be recorded. Mr. Meeson would write down the initial letter of the investigator's surname against each statement, for example:

R. (A visitor called Ryan). A white object came up by my right eye.

F. I saw it very well from where I am.

B. I saw it.

C. I also.

F. It looked to me like a boiled white cabbage.

R. It seemed to me like an ace of diamonds and about three inches
    from my right eye.[7]

The investigators were puzzled by what they saw and heard, but
it will be seen that the conditions under which Eusapia worked
were highly favorable to illusion.

1. The room was in semidarkness so that recognition of objects
was difficult and easily affected by other factors, such as suggestion.

2. The investigators were voicing aloud what they saw or experienced, thus tending to influence each other by suggestion.

3. During the séance, the medium was continually moving and,
for example, pinching the investigators' hands, thus distracting
their attention.

4. The investigators were having to attend to more than one
thing at the same time. They had to control the hands and feet of
the medium and, concurrently, watch in the dim light for any
"psychic manifestations."

5. The séances were held late at night or in the early morning,
introducing the element of fatigue. Eusapia always slept until mid-
day as she could not afford to be tired.

6. The investigators had a strong belief in the supernatural,
hence they would be emotionally involved.

7. The investigators were men. The subject was a woman. Thus,
control of her activities was hampered by the fact that they had to
observe the proprieties.

The Naples investigators were convinced that Eusapia was
genuine, and her prestige rose considerably. Since that time, many
writers have claimed that the conditions of this investigation ruled
out the possibility of deception. They have pointed out that
Baggally and Carrington were amateur magicians and could have
detected fraud had it been present. Looking back on Eusapia's
subsequent career, it is only too clear, however, that the important
point about an investigator is whether or not he believes in the

reality of the phenomena he is investigating. The disbelieving skeptic will approach a study in quite a different frame of mind from the believer.

For example, in 1909 when Eusapia visited the United States, escorted by Carrington, who acted as her manager, the investigators were of quite a different nature.

In a fanfare of publicity, Eusapia started giving sittings. The early ones were mainly for the benefit of the press, but at one held on November 19, 1909, a number of scientists were invited to attend, including R. W. Wood, Professor of Physics at Johns Hopkins; Augustus Trowbridge, Professor of Physics at Princeton; and J. D. Quackenbos, a physician and novelist. Very little of a psychical nature happened at the sittings with scientific observers until, on the night of December 18, 1909, Eusapia was, at last, caught in the act. On this occasion, she was supervised by Hugo Munsterburg, the well-known Harvard Psychologist, who showed himself to be a complete realist. His report, from which the following extract is taken, appeared in the *Metropolitan Magazine* for February 1910.

One week before Christmas, at the midnight hour, I sat again at Madame Palladino's favourite left side and a well-known scientist on her right. We had her under strictest supervision. Her left hand grasped my hand, her right hand was held by her right neighbour, her left foot rested on my foot while her right was pressing the foot of her other neighbour. For an hour the regulation performance had gone on. But now we sat in the darkened room in the highest expectancy while Mr. Carrington begged John to touch my arm and then to lift the table in the cabinet behind her and John really came. He touched me distinctly on my hip and then on my arm and at last he pulled my sleeve at the elbow. I plainly felt the thumb and the fingers. It was most uncanny. And, finally, John was to lift the table in the cabinet. We held both her hands, we felt both her feet, and yet the table three feet behind her began to scratch the floor and we expected it to be lifted. But instead, there suddenly came a wild, yelling scream. It was such a scream as I have never heard before in my life, not even in Sarah Bernhardt's most thrilling scenes. It was a scream as if a dagger had stabbed Eusapia right through the heart.

What had happened? Neither she nor Mr. Carrington had the slightest idea that a man was lying flat on the floor and had succeeded in slipping noiselessly like a snail below the curtain into the cabinet. I had told him that I expected wires stretched out from her body and he looked out for them. What a surprise when he saw that she had simply freed her foot from her shoe and with an athletic backward movement of the leg was reaching out and fishing with her toes for the guitar and the table in the cabinet! And then lying on the floor he grasped her foot and caught her heel with firm hand, and she responded with the wild scream which indicated that she knew that at last she was trapped and her glory shattered.

Her achievement was splendid. She had lifted her unshod foot to the height of my arm when she touched me under cover of the curtain, without changing in the least the position of her body. When her foot played thumb and fingers the game was also neat throughout. To be sure, I remember before she was to reach out for the table behind her, she suddenly felt need of touching my left hand too, and for that purpose she leaned heavily over the table at which we were sitting. She said that she must do it because her spiritual fluid had become too strong and the touch would relieve her. As a matter of course in leaning forward with the upper half of her body she became able to push her foot further backward and thus to reach the light table, which probably stood a few inches too far. And then came the scream and the doom.[8]

But even that was not enough. Eusapia had clearly been indulging in trickery on this particular occasion, but what about all the things that had happened at other sittings? She was, according to her supporters, only 60 per cent fraudulent; she would use a trick if the real thing was not at hand. Anybody could catch her using a trick; the task was to show that she could not produce any unusual phenomena when she was stopped from using tricks. This presented some difficulty, as she and her manager, Hereward Carrington, laid down the conditions under which séances should be held.

In January 1910, a series of 6 sittings was held at Columbia University. A number of scientists attended, including R. W. Wood, C. L. Dana, a Professor of Psychology at Cornell, and E. B. Wilson, a Professor of Biology at Princeton. The sittings were organized by Dickinson Miller, a Professor of Philosophy at Columbia University.

The séances were held in the Physics Laboratory of Columbia university, and the committee managed to complete the case against her after enlisting the aid of 3 professional magicians, W. S. Davis, J. L. Kellogg, and J. W. Sargent, together with J. F. Rinn, an amateur magician who spent much of his time hounding mediums. The magicians, who attended the last 2 sittings, were introduced to Eusapia as professors so that she should suspect nothing. At a séance held on April 17, 1910, Davis and Kellogg sat on either side of Eusapia, controlling her hands and feet. Rinn and a Columbia student, Warren G. Pyne, had hidden themselves under the séance table where they could observe Eusapia's footwork at close range. During this séance, she was left free to do as she pleased, and the magicians showed appropriate surprise at the various phenomena.

At a sitting held a week later, on April 24, 1910, Kellogg and Davis again sat on either side of Eusapia controlling her arms, legs, and feet. On this occasion, it was arranged that conditions should be lax at the start so that Eusapia should have every opportunity to put up a good performance. Levitations and transportations were abundant under these conditions. Then, at a prearranged signal, Kellogg and Davis made their control expert and from then on nothing happened.

A full report was issued in the journal *Science*, with statements by the scientists who had attended. Miller stated that after her techniques had been observed and controlled there were no manifestations of psychic phenomena.[9]

Rinn, from his vantage point beneath the table, saw the medium free her left leg by maneuvering her right foot so that her heel rested on Davis' toe and her toe on Kellogg's toe. The following statement which Rinn made was published in *Collier's Weekly* in an article by Joseph Jastrow, Professor of Psychology at the University of Wisconsin, who was present at the séance held on April 24, 1910:

> In a few moments, after some ejaculations in Italian from the medium, the table began to wobble from side to side; and a foot came from underneath the dress of the medium and placed the toe underneath the leg of the table on the left side of the medium, and, pressing upward, gave it a little chuck into the air. . . . A short time after the lights were lowered she swung her left foot

free from her dress at the back and kicked the curtain of the cabinet quickly, which caused it to bulge out toward the sitters. This was done several times so daringly that under the chairs where I lay it seemed almost impossible that the people above the table could not have observed it.

Later the medium placed her left leg back into the cabinet and pulled out from behind the curtain a small table with certain articles upon it, which was dashed to the floor in front of the cabinet on the left-hand side. It remained there in varying positions and was kicked by the medium a number of times. At one time the medium juggled the table that had been kicked out from behind the curtain on the end of her left toe in a very clever manner, so that it gave the appearance as if the table was floating in the air.[10]

Eusapia had survived many investigative committees, and she might well have survived that at Columbia University, since few people who visit mediums read scientific periodicals such as *Science*, and for every newspaper account Carrington could produce a ready reply. But she now had to contend with magicians, who at that time were at loggerheads with the mediums. The magician earns an honest living entertaining people with tricks. He regards the medium as prostituting his art, for she uses tricks to convince people of her supernatural powers in order to make money. With much publicity, Eusapia was challenged by Rinn to a contest, and she was offered $1,000 if she could perform any trick that the magicians could not duplicate under similar control conditions. A great deal of haggling went on, with much newspaper publicity as to the conditions to be observed. Eusapia would not agree to being encased in a bag nor with being tied with thin thread. Eventually, the conditions appear to have been agreed upon, but Eusapia did not turn up for the contest and later returned to Italy.

One further investigation was reported. Fielding went to Naples in December 1910, and a series of 5 séances were held. This time, he observed only tricks. If there was any residual element of genuine phenomena present in Eusapia's performance, it made no appearance. Little further was heard of her, and she died on May 16, 1918.

It was at enormous expense of time and money—she was paid $125 per sitting while in the United States—that the secrets of Eusapia Palladino were finally revealed. Many parapsychologists are still convinced that not all of her act was fraudulent.

MARGERY CRANDON

The exposure of Eusapia Palladino by no means marked the end of scientific interest in séance-room phenomena. Numerous other mediums were headline news, and then in May 1923, Margery Crandon, the most famous of all American mediums, first came before the public eye. She was the wife of L. R. G. Crandon, a distinguished Boston surgeon who was present at all her séances and who, many of the investigators believed, was responsible for much of what went on.

Her performance was in some ways similar to that of Eusapia Palladino, but she had many new tricks in her repertoire. During a séance, she went into a trancelike state during which "Walter," purportedly her deceased brother and her master of ceremonies, manifested himself. Walter's voice emanated from Margery's mouth, and sometimes his hand would be seen. He had a great sense of humor, although some of his utterances were calculated to make any nice girl blush.

Margery operated under conditions very much in her favor compared with those enjoyed by Eusapia Palladino. Her séances usually took place in complete darkness relieved only by a flash of red light provided by an apparatus fixed up by Crandon and operated when Walter gave the signal. Also, investigators had to agree to rigid conditions laid down by the Crandons before they were allowed to take part in a séance.

Margery was also much better able to win the sympathy of her investigators than was Eusapia. She was young, witty, and attractive. Even in a photograph, in which a considerable quantity of what look like jellied eels have deposited themselves on her right ear, it is clear that her physical charms far surpassed those of the rather stout Eusapia.

Margery, like Eusapia, was studied by several groups of investigators. The first research was carried out by four Harvard psychol-

ogists, William McDougall, A. A. Roback, Gardner Murphy, and
Harry Helson. They were not favorably impressed, but a report was
not issued at the time.

The second investigation was made by a committee appointed by
the *Scientific American*, which had offered $5,000 to anyone who
could exhibit genuine psychic phenomena. The great American
magician Harry Houdini was a member of the committee, but he
was ignored until some 80 sittings had been held and Margery was
about to get the prize. He was eventually asked to participate at a
séance held on July 23, 1924. After he had detected trickery, the
committee withheld the prize, although one of its members, J. M.
Bird, an associate editor of *Scientific American* appears to have
been convinced that Margery was at least 40 per cent genuine.

One of Margery's tricks was described by Houdini as follows:

During the second intermission "Walter" asked for an illumi-
nated plaque to be placed on the lid of the box which held the bell
and Bird went to get it. This left the right hand and foot of the
medium free. Bird had difficulty in finding the plaque and while
he was searching "Walter" suddenly called for "control."

Mrs. Crandon placed her right hand in mine and gave me to
understand that I had both her hands. Bird was requested to stand
in the doorway, but without any warning, before he could obey,
the cabinet was thrown over backwards violently. *The medium
then gave me her right foot also, saying:*

"You have now both hands and both feet."

Then "Walter" called out:

"The megaphone is in the air. Have Houdini tell me where to
throw it."

"Towards me," I replied, and in an instant it fell at my feet. The
way she did these tricks is as follows: when Bird left the room it
freed her right foot and hand. With her right hand she tilted the
corner of the cabinet enough to get her free foot under it, then
picking up the megaphone she placed it on her head, dunce-cap
fashion. Then she threw the cabinet over with her right foot. As
she did so I distinctly felt her body give and sway as though she
had made a vigorous lunge. As soon as this was done "Walter"
called for "Better control" and she gave me her right foot. Then
she simply jerked her head, causing the megaphone to fall at my
feet. Of course with the megaphone on her head it was easy and
simple for her to ask me or anyone else to hold both of her feet

and also her hands, and still she could snap the megaphone off her head in any direction requested. This was the *"slickest"* ruse I have ever detected, and it has converted all sceptics.[11]

Houdini's exposure did not convince those who believed in the supernatural. In 1925, Margery was investigated by E. J. Dingwall of the British Society for Psychical Research. His report is difficult to assess. He showed that most of the phenomena could have been produced by trickery on the part of Margery and her husband, but he seemed loath to come to any definite conclusion. Dingwall's underlying belief in the possibility of such things as ectoplasm almost certainly affected his actions and interpretations.

Toward the end of Dingwall's investigation, Hudson Hoagland, a young Harvard psychologist later to become well known in experimental psychology, became interested in the affair. Subsequently, a committee was formed consisting of Hoagland and four instructors from the University. A number of senior members of the University also attended some sittings and associated themselves with the findings.

In November 1925, Hoagland published an article in the *Atlantic Monthly* in which more than 20 separate items of evidence were produced to support the fact that Margery was a trickster. Although the Harvard committee had pronounced Margery fraudulent, the American Society for Psychical Research was not satisfied and wanted a further investigation.

Another committee was formed consisting of R. W. Wood, who had been on the committee investigating Eusapia Palladino; a skeptical psychologist, Knight Dunlap, of the Johns Hopkins faculty; and G. McComas, Associate Professor of Psychology at Princeton. The Crandons terminated the proceedings after the fourth sitting with this committee when the following episode took place.

Wood very cautiously *touched* and finally *pinched* the end of the "ectoplasm" that issued from Margery's mouth, without any sign of detection on her part. The significant point here is that a medium always insists that even *touching* the ectoplasm is sure to result in her illness or possible death. Wood states that it felt like a steel knitting needle covered with one or two layers of soft leather. As Wood, at the conclusion of the séance, solemnly dictated this stunt into the record, Margery shrieked and pretended to faint, and *that* was the end of the committee's séances with *her*. A full report of the committee's findings was sent to the American Society for Psychical Research, but the Society never saw fit to publish it.[12]

In 1929, Margery gave 3 séances in London in the rooms of the Society for Psychical Research. By this time, an important part of her act consisted of fingerprints that Walter impressed on a lump of wax. It was found that some of the fingerprints were Margery's, although her hands were supposed to have been controlled throughout the séances, other fingerprints belonged to no one present— except perhaps Walter.

The main supporter of Margery, apart from her husband, had been J. M. Bird. He had been fired from the *Scientific American* after their investigation and had become Research Officer of the American Society for Psychical Research of New York. Another staunch supporter was a member of the Boston Society for Psychical Research, E. E. Dudley. It was Dudley who eventually made the discovery that gave the *coup de grace* to Margery.

In March 1932, Dudley found that fingerprints left behind by Walter were those of Margery's dentist, who had attended many of her séances prior to 1925. It was also found that prints left behind by Walter in London were those of the dentist. The New York Society for Psychical Research refused to publish Dudley's findings, but they were eventually published by its rival, the Boston Society for Psychical Research. Walter Franklin Prince, the principal Research Officer of the Boston Society, declared that the Margery case would come to be considered the most ingenious, persistent, and fantastic complex of fraud in the history of psychic research, but that was 30 years ago.

She continued to give séances until 1938, when her husband died, after which she lost her powers. She died on November 1, 1941, at her home in Boston.

It may well be asked why it is necessary to explore in so much detail these ridiculous episodes in the history of psychical research. But it should be realized that, at the time, such things were taken very seriously by completely sane men. At great expense of time and energy, many eminent men provided evidence of the background of trickery that was responsible for the alleged psychic phenomena. Such efforts should not be required in a rational community but it is evident that, even in the twentieth century, superstition is far from dead.

Commenting on Professor Miller's report on the exposure of Eusapia Palladino, an editorial in the *New York Times* of May 10, 1910, concluded with the words: "But no one can read his trenchant analysis of her repeated and long continued conquests without feeling that the men of science have been her willing dupes and her abettors in a sort of conspiracy to mystify society." [13]

That sentence contained some truth. Both Eusapia Palladino and Margery Crandon were investigated by committee after committee, but it is significant that on all those occasions when professional magicians were present, the mediums were completely exposed. Neither Eusapia nor Margery could fool the magicians because they knew all the tricks and how to combat them.

If another Eusapia or Margery were to arise tomorrow, how would she succeed? The answer is quite clear. If she could avoid the attention of investigating committees, she would find public credulity no less than it was in 1889 or 1924. The present spate of television programs dealing with the supernatural indicates how popular allegedly true accounts of supernatural happenings are and how strong must be people's underlying beliefs.

Today, there are Eusapias and Margerys by the thousand, but they are more concerned with making money than with convincing investigating committees of their abilities. Man will pay for what he needs. He pays heavily for quack medical remedies, since health is an invaluable commodity. He will also pay heavily a spiritualist who claims to be able to contact a departed relative, for this is a service that no one else claims to provide.

CHAPTER 16

Mental Mediums

THE stock in trade of the mediums so far discussed was the production of physical phenomena—objects moved, things were seen, and noises were heard. The phenomena produced by these mediums were readily reproducible by stage magicians, and claims about the cause of such effects could be checked by seeing whether they still occurred when the possibility of trickery was removed. The medium's usual defense against detection lay in the imposition of "rules" and conditions to limit the scope of the investigator: the sitting took place in darkness or semidarkness so that visibility was poor, and the investigators had to be kept under control during the sitting—best done by making them "control" the medium. As soon as the researchers by-passed these conditions, the medium either lost his "powers" or was shown to be a fraud.

Since the introduction of infrared telescopes and cameras, physical mediums have ceased to offer themselves for investigation. Subsequent studies have been largely limited to the examination of evidence provided by the *mental mediums,* who profess to produce communications that originate from dead persons. This technique is more subtle and evasive than that of the physical mediums, since it relies on psychological rather than physical processes. A physical medium could be caught using his feet to levitate a table, but the mental medium cannot be caught in this manner. The phenomena produced by mental mediums are, on the other hand, far less unusual to an observer, and many people would deny that there is anything in their performance that the average educated person should find puzzling. Attention will here be confined to the American medium, Mrs. Leonore Evelina Piper and the British medium, Mrs. Gladys Osborne Leonard, both of whom psychical researchers claimed had supernatural powers and who have been studied extensively.

There are 3 main techniques used by mental mediums.

1. The medium apparently goes into a trance during which her body is said to be taken over by one or more spirit "controls." These are supposed to be the spirits of deceased persons who try to pass on the message from other spirits, or *communicators* to the medium's clients, or *sitters*. Their attempts at communication utilize the medium's voice and handwriting, but the controls have their own characteristics and distinguishing features, which are different from those of the medium.

2. The medium acts as if one of the communicators is responsible for her speech and behavior and is in "direct control" of her.

3. The medium produces messages by automatic writing or similar processes while retaining consciousness and apparently being her normal self throughout the proceedings.

In each case, the ability of the medium is usually assessed by her clients and investigators in terms of the amount of transmitted information that she would not be expected to have in her possession, in the normal run of events.

The standard procedures of fake mediums are well known. The prospective client may have to arrange a sitting in advance, leaving his name and address. This enables the medium, if the financial prospects justify the trouble, to assemble facts about the sitter's background. These are then produced for the benefit of the customer at later sittings to establish the medium's supernatural powers. Further information is gleaned from the sitter's reactions to generalized but interrogatory remarks and by the interpretation of responses to feelers. Opportunities may meanwhile present themselves for the medium or her assistants to add to their dossiers on clients by examination of the contents of coat pockets and purses. Information about other prospective clients may be gleaned from sitters, especially when people of eminence or known credulity are involved. Investigators may even be sent to the client's home town to gather information.

The main point at issue is whether the use of such mundane methods is limited to fake mediums. How is the fake to be differentiated from the real? No medium ever studied has been found to be free of deceit. However, the committed investigator always has an out. He will reply that the true "sensitive" may indeed employ trickery, but only when disturbed by incompetent investigators.

Investigators have been, it is true, only too well aware of the unspiritual activities of the majority of mediums, and they have always claimed that the most stringent precautions have been taken to render fraud impossible. However, this is a claim characteristic of psychical researchers generally. Having seen to what little extent such precautions were efficacious in the case of physical mediums where conditions were relatively simple, we may well be apprehensive as to any claims made concerning precautions to prevent fraud by mental mediums. With them there is nothing tangible to grasp. Their performance can only be understood through a knowledge of the psychological factors present in the séance room, the gullibility of the average sitter, and the inaccuracy of human memory.

Today, it is becoming unfashionable to explain mediumistic phenomena in spiritualistic terms, and the current tendency is to invoke theories of ESP. The medium is said not to communicate with the dead, but to receive information by telepathy from her client.

MRS. PIPER

Perhaps the most closely studied of all mental mediums was the American, Mrs. Leonore Piper. She first came to the notice of the distinguished American psychologist William James in 1886, and he introduced her to Richard Hodgson, the secretary of the American Society for Psychical Research. These two men studied and reported upon her trances from 1886 to 1892. In 1889, she visited England to be studied by the British Society for Psychical Research, which appointed for the purpose a committee headed by Sir Oliver Lodge. Reports on the period from 1892 to 1897 were made by Hodgson and Professor Romaine Newbold (1865–1926), Professor of Philosophy at the University of Pennsylvania. James Hyslop, (1854–1920), Professor of Logic and Ethics at Columbia University, reported on her trance activities from 1897 to 1905.

Mrs. Piper was regarded by her investigators as being of reasonable intelligence, education, and integrity. In 1884, she paid visits to a "psychic healer," a person who claims to cure disease through the intervention of spirits, for medical advice. During her second visit, she went into a trance herself and soon became able to do this at will. During her trances she seemed to assume other personalities and speak or write on matters of which she was ignorant after she regained her normal state. Soon a regular "control" appeared; this was the spirit of a French physician named Phinuit. However, in 1892, Phinuit was largely replaced as "control" by the spirit of "G. P." The initials "G. P." were thought to be those of George Pellham, this being a pseudonym for George Pellew, a young English friend of Hodgson whose sudden death had occurred a few weeks previously.

The sittings with G. P. as control were reported at length over the next 4 years, and while Mrs. Piper's claim to put herself in contact with spirits was doubted, the findings were long regarded as providing convincing evidence for extrasensory perception. Mrs. Piper, it was reported, had met Pellew only on one occasion and, in fact, was not aware of this until much later. But, when under G. P.'s control, she spoke of matters confidential to Pellew, and she is said to have recognized 30 of his past friends out of 150 strangers who attended sittings. She was also able to describe the location of a tin box containing some of Pellew's private papers, which had been missing since his death. Eventually, Hodgson, who up till then had been skeptical about the whole affair, was so impressed by this accumulation of evidence that he announced his conversion to spiritualism. Then, after his death in 1906, he became Mrs. Piper's control, only to be eventually ousted by the spirits of such celebrities as George Eliot and Julius Caesar.

Despite the voluminous reports and the eminence of the investigators, it is clear that the case for Mrs. Piper's extrasensory powers rests mainly on the G. P. series. For Phinuit turned out to know little French and less medicine. He explained the former fact by claiming that in life he had lived so long in an English community in Marseilles that he had forgotten his native tongue. Of more likely significance is the fact that Mrs. Piper had only learned a little French at school. Phinuit could give little information regarding his life on earth, which is not surprising as inquiries in France yielded no record of his birth, life, or death. On the other hand, he was adept at fishing for information and often contradicted himself.

Also, he often displayed signs of temporary deafness when posed with a difficult question. Much of his "communication" was garbled, incomplete, or merely gibberish; but of more concern to the investigators was the fact that he was unable to demonstrate, even to their satisfaction, that he was in direct contact with the spirits of deceased people.

The later period of Mrs. Piper's career as a medium produced results that can only be regarded as farcical. The band of spirits who took over control seemed bent on communicating rubbish, and the researchers sadly, but honestly, reported long sessions during which they were regaled with nonsense from the spirit world. And yet such was their faith that they were completely blind to any rational explanation.

There remains the G. P. series. The validity of this investigation is weakened by two points that are overlooked by writers sympathetic to the demonstration of psychic phenomena. First, it was never thought necessary to check G. P.'s statements about his earthly life. This was largely due to the tone of the reports submitted by Hodgson to the Society for Psychical Research. In them it was repeatedly implied that Pellew's parents supported the statements made by G. P. and that they were occasionally present in person at the séances. Later, the Pellew family, which had pointedly remained aloof from the excitement and publicity about G. P., flatly denied that any material reported from Mrs. Piper's séances had any connection with George Pellew. His mother, when refusing an invitation from Hodgson to join the American Society for Psychical Research, referred to G. P.'s communications as "utter drivel and inanity." [1]

George's brother, C. E. Pellew, Professor of Literature at Columbia University, stated that the famous tin box was in fact empty and that the papers referred to by G. P. had been in the possession of a friend for many years. He referred scornfully to the "absolute unreliability of any statement of the believers in the Mrs. Piper cult." [2] He wrote in a letter to a friend (Edward Clodd), "I was finally persuaded to see Mrs. Piper, and found her a bright, shrewd, ill-educated, commonplace woman who answered glibly enough questions where guessing was easy, or where she might have obtained previous information. But whenever I asked anything that would be known only to George himself, she was either silent or entirely wrong." [3]

MRS. LEONARD

Mrs. Gladys Osborne Leonard baffled psychical researchers for some 40 years. Although she was a professional medium, she claimed to have entered the field only to bring comfort to those bereaved during World War I. Thus, her stock opening for new sitters was the presentation of messages from the spirits of young men who had recently died. These men were almost always described as soldiers, always officers. Mrs. Leonard's control was an Indian girl called "Feda." She was described as a gay, lovable child with an impish sense of humor. Feda had pet baby names for her regular sitters, and she seems to have elicited warm affection from many of the investigators. She was very cooperative and insisted that her communications should be delivered at a speed convenient to the recorder. Thus, the English writer Radclyffe Hall and Lady Una Troubridge end the introduction to their major report with acknowledgements, not to Mrs. Leonard, but to Feda.

> Our thanks are due to Feda for the full and accurate records which we have been able to obtain. She has always shown the greatest solicitude on this point, repeating slowly and carefully, more than once, anything intricate that appeared to her to be of evidential value . . . [she] has been known to rebuke the communicator, saying "Don't speak so quickly, Mrs. Twonnie" (or "Mrs. Una," as the case may be) hasn't got that down yet . . . a very real mutual liking has grown up between ourselves and Feda.[4]

Feda showed an admirable awareness of the need for clear evidence. She would urge her spirit communicators to provide verifiable facts and not hackneyed references to lost letters and mothers' love.

Despite this desire to provide objective data and the enthusiasm with which it was received by a series of investigators, Feda's pronouncements were seldom impressive. Many authorities, however, have written as if her communications provide undoubted proof, if not for a spirit world, at least for Mrs. Leonard's remarkable powers of extrasensory perception.

Feda's communications were typically mediumistic. They were characterized by ambivalence, platitudes, and evasion. Although packed with allusions and generalities, there was never anything as definite as a simple statement of name, address, and date of birth.

The veracity of Mrs. Leonard's claims was accepted as being especially established by Feda's communications with the departed spirits of Raymond Lodge and "A. V. B." Raymond was the young officer son of Sir Oliver Lodge. A. V. B. was an old friend of Radclyffe Hall. It is of interest to see how these identifications were "proved" at the first sittings. The description Feda gave of Raymond was as follows:

> Is a young man, rather above the medium height; rather well-built, not thick set or heavy, but well-built, he holds himself up well. He has not been over long. His hair is between colours. He is not easy to be described, because he is not building himself up too solid as some do. He has greyish eyes; hair brown, short at the sides; a fine shaped head; eyebrows also brown, not much arched; nice shaped nose, fairly straight broader at the nostrils a little; a nice shaped mouth a good sized mouth it is, but it does not look large because he holds the lips nicely together; chin not heavy; face oval.[5]

A check by Mrs. W. H. Salter, a Research Officer of the British Society for Psychical Research, of the descriptions of 14 young men given by Feda at first sittings reveals this as her stock description of any departed male.[6] In all 14 cases in which height is mentioned, the young man is described as being "tall" or "above medium height." Nine of these were also described as "well-built." In the 12 cases when the color of the hair is given, it is brown. It is always cut or "cutted short at the sides." The 14 times that the color of the eyebrows is given, it is brown; 11 sets of eyebrows are "a little arched." Twelve times the shape of the nose is described as "straight or almost straight," while 11 noses are further described as having "rounded tips" or as being "broader at the nostrils." Six mouths have "a nice shape." As a matter of interest, about half the sitters found the descriptions given them to be fairly good of some relative or friend killed in the war. Feda had evidently developed a model of the average young British officer as remembered by the average mother: a young man, tall and well-built with brown hair cut short at the sides, a straight nose broadening at the tip, and slightly arched brown eyebrows. A few other variables are permutated; faces are either oval or between round and oval, hair is always brushed back and often sticks up at the top, and eyes are either blue gray or gray.

One further regular feature of Feda's officer-communicator is that he often spoke of group photographs, a fairly safe bet, as it must be quite exceptional for a British officer to avoid regimental and mess photographs. But Sir Oliver was very impressed when "Raymond" mentioned such a portrait, which only subsequently turned up at the Lodge's home.

When Radclyffe Hall first visited Mrs. Leonard, it was as an investigator only. But Feda, doubtless taking it for granted that she was one of the run-of-the-mill bereaved relatives, immediately produced the spirit of a young soldier. Radclyffe Hall disclaimed any romantic affiliations with army officers, and Feda then adopted her usual second line of approach—an elderly lady. The description of this lady, whose initials were A. V. B., was eventually elicited as:

> F[eda]: The lady is of medium height has rather a good figure but is inclined to be fat, Feda thinks; she has a straight nose, a well-shaped face, but the face is inclined to lose its outline a little. The eyebrows are slightly arched, her hair is not done fashionably.
> R. H.: Is it worn in the neck?
> F. : No it's done on the crown of her head . . .[7]

Of Feda's 10 descriptions of women that Mrs. Salter reports, 8 are called elderly or past middle age. In the 9 cases where height is mentioned, 8 ladies are "of medium height," while three are specified as having "a good figure." All 5 references to noses describe them as "straight," and 3 faces are mentioned as "losing their outline." Three sets of eyebrows are "slightly arched." Of 8 hair styles referred to, 6 are "on the crown of the head."

SUMMARY

The *Proceedings* of the Society for Psychical Research are crammed with "evidence" consisting of material of this sort. Performances like those of Mrs. Piper and Mrs. Leonard, essentially similar to those of fairground fortune tellers, have attracted the attention of psychical-research investigators for years. Such women will always be around, either as professional mediums who bring consolation to the bereaved at considerable financial gain to themselves, or as amateurs, who, at least part of the time, may not really understand what they are doing.

The trance medium, if she is not merely shamming, is a person who finds herself experiencing fits, or states of changed consciousness. These occur involuntarily, but at some stage she finds it possible to elicit one at will. While in one of these states, she is no longer able to function normally. She hears imaginary voices and may suffer from visual and kinesthetic delusions. Some other person seems to take over her body and her mind. His voice speaks through her vocal chords expressing thoughts and experiences of which she has no knowledge. She may write or communicate by gesture in some manner characteristic of the control. She is in fact suffering from dissociation. Conscious awareness of everyday events may still exist during such a state, but even so, the ability to think and communicate is changed. When herself again, she may sometimes display a *retrograde amnesia,* that is, a loss of memory for the events that took place during the fit. There is little doubt that if she complained she was unhappy about this state of affairs or if she presumed that the person who took over from her was the representative of some political or religious organization, no psychiatrist would hesitate to diagnose mental illness. Such a person shows features common to several psychotic as well as neurotic disorders, although hysteria would seem to be the most likely diagnosis. Thus, J. Ehrenwald, an English psychiatrist and a member of the Society for Psychical Research states:

What is mediumistic trance? Its psychiatric interpretation is obvious. It is a state of mental dissociation hysteric in origin, induced by suggestion or auto-suggestion in persons with a particular tendency to give way to such influences. The trance state, once established as an habitual pattern of reaction, gives the person concerned an outlet for unconscious or repressed tendencies which are prevented from being expressed in ordinary life. The productions of the mediumistic trance are in this way largely comparable with the familiar symptoms of hysteria and especially of hysteric multiple personality.[8]

There is a serious possibility that such mediums should be treated rather than investigated. The phenomena of mediumship is curiously summed up in a letter written by Mrs. Piper to the New York *Herald* on October 20, 1901. In it she denied that she was a spiritualist or had ever experienced any proof of spirit return. She then asked herself why she had remained with the Society for Psychical Research for so long and replied: "Because of my desire to learn if I were possessed or obsessed." [9]

Looking back over the investigations of famous mediums, it may seem remarkable that they should have been taken seriously as providing evidence for any supernatural powers. But, in fact, a large number of eminent men were greatly impressed when they encountered these mediums under séance-room conditions. One reason for this may be that most of the men concerned had an inherent belief in the processes they were investigating. The reports on mediums given by skeptics such as J. F. Rinn and Harry Houdini are remarkably different from those published in the journals of the societies for psychical research. A second factor is that the conditions in which a mediumistic sitting is held are ill suited to exact observation. The observer, who is usually also the sitter, has to note not only what the medium says, but also his own statements to the medium and any other responses that he may give—and this is clearly quite an impossible task. The observer will report on only those utterances that attract his attention, he cannot possibly record or even become aware of every sound in the séance room and every change of expression or intonation of voice.

Anyone reporting on the performance of a performer who finds hidden objects by using audience reactions would be at the same disadvantage. He is unlikely to be able to become aware of the cues utilized by the performer even if they are pointed out to him.

In 1960, the British Broadcasting Corporation televised a sitting between a professional medium, Douglas Johnson, and a complete stranger to him. In his book, *Psychical Research Today*, Donald West, a psychiatrist who is Assistant Director of Research at the Cambridge University Institute of Criminology and a former Research Officer of the British Society for Psychical Research, comments, "The medium scored some striking hits and many viewers, including the present writer, were impressed by his success." [10] The program was recorded and rebroadcast later with a critical commentary by Christopher Scott, who is now Regional Statistical Adviser to the United Nations. West later commented that it then became apparent to him that almost everything the medium said could have been deduced from changes in facial expression and tone of voice induced in the sitter by the medium's leading questions. Many persons attributed to the medium statements that seemed in remarkable accordance with the facts as revealed by the sitter at the end of the original program, but when the sitting was seen for the second time, it was found that some of these were never uttered. Without the availability of a complete audiovisual recording, the medium's performance would have been greatly overrated both by the ordinary viewer and by experts like West.

If mediums such as Mrs. Piper and Mrs. Leonard utilized auditory and visual cues provided by their sitters, this could have been established by systematically removing such cues. Since each of these ladies retained her clairvoyant abilities for more than 20 years, they would have constituted admirable subjects for ESP research.

CHAPTER **17**

Conclusion

IS ESP A FACT?

THE basic problem of parapsychology is relatively simple when compared with problems in politics or aesthetics. Either it is possible for at least some people to communicate by extrasensory perception, or else ESP does not and cannot exist because the underlying processes necessary for its occurrence do not exist. A great deal of experimental work has failed to provide a clear case for the existence of ESP, but at least two facts have been established: first, subjects when trying to guess card symbols have obtained scores that cannot be attributed to chance; second, some of those taking part in ESP experiments have cheated to produce high scores.

The first fact cannot be disputed. Results such as those obtained by Hubert Pearce or by Riess's high-scoring subject need no statistical analysis for the purpose of establishing that something was happening during the experiments other than pure guesswork. The second fact that those taking part in experiments sometimes cheat is known from admissions of trickery. The first 2 major experiments in Great Britain on the Creery sisters and on Smith and Blackburn in 1882, involved 8 subjects, 7 of whom admitted to cheating, and the other did cheat according to his partner in the act. The last major investigation in Great Britain, on the Welsh schoolboys in 1955–1957, involved 2 subjects, both of whom admitted to cheating after being caught in the act. It would be remarkable if such attempts to assist the natural course of events ceased altogether in parapsychology between the years 1882 and 1956. In fact, close examination of the most spectacular findings in parapsychology invariably points to some form of trickery as an alternative to ESP. To the skeptic, psychical research seems to have been as much a history of the manner in which the artful can

233

mislead the innocent as it is a reflection of any more esoteric activity.

IS ESP A FRAUD?

Cheating in one form or another is one of the commonest of human activities. If it never occurred, much of the expense and complication of modern life would be avoided. The paper work involved in accounting and auditing—tickets, bills, counterfoils, invoices—would no longer be necessary. Games, examinations, competitions, and numerous such activities would be simplified. On the other hand, it is unlikely that more than a small number of experiments on ESP are affected by cheating, since the investigator does his best to ensure that his subjects cannot cheat and, no doubt, usually succeeds. The majority of investigators are likely to have sufficient faith in the reality of ESP to believe that it will manifest itself without outside aid. It may then seem strange to the reader that so much space has been given here to the matter of trickery. Why in the case of each of the so-called conclusive experiments should trickery invariably emerge as a likely alternative to ESP?

One reason is that an experiment is not classified as conclusive unless the known causes of experimental error have been eliminated in its design. If a trick is used in an experiment, it might be expected to produce an impressive result having large odds against arising by chance and, if the experiment is of the "conclusive" category, trickery would be the only alternative explanation to ESP. Thus, the process by which conclusive experiments are weeded out will also bring to light experiments in which a trick has been used.

A trick also involves a trickster. The following remarks made by George R. Price are very relevant.

> The wise procedure, when we seek to evaluate probability of fraud, is to try to ignore all vague, psychological criteria and base our reasoning (i) on such evidence as would impress a court and (ii) on purely statistical considerations. And here we must recognise that we usually make a certain gross statistical error. When we consider the possibility of fraud, almost invariably we think of particular individuals and ask ourselves whether it is possible that this particular man, this Professor X, could be dishonest. The probability seems small, but the procedure is incorrect. The correct

procedure is to consider that we very likely would not have heard of Professor X at all except for his psychic findings. Accordingly, the probability of interest to us is the probability of there having been anywhere in the world, among its more than 2 billion inhabitants, a few people with the desire and ability to produce false evidence for the supernatural.[1]

There is one psychological criterion, however, that even a court of law would regard as impressive. That is the question of motive. Why should people go to all the trouble of entering into complicated conspiracies merely to deceive their fellows? It should first be noted that there are many cases of known trickery in science where the motive is not clear. The Piltdown skull discovered in 1912 that at first appeared to be an important piece of evidence in the history of man's development involved the trickster in a lot of work for little apparent gain.

However, in the case of many individuals acting as subjects in parapsychology there is often a very clear motive. Mediums at one time in the United States were said to constitute the second highest paid profession open to women, and where monetary gain is not involved, there may be the desire to impress or to gain prestige. In the case of each of the major experimental investigations to which a chapter has been given in this book, there is a possible monetary or prestige motive for trickery.

In the early 1930's at Duke University, during the Depression, students who acted as subjects in ESP experiments were paid an hourly wage for their services. If Pearce was paid to act as a subject, he had every incentive to continue in that capacity. The Pratt-Woodruff experiment was a continuation of work started by Woodruff constituting part of the requirement for a higher degree. The Soal-Goldney experiment gained Soal his Doctorate of Science at London University. Would that degree have been given for a series of negative experiments? Mrs. Stewart was paid for her services. The Jones boys earned large rewards for high scores.

Parapsychologists are themselves to blame for the emphasis that has to be placed on cheating when considering their work. In science generally it is likely that, at times, investigators indulge in underhanded activities, but their experiments are shown up when other scientists fail to confirm their result. In such cases it may not be necessary to hold a long postmortem on the earlier experiment; it is just forgotten. However, parapsychologists—or at least some of the more vociferous of them—in denying the necessity to confirm experiments by repetition, make it essential to examine every experiment in detail in order to ensure that the result could not have been caused by cheating.

It is often difficult to discuss the possibility of cheating objectively. Parapsychologists tend to present their critics with a *fait accompli*. A similar situation would arise in orthodox science if a chemist reported an experimental result that contradicted all the previous research findings and theories of his fellow chemists, together with the statement "Either this finding must be accepted as valid or else you must accuse me of being a cheat and a liar. Do you accept it?" In such circumstances, orthodox chemists might feel diffident about openly expressing their doubts. They might, however, repeat the experiment to see whether they got the same result. If they failed to confirm his result, they would not go into a long discussion as to whether the original investigator was a liar or a cheat. They would just take with a grain of salt any further experimental reports from the same source.

The trickster has often been assisted by the investigator's overwhelming confidence in his ability to detect trickery. Observers, however careful, must be prepared to make mistakes. But in psychical research many of the investigators have considered themselves infallible. Soal claimed that boys of the caliber of Glyn and Ieuan could never hope to deceive him.

If a trick is used in an experiment, this fact might be expected to make itself apparent in the course of further research. But parapsychologists have erected a system that aids the trickster and at the same time preserves experimental findings.

SURVIVAL CHARACTERISTICS OF ESP

Scientists in general have been little influenced by philosophers who strive to inform them about the methodology and logic of their subject. Science has a basic methodological principle that is self-generating. It was not formulated by anybody, but it has the same empirical basis and underlying logic as the principle of natural selection in evolution. Investigators are continually producing reports of their experimental findings, which may be classified, for convenience, as good and bad. The good ones survive because they are confirmed in further research. The bad ones are forgotten because they cannot be confirmed. Science advances through a process of natural selection. New findings become targets for criticism, and a finding must be confirmed by critics under their own experimental conditions; it then soon becomes clear when it is to be rejected.

If anyone invents a pseudoscience in which this principle ceases to operate, the result soon becomes apparent, for the new "science" fails to have predictive value and leads to more and more findings and theories that are incompatible with orthodox science. This is what has happened in parapsychology. When critics fail to confirm ESP, this is not accepted as a reason for dropping the subject; on the contrary, belief in the reality of ESP is so strong that the principle of repeatability has been rejected or rendered impotent by the invoking of new processes which are claimed as subsidiary characteristics of the phenomenon. Thus, given a high-scoring subject, it would in the normal course of events be only a matter of time before every critic could be silenced, but these subjects cease to score high when tested by critics. Extrasensory perception only manifests itself before uncritical investigators. Again, Rhine and Pratt have observed, "Another major difficulty can be seen in the fact that some experimenters after a period of earlier success in obtaining extra-chance results in psi experiments have proved less effective in their later efforts. In such instances something apparently has been lost that was once a potent factor. The element most likely to change under prolonged testing would seem to be the quality of infectious enthusiasm that accompanies the initial discoveries of the research worker. Those who never succeed at all may, of course, be suspected of not ever having felt such contagious or communicable interest as would help to create a favorable test environment for their subjects." [2] In other words, experimenters fail to confirm their own results. And a further subsidiary characteristic emerges: ESP is affected by the mental state of the person investigating it.

If fresh characteristics are postulated in this manner, it is possible to survive almost any form of criticism. An experimental result cannot be confirmed or refuted since ESP does not operate in front of critics. After tightening up his experimental conditions, an investigator cannot disclaim the findings of his earlier work; failure in later work reveals that he has lost his enthusiasm.

Since the chief characteristic of the exploratory stage, according to the statement of Rhine and Pratt given on pages 22–23, is that the investigator carries out his work "without being burdened with too much precautionary concern." [3] failure to confirm earlier work is likely to arise when the investigator graduates from the exploratory stage to one where he takes more care with his work. After an investigator becomes burdened with concern, his precautions will, presumably, be against error and trickery rather than against ESP. It may be assumed that any change in his experimental results is due to the effectiveness of his precautions.

A REVISED APPROACH

At the present time, there are signs that the arguments put forward to support the work on ESP may be changing. Rhine and Pratt in recent writings imply that the case for ESP does not, after all, depend on conclusive experiments, but on general features that emerge from the whole mass of studies, conclusive or inconclusive; it is as if quantity can make up for quality when the latter has been found lacking. They write:

> The body of fact in parapsychology is like a many-celled organism. Its strength is that of a growth-relationship, consisting not only of the compounding of one cell with another, but also of the many lawful inter-relations that emerge in the growing structure. Going back as Hansel has done, with a one-cell perspective, to fix attention on some incomplete stage of development within a single experimental research is hard to understand in terms of healthy scientific motivation. [4]

What is the point of presenting conclusive experiments for the consideration of the scientific world if they cannot be criticized? How can an experiment be criticized until it has first been isolated? If experiments are to be considered en masse, will not data be confused with results such as those obtained with the Creery sisters and Smith and Blackburn? But as soon as criteria by means of which experiments are selected or rejected are set up, it becomes necessary to isolate each experiment to see whether it satisfies those criteria.

Moreover, what precisely are the "lawful inter-relationships" within the body of fact in parapsychology to which Rhine refers. To date, not a single lawful inter-relationship appears to have been established. How, for example, does distance affect extrasensory perception? The relationship between scoring rate and distance is completely chaotic, apparently dependent on the investigator, the subject, and the experimental conditions. If it were possible to give a standardized test for ESP to different groups of subjects, systematically varying factors such as age, nationality, intelligence, previous practice, distance, and so on, some lawful inter-relationships might eventually be expected to reveal themselves. But each of the reported investigations yields a result that has little relationship to any of the others.

Extrasensory perception is not a fact but a theory put forward to account for observations consisting of high scores obtained during the course of experiments. Parapsychologists have made such observations under a diversity of research conditions from which a number of facts emerge. If these facts can be related to one another by a theory that enables any one to be deducible from knowledge of the others, that theory has some value and plausibility. By means of it predictions might be made of what will happen in further experiments so that it can be put to further test. However, a theory that fails to account for a variety of facts and that cannot predict what will happen in further tests is of no value.

If some facts gleaned from the literature on ESP are assembled, they might appear as follows:

1. Subjects, when attempting to guess card symbols, have obtained scores that cannot be attributed to chance.

2. Some of those taking part in ESP experiments have indulged in trickery.

3. Subjects who obtain high scores cannot do so on all occasions.

4. Subjects tend to lose their ability to obtain high scores. This loss often coincides with the termination of an experiment.

5. A successful subject is sometimes unable to obtain high scores when tested by a critical investigator.

6. Some investigators often observe high scores in the subjects they test; others invariably fail to observe such scores.

7. A subject may obtain high scores under one set of experimental conditions and fail to do so under other experimental conditions.

8. No subject has ever demonstrated his ability to obtain high scores when the test procedure is completely mechanized.

Fact 1 is directly applicable to an hypothesis of the existence of ESP. Fact 2 is not relevant to such an hypothesis. Facts 3 and 4 are not predictable but could be said to provide further information about ESP; that is, it appears to be spasmodic and temporary. The remaining facts (5–8) are not predictable, and in the case of any other supposed process investigated by psychologists, would throw doubt on its authenticity. These facts can only be explained by invoking subsidiary characteristics of ESP.

Again, fact 1 is directly applicable to an hypothesis predicting trickery. Fact 2 demonstrates that such an hypothesis is correct in the case of certain experiments. The remaining facts (3–4) are all predictable from what is well known about trickery.

Lawful relationships can readily be seen among the facts when they are interpreted in accordance with the hypothesis of trickery. Thus, for example, from fact 7 it might be predicted that those experimental conditions that eliminate the possibility of trickery will also be the ones in which high scores do not arise. This is confirmed by fact 8, and also by examining the experimental conditions under 7 in which high scores have and have not been observed.

Thus the set of facts given above display lawful inter-relationships when interpreted in terms of the hypothesis of trickery, but they are difficult to reconcile with an hypothesis based on the existence of ESP.

A number of other facts could be added to the above list to which neither an hypothesis of ESP nor that of trickery would be applicable. This is to be expected, since a great deal of research both in parapsychology and elsewhere has revealed the manner in which high scores can arise through experimental error.

SUMMARY

During the past 85 years, a large number of investigations have been reported, the majority of which no responsible parapsychologist would claim as having been designed or intended for the purpose of providing conclusive evidence for ESP. Only a small number of studies were begun with the intent to provide such evidence.

The aim of this book has been to isolate the conclusive experiments and then to indicate that other explanations than ESP can account for their results. In the case of each of these conclusive experiments, the result could have arisen through a trick on the part of one or more of those taking part. In addition, closer examination of the experiments to see how far the hypothesis of trickery is consistent with information concerning the experiments in no case invalidates the hypothesis and in some cases strengthens it.

It cannot be stated categorically that trickery was responsible for the results of these experiments, but so long as the possibility is present, the experiments cannot be regarded as satisfying the aims of their originators or as supplying conclusive evidence for ESP.

A great deal of time, effort, and money has been expended but an acceptable demonstration of the existence of extrasensory perception has not been given. Critics have themselves been criticized for making the conditions of a satisfactory demonstration impossible to obtain. An acceptable model for future research with which the argument could rapidly be settled one way or the other has now been made available by the investigators at the United States Air Force Research Laboratories. If 12 months' research on VERITAC can establish the existence of ESP, the past research will not have been in vain. If ESP is not established, much further effort could be spared and the energies of many young scientists could be directed to more worthwhile research.

REFERENCE NOTES

INTRODUCTION

1. Originally printed in the *American Magazine* for October, 1910; reprinted as "The Final Impressions of a Psychical Researcher," in WILLIAM JAMES, *Memories and Studies* (New York: Longmans, Green, 1911), pp. 181–183; and also in GARDNER MURPHY and R. O. BALLOU, eds., *William James on Psychical Research* (New York: Viking Press, Inc., 1960), pp. 313 f.
2. LEON FESTINGER, H. W. RIECKEN, and STANLEY SCHACHTER, *When Prophecy Fails* (Minneapolis: University of Minnesota Press, 1956). See also the general discussion in LEON FESTINGER, *A Theory of Cognitive Dissonance* [Evanston, Ill.: Row, Peterson & Co., 1957 (reprinted by the Stanford University Press, 1962)].
3. See E. G. BORING, "Cognitive Dissonance, Its Use in Science," *Science*, CXLV (1964), 680–685.
4. MURPHY and BALLOU, eds. *William James on Psychical Research;* E. G. BORING, "The Spirits against Bosh," *Contemporary Psychology*, VI (1961), 149–151.
5. On the many definitions of chance, see A. J. AYER, "Chance," *Scientific American*, CCXIII (October, 1965), 44–54.
6. GEORGE BOOLE, *An Investigation into the Laws of Thought* (London: Macmillan & Co. Ltd., 1854), pp. 368–375.
7. JOHANNES VON KRIES, *Die Principien der Wahrscheinlichkeitsrechnung* (Freiburg: J. C. B. Mohr, 1886), pp. 5–15.
8. J. M. KEYNES, *A Treatise on Probability* [London: Macmillan & Co. Ltd., 1921 (reprinted variously and by Harper & Row, 1962)], pp. 41–64.
9. AYER, *Scientific American* (1965), p. 44.
10. E. G. BORING, "Statistical Frequencies as Dynamic Equilibria," *Psychological Review*, XLVIII (1941), 279–301.
11. *Ibid.*, p. 295.
12. E. G. BORING, "The Nature and History of Experimental Control," *American Journal of Psychology*, LXVII (1954), 573–589, and especially on a fact's being a difference, p. 575.
13. BORING, *Psychological Review* (1941), p. 296.
14. AYER, *Scientific American* (1965), p. 51.

CHAPTER 1

1. D'ARCY THOMPSON, *Growth and Form* (Cambridge, England: Cambridge University Press, 1942), p. 13.
2. MARGARET KNIGHT, "Theoretical Implications of Telepathy," *Science News*, No. 18 (London: Penguin Books Ltd., 1950), p. 20.
3. H. J. EYSENCK, *Sense and Nonsense in Psychology* (London: Penguin Books Ltd., 1957), p. 13.

4. S. G. SOAL and F. BATEMAN, *Modern Experiments in Telepathy* (London: Faber & Faber Ltd., 1954), p. 24.
5. Quoted in ROSALIND HEYWOOD, *Beyond the Reach of Sense* (New York: E. P. Dutton & Co., Inc., 1961), p. 11.
6. D. O. HEBB, "The Role of Neurological Ideas in Psychology," *Journal of Personality*, XX (1951), 45.
7. ALDOUS HUXLEY, *Life*, XXXVI, No. 2 (1954), 96.
8. R. H. THOULESS, "Thought Transference and Related Phenomena, 1950," from SOAL and BATEMAN, *Modern Experiments in Telepathy*, p. 357.

CHAPTER 3

1. ARTHUR KOESTLER, *The Observer* (London), May 7, 1961, p. 23.
2. C. D. BROAD, "Discussion: the Experimental Establishment of Telepathic Precognition," *Philosophy*, XIX, No. 74 (1944), 261.
3. J. B. RHINE and J. G. PRATT, *Parapsychology: Frontier Science of the Mind* (Springfield, Ill.: Charles C. Thomas, Publisher, 1957), p. 140.
4. *Ibid.*, p. 19.
5. G. E. WOLSTENHOLME and ELAINE C. P. MILLAR, eds., *Extrasensory Perception*, Ciba Foundation Symposium (London: J. & A. Churchill Ltd., 1956), p. 32.
6. J. G. PRATT, J. B. RHINE, BURKE M. SMITH, CHARLES E. STUART, and JOSEPH A. GREENWOOD, *Extra-Sensory Perception after Sixty Years* (Boston: Bruce Humphries, Publishers, 1940).
7. WOLSTENHOLME and MILLAR, eds., *Extrasensory Perception*, p. 51.

CHAPTER 4

1. H. SIDGWICK, "Presidential Address," *Proceedings of the Society for Psychical Research*, I, Part I (1882), 12.
2. W. F. BARRETT, EDMUND GURNEY, and F. W. H. MYERS, "First Report on Thought Reading," *Proceedings of the Society for Psychical Research*, I, Part I (1882), 63.
3. *Daily News* (London), September 1, 1911.
4. SIR JAMES CRICHTON-BROWNE, letter in *Westminster Gazette*, January 29, 1908.
5. *Daily News* (London), *op. cit.*
6. *Ibid.*
7. *Ibid.*
8. M. E. CHEVREUL, *De la baquette divinatoire, du pendule dit explorateur et des tables tournantes* (Paris: Malet Bachelier, 1854).
9. W. F. BARRETT and T. BESTERMAN, *The Divining Rod; an Experimental and Psychological Investigation* (London: Methuen & Co. Ltd., 1926).
10. O. PFUNGST, *Clever Hans*, trans. CARL L. REHN (New York: Holt, Rinehart & Winston, Inc., 1911).
11. SOAL and BATEMAN, *Modern Experiments in Telepathy*, p. 16.
12. INA JEPHSON, "Evidence for Clairvoyance in Card-Guessing," *Proceedings of the Society for Psychical Research*, XXXVII, Part CIX (1929), 223–268.
13. T. BESTERMAN, S. G. SOAL, and INA JEPHSON, "Report of a Series of Experiments in Clairvoyance Conducted at a Distance under Approxi-

mately Fraud-Proof Conditions," *Proceedings of the Society for Psychical Research*, XXXIX, Part CXVIII (1931), 374–414.

14. G. N. M. TYRRELL, "Further Research in Extra-Sensory Perception," *Proceedings of the Society for Psychical Research*, XLIV, Part CXLVII (1936), 99–166.

15. J. L. KENNEDY, "A Methodological Review of Extra-Sensory Perception," *Psychological Bulletin*, XXXVI (1939), 59–103.

CHAPTER 5

1. J. B. RHINE, "An Investigation of a Mind Reading Horse," *Journal of Abnormal and Social Psychology*, XXIII (1929).

2. J. B. RHINE, *Extra-Sensory Perception* (Boston: Boston Society for Psychic Research, 1934). Reprinted by permission of Faber & Faber Ltd., and J. B. Rhine. Page numbers that follow refer to edition published in England (London: Faber & Faber Ltd.).

3. *Ibid.*, p. 229.

4. *Ibid.*, p. 83.

5. *Ibid.*, p. 113–114.

CHAPTER 6

1. W. S. COX, "An Experiment in ESP," *Journal of Experimental Psychology*, XII, No. 4 (1936), 437.

2. E. T. ADAMS, "A Summary of some Negative Experiments," *Journal of Parapsychology*, II, No. 3 (1938), 232–236.

3. J. C. CRUMBAUGH, "An Experimental Study of Extra-Sensory Perception" (Master's thesis, Southern Methodist University, 1938).

4. R. R. WILLOUGHBY, "Further Card-Guessing Experiments," *Journal of General Psychology*, XVIII (1938), 3–13.

5. C. P. HEINLEIN and J. H. HEINLEIN, "Critique of the Premises and Statistical Methodology of Parapsychology," *Journal of Psychology*, V (1938), 135–148.

6. SOAL and BATEMAN, *Modern Experiments in Telepathy*, pp. 135–148.

7. J. L. KENNEDY, "The Visual Cues from the Backs of ESP Cards," *Journal of Psychology*, VI (1938), 149–153.

8. C. V. C. HERBERT, "Experiments in Extra-Sensory Perception 1. A Note on Types of Zener Cards," *Journal of the Society for Psychical Research*, XXX, No. 545 (1938), 215–218.

9. J. L KENNEDY, *Psychological Bulletin* (1939).

10. *Ibid.*, p. 94.

11. L. WARNER, "A Test Case," *Journal of Parapsychology*, I, No. 4 (1937), 234–238.

12. B. F. RIESS, "A Case of High Scores in Card Guessing at a Distance," *Journal of Parapsychology*, I, No. 4 (1937), 260–263.

13. *Ibid.*, p. 263.

14. J. L. KENNEDY, *Psychological Bulletin* (1939), p. 91.

15. SOAL and BATEMAN, *Modern Experiments in Telepathy*, p. 49.

16. PRATT, *et al.*, *Extra-Sensory Perception after Sixty Years*, p. 163.

17. *Ibid.*, p. 165.

18. *Ibid.*
19. *Ibid.*, p. 165, 166.

CHAPTER 7

1. J. B. RHINE and J. G. PRATT, "A Review of the Pearce-Pratt Distance Series of ESP Tests," *Journal of Parapsychology*, XVIII, No. 3 (1954), 165–177.
2. J. B. RHINE, *New Frontiers of the Mind* (London: Faber & Faber Ltd., 1938), p. 222. Reprinted by permission of Faber & Faber Ltd., and Holt, Rinehart and Winston, Inc.
3. J. B. RHINE and J. G. PRATT, "A Reply to the Hansel Critique of the Pearce-Pratt Series," *Journal of Parapsychology*, XXV, No. 2 (1961), 93, 94.
4. J. G. PRATT, *Parapsychology: An Insider's View of ESP* (London: W. H. Allen & Co., 1964), p. 49. Reprinted by permission of W. H. Allen & Co., and Doubleday and Company, Inc.
5. RHINE, *New Frontiers of the Mind*, p. 226.
6. RHINE and PRATT, *Journal of Parapsychology* (1954), p. 165.

CHAPTER 8

1. J. G. PRATT and J. L. WOODRUFF, "Size of Stimulus Symbols in Extra-Sensory Perception," *Journal of Parapsychology*, III, No. 2 (1939), 121–158.
2. RHINE and PRATT, *Parapsychology*, p. 30.
3. J. B. RHINE, *New World of the Mind* (London: Faber & Faber Ltd., 1954), p. 55. Copyright © 1953 by J. B. Rhine. Reprinted by permission of Faber & Faber Ltd., William Sloane Associates, and J. B. Rhine.
4. D. H. RAWCLIFFE, *Illusions and Delusions of the Supernatural and the Occult* (New York: Dover Publications, Inc., 1959), p. 388. Reprinted through permission of the publisher.
5. J. G. PRATT and J. L. WOODRUFF, "Refutation of Hansel's Allegation Concerning the Pratt-Woodruff Series," *Journal of Parapsychology*, XXV, No. 2 (1961), 123.

CHAPTER 9

1. S. G. SOAL and K. M. GOLDNEY, "Experiments in Precognitive Telepathy," *Proceedings of the Society for Psychical Research*, XLVII, Part CLXVII (1943), 21–150.
2. BROAD, *Philosophy* (1944), p. 261.
3. G. E. HUTCHINSON, "Marginalia," *American Scientist*, XXVI (1948), 291.
4. RHINE, *New World of the Mind*, p. 59.
5. G. R. PRICE, "Science and the Supernatural," *Science* CXXII, No. 3165 (August 26, 1955), 362.
6. *Ibid.*
7. *Ibid.*
8. S. G. SOAL and K. M. GOLDNEY, "The Shackleton Report," *Journal of the Society for Psychical Research*, XL, No. 705 (1960), 378. Dr. Soal's answer to Mrs. Albert's statement is to be noted in the same article.

9. SOAL and GOLDNEY, *Proceedings of the Society for Psychical Research* (1943), p. 128.
10. SOAL and BATEMAN, *Modern Experiments in Telepathy*, pp. 346, 347.
11. S. G. SOAL and H. T. BOWDEN, *The Mind Readers* (London: Faber & Faber Ltd, 1959), p. 192.
12. SOAL and BATEMAN, *Modern Experiments in Telepathy*, p. 203.
13. J. F. NICOL, "The Statistical Controversy in Quantitative Research," *International Journal of Parapsychology*, I, No. 1 (1959), 56.

CHAPTER 10

1. SIR CYRIL BURT, "Experiments on Telepathy in Children," *British Journal of Statistical Psychology*, XII, Part I (1959), 72.
2. SOAL and BOWDEN, *The Mind Readers*, p. 48.
3. *Ibid.*, p. 26.
4. *Ibid.*, p. 282.
5. *Ibid.*, p. 61.
6. *Ibid.*, p. 281.
7. *Ibid.*, p. 81.
8. *Ibid.*, p. 177.
9. *Ibid.*, p. 178.
10. CHRISTOPHER SCOTT and K. M. GOLDNEY, "The Jones Boys and the Ultrasonic Whistle," *Journal of the Society for Psychical Research*, XL, No. 703 (1960), 249–260.
11. FRANCIS GALTON, *Inquiries into Human Faculty* (London: J. M. Dent & Sons Ltd., 1907), p. 235.
12. D. J. WEST, *Psychical Research Today* (London: Penguin Books Ltd., 1962); and R. H. THOULESS, *Experimental Psychical Research* (London: Penguin Books Ltd., 1963).
13. SOAL and BOWDEN, *The Mind Readers*, p. 235.

CHAPTER 11

1. MICHAEL FARADAY, "Experimental Investigation of Table-moving," *The Athenaeum*, July, 1853, pp. 801–803.
2. RHINE, *New World of the Mind*, p. 37.
3. J. F. NICOL, "Some Difficulties in the Way of Scientific Recognition of Extrasensory Perception," *Extrasensory Perception*, eds. WOLSTENHOLME and MILLAR, p. 36.
4. E. GIRDEN, "A Review of Psychokinesis," *Psychological Bulletin*, LIX (1962), 353–388.
5. J. B. RHINE and BETTY M. HUMPHREY, "The PK Effect with Sixty Dice per Throw," *Journal of Parapsychology*, IX, No. 3 (1945), 215.
6. GIRDEN, *Psychological Bulletin*, p. 361.
7. J. F. NICOL and W. CARINGTON, "Some Experiments in Willed Die-Throwing," *Proceedings of the Society for Psychical Research*, XLVIII, Part CLXXIII (1946), 164–175.
8. C. B. NASH, "PK Tests of a Large Population," *Journal of Parapsychology*, VIII, No. 4 (1944), 304–310.
9. ELIZABETH McMAHON, "A PK Experiment under Light and Dark Conditions," *Journal of Parapsychology*, IX, No. 4 (1945), 249–263.

10. R. H. THOULESS, "Some Experiments on PK Effects in Coin Spinning," *Journal of Parapsychology,* IX, No. 3 (1945), 169–175.
11. DOROTHY POPE, "Bailey's Comparison of a Coin and a Die in PK Tests," *Journal of Parapsychology,* X, No. 3 (1946), 213–215.
12. S. R. BINSKI, "Report on Two Exploratory PK Series," *Journal of Parapsychology,* XXI, No. 4 (1957), 284–295.
13. H. FORWALD, "A Continuation of the Experiments on Placement PK," *Journal of Parapsychology,* XVI, No. 4 (1952), 273–283.
14. C. C. L. GREGORY, letter in *Psychic News,* May 9, 1959.
15. J. F. NICOL, "The Design of Experiments in Psychokinesis," *Journal of the Society for Psychical Research,* XXXVII, No. 681 (1954), 355.
16. W. E. COX, "The Effect of PK on the Placement of Falling Objects," *Journal of Parapsychology,* XV, No. 1 (1951), 40–48.
17. ELSIE A. G. KNOWLES, "Report of an Experiment Concerning the Influence of Mind over Matter," *Journal of Parapsychology,* XIII, No. 3 (1949), 186–196.
18. MARTIN GARDNER, *Fads and Fallacies in the Name of Science* (New York: Dover Publications, Inc., 1957), p. 307. Copyright 1952, 1957, by Martin Gardner. Reprinted through permission of the publisher.
19. *Ibid.,* p. 353.

CHAPTER 12

1. BETTY M. HUMPHREY, "Success in ESP as Related to Form of Response Drawings 1. Clairvoyance Experiments," *Journal of Parapsychology,* X, No. 2 (1946), 78–106.
2. J. F. NICOL and BETTY M. HUMPHREY, "The Exploration of ESP and Human Personality," *Journal of the American Society for Psychical Research,* XLVII, No. 4 (1953), 133–178.
3. D. J. WEST, "ESP Performance and the Expansion-Compression Rating," *Journal of the Society for Psychical Research,* XXXV, No. 660 (1950), 295–308.
4. G. R. SCHMEIDLER, "Separating the Sheep from the Goats," *Journal of the American Society for Psychical Research,* XXXIX, No. 1 (1945), 47–50.
5. W. R. SMITH, E. F. DAGLE, M. D. HILL, and J. MOTT-SMITH, Testing for Extrasensory Perception with a Machine, *Data Sciences Laboratory Project 4610,* AFCRL–63–141, May, 1963; and S. D. KAHN, "Studies in Extrasensory Perception," *Proceedings of the American Society for Psychical Research,* XXV (October, 1952), 1–48.
6. M. ANDERSON and R. WHITE, "Teacher-Pupil Attitudes and Clairvoyance Test Results," *Journal of Parapsychology,* XX, No. 3 (1956), 141–157.
7. M. E. RILLING, CLARE PETTIJOHN, and JOHN Q. ADAMS, "A Two Experimenter Investigation of Teacher Pupil Attitudes," *Journal of Parapsychology,* XXV, No. 4 (1961), 247–259; and R. WHITE and J. ANGSTADT, "A Résumée of Research into Teacher-Pupil Attitudes," *Journal of the American Society for Psychical Research,* LV (October, 1961), 142–147.
8. SOAL and BATEMAN, *Modern Experiments in Telepathy,* p. 251.
9. KAHN, *Proceedings of the American Society for Psychical Research* (1952).

10. SMITH, *et al., Data Sciences Laboratory Project 4610.*
11. L. L. VASILIEV, *Experiments in Mental Suggestion,* trans. not given (Church Crookham, Hants., England: Institute of Mental Images, 1963), p. 6.
12. Originally published in Russian as *Suggestions at a Distance* (Moscow: Gospolitis, The State Publishing Company, 1962).
13. VASILIEV, *Experiments in Mental Suggestion,* p. 74.

CHAPTER 13

1. RHINE and PRATT, *Journal of Parapsychology* (1961), p. 97.
2. RHINE and PRATT, *Journal of Parapsychology* (1954), p. 175.

CHAPTER 14

1. E. GURNEY and F. W. H. MYERS, "Visible Apparitions," *Nineteenth Century,* XVI (July, 1884), 89–91. Reprinted through permission of *The Twentieth Century.*
2. *Nineteenth Century,* XVI (November, 1884), 451.
3. J. E. COOVER, "Metaphysics and the Incredulity of Psychologists," ed. CARL MURCHISON, *The Case for and against Psychic Belief* (Worcester, Mass.: Clark University, 1927), p. 261.
4. From G. N. M. TYRRELL, *The Personality of Man* (London: Pelican Books, 1947), p. 63. Originally published in *Journal of the Society for Psychical Research,* VI, No. 103 (1893), 129.
5. *Ibid.*
6. Notice inside back cover, *Proceedings of the Society for Psychical Research,* VI, Part XVII (1888).
7. D. BLACKBURN, *Daily News* (London), September 1, 1911.
8. JACK HARRISON POLLACK, "Crime Busting with ESP," *This Week,* February 26, 1961, p. 21.
9. In a letter to the author. Printed by permission of E. D. Maaldrink.
10. SIDNEY KATZ, "First Report on Extra-Sensory Perception," *Maclean's,* July 29, 1961, p. 44.
11. F. BRINK, "Parapsychology and Criminal Investigation," *International Criminal Police Review,* No. 134 (January, 1960), p. 8.
12. S. H. POSINSKY, "The Case of John Tarmon: Telepathy and the Law," *The Psychiatric Quarterly,* XXXV, No. 1 (January, 1961), pp. 165–166.

CHAPTER 15

1. WILLIAM CROOKES, *Researches in the Phenomena of Spiritualism* (London: Burns & Oates, 1874), p. 88.
2. RENÉE HAYNES, *The Hidden Springs* (New York: The Devin-Adair Co., 1961), p. 223. First published in England by Hollis & Carter, 1961. Copyright 1961 by Renée Haynes.
3. E. J. DINGWALL, *Very Peculiar People* (London: Rider & Company, 1950), p. 190.
4. HERBERT THURSTON, *The Physical Phenomena of Spiritualism* (London: Burns & Oates, 1936), p. 336.

5. E. FIELDING, W. W. BAGGALLY, and H. CARRINGTON, "Report of a Series of Sittings with Eusapia Palladino," *Proceedings of the Society for Psychical Research,* XXIII, Part LIX (1909).
6. *Ibid.,* p. 328.
7. *Ibid.,* p. 359.
8. H. MUNSTERBURG, "Report on a Sitting with Eusapia Palladino," *Metropolitan Magazine,* February, 1910.
9. D. S. MILLER, "Report of an Investigation of the Phenomena Connected with Eusapia Palladino," *Science,* LXXVII (1910).
10. J. JASTROW, "Unmasking of Paladino," *Collier's Weekly,* Vol. XLV (May 14, 1910), 21–22.
11. W. B. GIBSON and MORRIS N. YOUNG, eds., *Houdini on Magic* (New York: Dover Publications, Inc., 1953), pp. 141–142. Copyright 1953 by Dover Publications, Inc. Reprinted through permission of the publisher.
12. W. B. SEABROOK, *Doctor Wood: Modern Wizard of the Laboratory* (New York: Harcourt Brace & World, Inc., 1941), p. 215.
13. Editorial, *New York Times,* May 10, 1910.

CHAPTER 16

1. Quoted in J. F. RINN, *Searchlight on Psychical Research* (London: Rider & Company, 1954), p. 126.
2. *Ibid.*
3. *Ibid.*
4. RADCLYFFE HALL and U. V. TROUBRIDGE, "On a Series of Sittings with Mrs. Osborne Leonard," *Proceedings of the Society for Psychical Research,* XXX, Part LXXVIII (1919), 346–347.
5. OLIVER LODGE, *Raymond or Life and Death* (London: Methuen & Co. Ltd., 1916), p. 125.
6. W. H. SALTER, "A Further Report on Sittings with Mrs. Leonard," *Proceedings of the Society for Psychical Research,* XXXII, Part LXXXII (1921), 74–85.
7. HALL and TROUBRIDGE, *Proceedings of the Society for Psychical Research* (1919), p. 348.
8. J. EHRENWALD, *Telepathy and Medical Psychology* (London: George Allen and Unwin, Ltd., 1947), p. 402 n.
9. LEONORE PIPER, New York *Herald,* October 20, 1901.
10. D. J. WEST, *Psychical Research Today* (London: Penguin Books Ltd., 1962), p. 101.

CHAPTER 17

1. G. R. PRICE, *Science* (1955), p. 363.
2. RHINE and PRATT, *Parapsychology,* p. 132.
3. *Ibid.,* p. 19.
4. RHINE and PRATT, *Journal of Parapsychology* (1961), p. 94.

GLOSSARY

agent: The person who sees the card, or object and acts as "sender" or "transmitter" in a telepathy test.

bit: A binary unit of information. It's name is an acronym coming from binary dig*it*. A bit of information could be passed to a subject in an ESP test by means of a signal that assumed one of two states during each trial, for example, a light operated by a Morse key that was either on or off. Two such lights (*A* and *B*) could convey two bits of information and enable the subject to identify correctly any one of four possible choices. (*A* on, *B* on; *A* off, *B* off; *A* on, *B* off; *A* off, *B* on). In general if *N* represents the number of bits and *C* the number of choices, $C = 2^n$ or $N = \log_2 C$. Thus, to identify one of six alternatives, 2.6 bits are required.

BT: A clairvoyance-testing technique identified variously as (1) *Basic Technique* (Rhine) in which each card is laid aside by the experimenter as it is called by the subject; (2) *Before Touching* (Rhine) in which each card is called before it is touched by any one; (3) *Broken Technique* (Soal) in which each card is lifted off the pack by the experimenter as the percipient makes his guess.

call: The symbol selected by the percipient when he attempts to guess a target.

clairvoyance: Awareness of, or response to, objects or events without the mediation of the senses; see also, ESP.

control series: A control series consists of a set of observations made under identical conditions to an experimental series, except that, in the control series, the process being investigated cannot operate. For example, Soal included runs in his telepathy tests in which the agent did not look at the cards. These runs constitute a control series in respect to telepathy.

cross check: In order to answer the criticism that high scores in ESP tests may be due to statistical artifacts, the experimenters have checked the subjects' calls for each run against targets used in some other run for which they were not intended. This procedure produces a control series in which statistical artifacts could operate but ESP could not.

DT (down through): A technique for testing clairvoyance in which the cards are called down through a deck before any cards are removed or checked.

ESP (extrasensory perception): A term coined by J. B. Rhine designating awareness of, or response to, objects, events (clairvoyance), or of another person's thoughts (telepathy) without the mediation of the senses.

mental healer: A person who claims to be able to cure disease through the laying on of hands or the intervention of the spirits of dead persons.

mental medium: A person who claims to produce messages from the spirits of the dead.

odds against chance: If there are odds of *N* to 1 against chance occurrence, this implies that if a large number of tests were carried out identical to the one under consideration but in which ESP could not operate, then a score as high as that obtained in the original experiment would be expected to arise approximately *M* times in $M(N + 1)$ such tests. "Calls" produced by a random-number generator could be employed to make such a test; see also, control series.

parapsychology: Another name for psychical research. The study of phenomena—such as ESP, PK, ghosts, mediums, and poltergeists—which are disclaimed or ignored by orthodox psychologists.

percipient: The person in an ESP test who attempts to guess another's thoughts or to identify symbols, objects, or events.

physical medium: A person who claims to invoke spirits of dead persons in order to produce movements of objects or visible spirit forms.

PK (psychokinesis): An alleged direct influence exerted by a person on a physical system without the use of any known form of physical energy.

placement test: A PK test in which the subject attempts to make an object move to a particular position.

placement wishing: The subject in a placement test is said to use placement wishing when he attempts to produce lateral displacement of an object or to make it fall in a particular position.

plus 1 (+1) hit: A hit on the target that will arise next in a target sequence.

precognition: ESP directed to future events (precognitive clairvoyance), or thoughts (precognitive telepathy).

probable error: See standard error.

psychokinesis: See PK.

psychical research: See parapsychology.

random series: A series in which each member is independent of earlier members. In such a series, it is not possible to infer, or to increase the probability of guessing, a later member from knowledge of earlier members of the series.

PT (pure telepathy): A technique for testing telepathy, as distinct from clairvoyance, in which cards are not used. The agent merely thinks of the target.

run: A series of trials in an ESP or PK test. A run of 25 trials has been most often used in ESP experiments and a run of 24 dice throws in PK tests.

salience effect: A tendency for hits to arise at particular positions on a score sheet.

séance: A gathering together of persons for the purpose of witnessing spiritualistic phenomena.

significance: A score is said to be statistically significant when it has large odds against arising by chance. The criterion often used is odds of 100 to 1 against chance.

sitting: Part of an ESP experiment consisting of all the trials made at one session.

spiritualist: A person who believes in the ability of mediums to contact the spirits of the dead.

standard error: The square root of the arithmetic mean of the squares of the deviations from the mean. Probable error equals 0.6745 times the standard error. It is usual to give a critical ratio in terms of the difference divided by its standard error.

target: The symbol being guessed at in an ESP test.

telepathy: Awareness of, or response to, another person's thoughts without the mediation of the senses; see also, ESP, this is sometimes known as Thought Tranference.

thought transference: See telepathy.

trial: Each single guess at a card, symbol, or object.

Zener cards: Cards bearing one of the five symbols: circle, plus sign, rectangle, star, or wavy lines, as originally used at Duke University.

SUGGESTIONS FOR FURTHER READING

GENERAL REVIEWS OF ESP RESEARCH

GARDNER, MARTIN. *Fads and Fallacies in the Name of Science.* New York: Dover Publications, Inc., 1957.

PRATT, J. G., RHINE, J. B., SMITH, M. BURKE, and STUART, CHARLES E. *Extra-Sensory Perception after Sixty Years.* Boston: Bruce Humphries, Publishers, 1940.

SOAL, S. G., and BATEMAN, F. *Modern Experiments in Telepathy.* London: Faber & Faber Ltd., 1954.

THOULESS, R. H. *Experimental Psychical Research.* London: Penguin Books Ltd., 1963.

WEST, D. J. *Psychical Research Today.* London: Penguin Books Ltd., 1962.

EARLY HISTORY OF THE SOCIETY FOR PSYCHICAL RESEARCH

HALL, TREVOR T. *The Strange Case of Edmund Gurney.* London: Gerald Duckworth & Co. Ltd., 1964.

SPIRITUALISM

COOVER, J. E. "Metaphysics and the Incredulity of Psychologists." In MURCHISON, CARL (ed.), *The Case for and against Psychic Belief.* Worcester, Mass.: Clark University, 1927, pp. 215–264.

RAWCLIFFE, D. H. *Illusions and Delusions of the Supernatural and the Occult.* New York: Dover Publications, Inc., 1959.

RINN, J. F. *Searchlight on Psychical Research.* London: Rider & Company, 1954.

SELECTED READINGS

GIRDEN, E. "A Review of Psychokinesis," *Psychological Bulletin,* LIX (1962), 353–388.

GRIDGEMAN, N. T. "Parapsychology and All That," *Queens Quarterly,* LXX, No. 4 (1964).

HANSEL, C. E. M. "Experiments on Telepathy," *New Scientist,* V, No. 119 (February, 1959), 457–459.

——. "Experimental Evidence for Extra-Sensory Perception," *Nature,* CLXXXIV (November 7, 1959), 1515–1516.

KENNEDY, J. L. "A Methodological Review of Extra-Sensory Perception," *Psychological Bulletin,* XXXVI (1939), 59–103.

NICOL, J. FRASER. "The Statistical Controversy in Quantitative Research," *International Journal of Parapsychology,* I, No. 1 (1959), 47–63.

——. "Some Difficulties in the Way of Scientific Recognition of Extrasensory Perception." In Wolstenholme, G. E., and Millar, Elaine C. P. (eds.). Ciba Foundation Symposium. London: J. & A. Churchill Ltd., 1956.

PRICE, G. R. "Science and the Supernatural," *Science,* CXXII, No. 3165 (August 26, 1955), 359–367.

SMITH, W. R., DAGLE, E. F., HILL, M. D., and MOTT-SMITH, J. Testing for Extrasensory Perception with a Machine, *Data Sciences Laboratory Project 4610,* AFCRL–63–141, May, 1963.

SOAL, S. G. "Experimental Evidence for Extra-Sensory Perception," *Nature,* CLXXXV, No. 4717 (March 26, 1960), 950–951.

———. "Experimental Evidence for Extra-Sensory Perception," *Nature,* CLXXXVII, No. 4732 (July 9, 1960), 171–172.

INDEX

ABOUT THE AUTHOR

C. E. M. HANSEL holds the Chair of Psychology at the University College of Swansea, University of Wales. Prior to this, he was a Senior Lecturer in the Department of Psychology at the University of Manchester. He attended Bournemouth Municipal College of Technology and Commerce and Cambridge University, where he received his B.A. and M.A. degrees. The co-author of a previous book, *Risk and Gambling,* and the author of numerous articles on various psychological topics, Professor Hansel has made a special study of extrasensory perception over the years, which has culminated in this authoritative and exhaustive work. He is married and has five children.